The Open University

S328 Ecology
Science: a third level course

ECOLOGY
Book Three
COMMUNITIES

The S328 Course Team

Course Team Chair:	Jonathan Silvertown
Course Manager:	Phil Parker
Authors:	Mary Bell
	Mike Gillman
	Dick Morris
	Phil Parker
	Irene Ridge
	Jonathan Silvertown
	Charles Turner
Course Secretary:	Val Shadbolt
Editors:	Gerry Bearman
	Sheila Dunleavy
	Gilly Riley
	Bina Sharma
	Margaret Swithenby
Graphic Design:	Mandy Anton
	Sarah Crompton
	Keith Howard
	Pam Owen
	Ros Wood
Course and Book 3 Assessor:	Professor Peter Edwards
Consultants:	Hilary Denny
	Robert J. Morley
Comments:	Eric Bowers
BBC:	Tony Jolly
	Liz Sugden
ACS:	Jon Rosewell

The Open University, Walton Hall, Milton Keynes, MK7 6AA.

First published 1996. Reprinted with corrections 2001.

Copyright © 1996 The Open University.

Edited, designed and typeset through AppleMac/QuarkXPress by The Open University.

Printed in the United Kingdom by Selwood Printing Ltd., Burgess Hill, West Sussex

ISBN 0 7492 51832

This text forms part of an Open University Third Level Course. If you would like a copy of *Studying with The Open University*, please write to the Central Enquiry Service, PO Box 200, The Open University, Walton Hall, Milton Keynes, MK7 6YZ. If you have not enrolled on the Course and would like to buy this or other Open University material, please write to Open University Educational Enterprises Ltd, 12 Cofferidge Close, Stony Stratford, Milton Keynes, MK11 1BY, United Kingdom.

S328book3i1.3

BOOK THREE COMMUNITIES

CONTENTS

Introduction to Book 3   7

Chapter 1   Biogeography   9

1.1	Introduction	9
	Summary of Section 1.1	12
1.2	Global biogeographical patterns	12
	1.2.1 Biogeographical regions	12
	1.2.2 Types of biogeographical distribution	20
	1.2.3 Dispersal and vicariance	23
	1.2.4 Species richness and diversity	24
	Summary of Section 1.2	26
1.3	Long-term biogeographical changes	27
	1.3.1 Continental drift and plate tectonics	27
	1.3.2 Plate tectonics and the distribution of organisms	31
	1.3.3 Palaeoclimate	36
	Summary of Section 1.3	37
1.4	Quaternary biogeographical changes	39
	1.4.1 The Quaternary Ice Age	39
	1.4.2 Palaeoecology and the Quaternary fossil record	42
	1.4.3 Pollen analysis	44
	1.4.4 Interglacial vegetational history – a case study	48
	1.4.5 Glacial stage environments	53
	Summary of Sections 1.4.1 to 1.4.5	55
	1.4.6 Southern Europe	58
	1.4.7 Temperate refugia	60
	1.4.8 Tropical refugia	63
	Summary of Sections 1.4.6 to 1.4.8	68
1.5	Flandrian environmental changes	69
	1.5.1 Blelham Tarn	70
	1.5.2 Late-glacial and Flandrian vegetational history	73
	1.5.3 Early human impacts during the Flandrian	78
	1.5.4 Early agriculture in East Anglia	82
	Summary of Sections 1.5.1 to 1.5.4	89
1.6	Recent biogeographical changes	90
	Summary of Section 1.6	94
1.7	Semi-natural vegetation	95
	1.7.1 Historical development and woodland classification	95
	1.7.2 Ancient woodland and its management	97
	1.7.3 Ancient woodland flora and fauna	101

1.7.4   Extinctions and conservation of isolated plant and
        animal populations   102
Summary of Section 1.7   106

Objectives for Chapter 1   107

References for Chapter 1   108

Chapter 2   Community composition, structure and function   109

2.1   Introduction   109

2.2   Definition and composition of ecological communities   109
      2.2.1   Interactions and area   109
      Summary of Section 2.2   114

2.3   An excursion into the tropical forest   114
      2.3.1   Guilds in the tropical forest   115
      2.3.2   Pollinators   116
      2.3.3   Frugivores   121
      Summary of Section 2.3   123

2.4   Themes of community composition, structure and function 125

2.5   Measurement of community complexity   126
      2.5.1   Defining and sampling species richness   126
      2.5.2   The measurement of species diversity   129
      2.5.3   Alpha, beta and gamma diversity   131
      2.5.4   Food web structure and the community matrix   132
      Summary of Section 2.5   134

2.6   Are complex communities more stable than simple ones?   135
      2.6.1   Charles Elton and Robert May   135
      2.6.2   Predictions from the community matrix   136
      2.6.3   Analysis of community stability in the field   137
      Summary of Section 2.6   139

2.7   Local and regional patterns of species richness   140
      2.7.1   The species–area curve   140
      2.7.2   Rarity and abundance   142
      2.7.3   Species richness of insects on trees   143
      Summary of Section 2.7   146

2.8   Regulation of communities   148
      2.8.1   Top-down and bottom-up   148
      2.8.2   Non-equilibrium processes   149
      Summary of Section 2.8   151

2.9   The relationship between species richness and latitude 152
      2.9.1   Hypotheses   152
      Summary of Section 2.9   155

Objectives for Chapter 2   157

References for Chapter 2   157

Chapter 3 Ecological succession **161**

3.1 Introduction 161

3.2 Three examples of successional change 161
 3.2.1 Old-field 161
 3.2.2 The hydrosere 165
 3.2.3 Volcanic islands 167
 Summary of Sections 3.1 and 3.2 169

3.3 Patterns of community change during succession 170
 3.3.1 Plant biomass and species richness 170
 3.3.2 Animals and fungi 176
 3.3.3 Life histories 179
 Summary of Section 3.3 180

3.4 The climax state 180
 Summary of Section 3.4 183

3.5 The mechanisms of succession 183
 3.5.1 Using experiments to investigate the role of animals 183
 3.5.2 An overview of the mechanisms of succession 188
 Summary of Section 3.5 192

3.6 Cyclic changes 194
 Summary of Section 3.6 195

Objectives for Chapter 3 196

References for Chapter 3 196

Answers to Questions **199**

Acknowledgements **212**

Index **214**

INTRODUCTION TO BOOK 3

The fact that all species of animals and plants live with and depend upon associations with other organisms is the most fundamental axiom in ecology. Books 1 and 2 have explored this fact and its consequences for numerous species. In Book 1, we introduced the idea that the complexity of ecological systems can be tackled by thinking about the problem in terms of a **hierarchy** of levels: the individual, the population, the community and the ecosystem. You have now worked your way from the individual (Book 1) to the population (Book 2) and are ready to embark on community ecology in this Book.

Community ecology is about the collective properties of species and addresses such questions as: 'Why do groups of species occur where they do?', 'Why do species occur in particular associations with other species?' and 'Why are there more species in some communities than in others?'.

A good way to get a feel for the subject matter and scope of Book 3 is to think of the different **scales** on which processes affecting ecological communities operate in time and space (Figure 1). Scale has been a recurring theme in the Course, so the notion that this is important in community ecology should not come as a surprise. However, what you might find surprising is the sheer magnitude of the geographical area and geological timescale over which processes affecting the composition of ecological communities have operated (Figure 1).

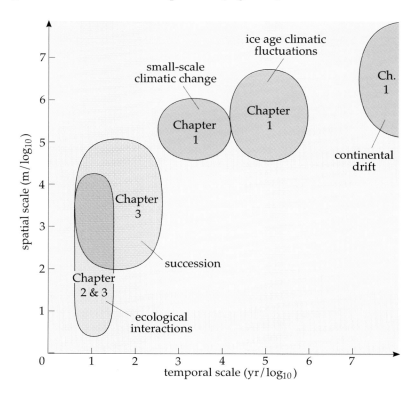

Figure 1   A diagrammatic representation of the spatial and temporal scales relevant to the patterns and processes discussed in this Book. The scales are logarithmic to the base 10, thus 3 on the temporal scale is 10^3 yr = 1000 yr; and 3 on the spatial is 10^3 m = 1 km. The boundaries of each pattern/process are only approximate.

Some of the questions in community ecology can only be answered by looking back thousands or even millions of years ago. Other questions demand a broad geographical perspective. Many of these large-scale questions are addressed in Chapter 1 on **biogeography**. Global patterns of species distribution and species richness often have their origin in very ancient events such as continental drift, or in the history of climate, both of which are dealt with in that Chapter. More local patterns, such as the composition of the plant communities found in Britain today, have a more recent origin but still require an historical perspective to be understood and these are also discussed in Chapter 1.

In Chapter 2, we consider ecological communities in the strict sense, functioning over relatively small temporal and spatial scales (compatible with the population analyses of Book 2). Patterns here include how the abundance of species changes with area sampled, as a result of processes such as predation, competition (already discussed in Book 2) and disturbance. Consideration of the temporal dynamics of communities is restricted to a discussion of the stability of hypothetical communities near assumed equilibria (as covered for populations in Book 2). In these situations, we are more concerned with the relative abundance of species in a community than with how species numbers or composition change.

This is in contrast to Chapter 3, which deals with the phenomenon of ecological succession (introduced in Book 1), where species turnover through time is very pronounced so that at the end of succession there may be none of the species left that were present at the start. Thus, the pattern here is the temporal dynamics of communities. The underlying ecological processes will be similar to those considered in Chapter 2, with an emphasis on particular interactions such as seed dispersal.

BIOGEOGRAPHY   CHAPTER 1

Prepared for the Course Team by Charles Turner and Robert J. Morley

1.1   Introduction

Biogeography is the study of geographical patterns in the distribution of organisms. These patterns can include those of major features, such as the distribution of biomes (Book 1, Figure 3.15) and of communities. It may also include the study of geographical trends in diversity and species richness, which are introduced in this Chapter, but chiefly discussed in Chapter 2. However, it is the study of the distribution of individual taxa, at different levels in the hierarchy of classification, and ultimately of species populations, that provides the basic data for understanding all these patterns.

From your study of the earlier books of this Course, you will already be familiar with various biotic and abiotic factors that influence or even control species distributions in particular regions, generally in combination, but there are also temporal factors in terms of long-term geological or more recent history which have barely been mentioned and form much of the topic of this Chapter. Moreover, distribution patterns can be represented at many different scales, and each scale may require a different approach to its explanation.

Figure 1.1   Present global distribution of the palm family Arecaceae.

The palm family Arecaceae exhibit a range of distribution patterns and reflect some of these controls (Figure 1.1). Palms are basically tropical and subtropical; one species – the dwarf palm *Chamaerops humilis* – just extends as a native plant into Europe, where it occurs naturally in a few places along the coast of the western Mediterranean. Another species, *Phoenix theophrasti*, a dwarf relative of the date palm *P. dactylifera*, is found only on the island of Crete. Although a number of other species of palm are cultivated in gardens farther north, the controlling factor seems to be that palms are very frost-sensitive, particularly because almost all have a single large apical growth point which is easily damaged. So this is an example of climatic control, affecting the whole family. Plant families with this kind of distribution are termed **megathermal** and are believed never to have occurred significantly outside areas of tropical or subtropical climates, so there is also an historical dimension to their distribution which will be discussed later.

If one looks at the distribution of individual genera of palms, a few are widespread across the Old World tropics, but most of the 250 or so genera have a distribution restricted to particular continents or even islands. Here, in addition to climatic factors, other factors such as evolutionary history and long-term geographical isolation must play a role. Some genera already begin to set puzzles. For example, the palm genus *Livistona* is represented by species in Australia and New Guinea and right across south-east Asia into India and China, whereas it is well known that the mammal faunas of Australia and south-east Asia are very different.

Turning to the distribution of individual species, many have narrow tolerances and restricted niches. A special case is that of the coconut palm *Cocos nucifera*. This is now widely cultivated throughout the tropics, but has no known wild native populations and is believed to have originated somewhere in the area of the Pacific. Here, the factor of human activities appears to be clearly paramount.

On a different scale, the distribution map (based on a 10 km² grid) for the black spleenwort fern *Asplenium adiantum-nigrum* in the British Isles also shows the influence of climate (Figure 1.2). Like most ferns it requires very humid conditions for its establishment, particularly during the inconspicuous and fragile gametophyte stage.

black spleenwort fern
Asplenium adiantum-nigrum

(× 0.12)

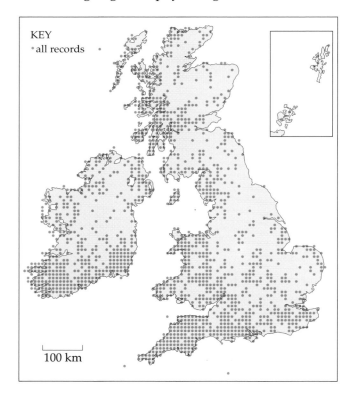

KEY
• all records

100 km

Figure 1.2 Distribution of the black spleenwort fern *Asplenium adiantum-nigrum* in the British Isles.

❑ How is this reflected in its distribution pattern?

■ The map demonstrates that it is much commoner in the western parts of Britain and Ireland. In the east it is sparser, except in some coastal areas. You would be correct in deducing that this distribution pattern can largely be correlated with relative humidity of the atmosphere and so indirectly with precipitation levels.

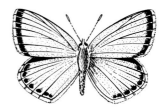

chalkhill blue   *Lysandra coridon* (× 1.1)

What this map cannot show you is that whereas in western areas this fern grows abundantly in hedgebanks, on rocky ground such as cliff faces, quarries and scree slopes, elsewhere it is a rather local plant, restricted to the sheltered side of damp, ancient walls, avoiding too much direct sunlight; so there are microhabitat patterns of distribution as well.

❑ Apart from abiotic factors, what other major set of factors have been already discussed, which clearly affect distribution patterns?

■ Interactions between species, including competitive exclusion, predation and various mutualistic relationships, as discussed in Book 1, Chapters 1 and 2, can be quite critical in this respect.

horseshoe vetch   *Hippocrepis comosa* (× 0.4)

Compare, for example, the distribution of the chalkhill blue butterfly *Lysandra corydon* in Britain and that of its preferred food plant the horseshoe vetch *Hippocrepis comosa* (Figure 1.3).

Can you suggest what might be the main factor controlling these distinctive distribution patterns?

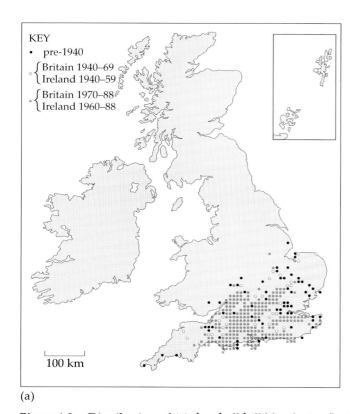

(a)

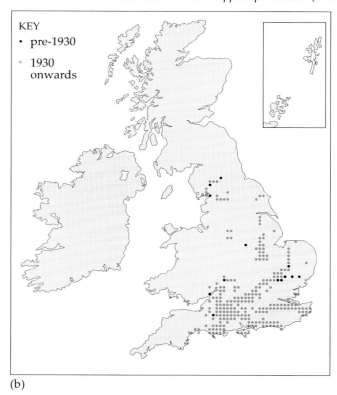

(b)

Figure 1.3   Distribution of (a) the chalkhill blue butterfly *Lysandra corydon* and (b) its food plant, horseshoe vetch *Hippocrepis comosa*, in Britain.

You may have realized that the pattern picked out, at least in southern England, is that of the Chalk Downs. *Hippocrepis* is essentially a calcicole plant that grows only in chalk or limestone grassland. Hence the underlying control is geological. Another fact suggested by this map is that both the plant and particularly the butterfly have been subject to recent local extinction. This is almost certainly due to either ploughing up of chalk and limestone grassland to extend agriculture or to the abandonment of sheep grazing, allowing closely cropped turf, in which *Hippocrepis* thrives, to be invaded and replaced by shrubs or coarse grasses.

Observational data of this kind can often provide explanations for such patterns, and these explanations can sometimes be tested and supported by experimental techniques. On the other hand, many biogeographical distribution patterns, especially when viewed from a regional or global perspective, cannot simply be explained in ecological terms but have arisen as a result of factors linked to evolutionary and geological history or to palaeoclimatic fluctuations over time ranges that vary from thousands to many millions of years. Such patterns are the concern of **historical biogeography**. To study them in detail requires a knowledge of many different disciplines. Biogeography, more than many other branches of the natural sciences, requires the broad understanding of the natural historian, rather than the narrow approach of the modern specialist.

Summary of Section 1.1

Biogeography is the study of geographical patterns in the distribution of organisms. It encompasses patterns of different kinds and at different scales. We attempt to explain such patterns in terms of abiotic and biotic factors, usually in combination, but often they are strongly linked to underlying temporal factors relating to geological processes in the past or to more recent historical events, especially involving the effects of human activities.

1.2   Global biogeographical patterns

1.2.1   Biogeographical regions

The terrestrial floras and faunas of widely separated geographical areas generally exhibit few taxa in common, even under almost identical climatic conditions and even though life forms in such regions may be closely comparable. The degree of similarity does not change uniformly with distance, but often sharply at major geographical boundaries. On the basis of these floral and faunal discontinuities, the world's floras and faunas can be divided globally into **Floral Kingdoms/Subkingdoms** and **Faunal Regions** respectively, the boundaries of which coincide in many respects, especially in the Northern Hemisphere and most of the tropics (Figure 1.4).

Both floral and faunal boundaries coincide with the major continental land masses, and, to some extent with the presence of major mountain belts, such as the Himalayas, and also with the sub-tropical high pressure zones. The position of the boundaries between Regions/Kingdoms is by no means coincidental, but reflects barriers of great geological antiquity. On the one hand, these reflect the boundaries of tectonic plates, which make up the surface of the Earth (see Figure 1.17). On the other, the positions of the subtropical high pressure belts which tend to be associated with regions of desert or dry savannah (Figure 1.5b) are determined by atmospheric circulation patterns (Figure 1.5a), and, can, from the geological record, be demonstrated not to have varied their latitudinal position significantly over most of geological time.

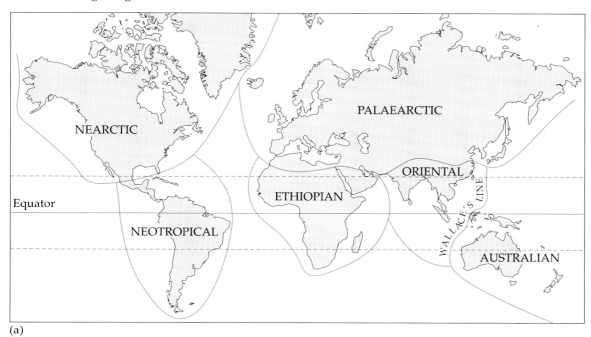

(a)

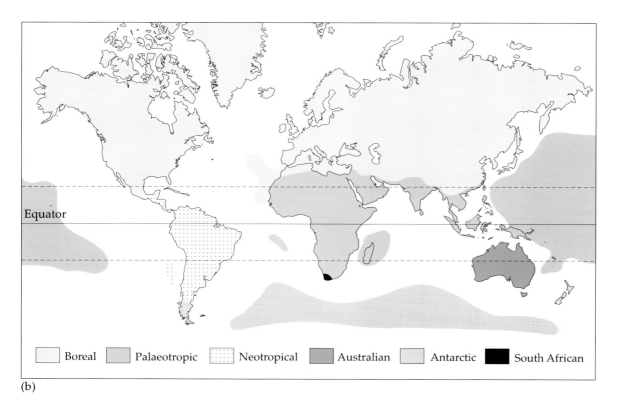

(b)

Figure 1.4   Faunal Regions and Floral Kingdoms compared. The following text provides an explanation for the names.

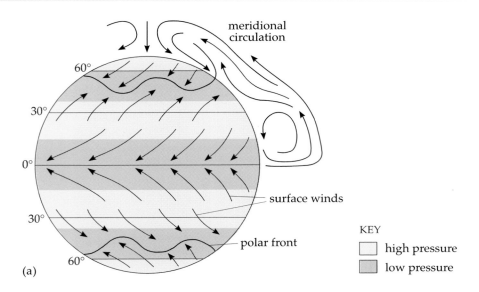

Figure 1.5 (a) Schematic diagram showing the zonal distribution of atmospheric circulation patterns for a hypothetical water-covered Earth. (b) Present-day latitudinal distribution of the Earth's climatic and vegetational belts.

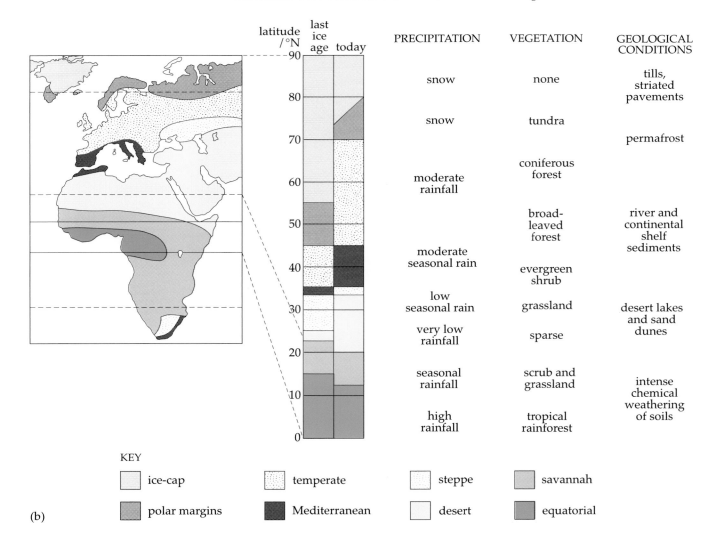

Within the constraints of these geological and climatic boundaries, the world's faunas and floras have evolved to some degree independently, giving rise to the present-day regional divisions.

Before you read on, try to complete the following exercise, summarizing some of the environmental and biological information about the various biogeographical regions.

❑ There are certain features of climate, topography and vegetation which characterize each region. From your general knowledge, try to fill in the spaces in Table 1.1, but do not spend too much time on it. Information in Book 1, Chapter 3, especially Figure 3.15, will help you complete the section on vegetation zones. Compare your answer with Table 1.2 (overleaf), where we have added more information on vertebrate faunas of the biogeographical regions.

Table 1.1   Characteristic climates, topography and vegetation in the biogeographical regions.

	Nearctic	Palaearctic	Ethiopian	Oriental	Neotropical	Australian
hemisphere						
special geographical features, e.g. mountains, rivers, lakes						
climate						
land connections with other regions						
vegetation zones						

The **Palaearctic** and **Nearctic** regions are often grouped together as the Holarctic region, because of their similarity. Floristically, this large area forms the **Boreal Kingdom**. The remarkable similarities of both floras and faunas across the Northern Hemisphere relate first to the absence of major climatic divides, and secondly to the presence of previous land connections between Eurasia and North America, whose importance will become clearer after you have read Section 1.3.1. There has been a connection across Beringia, the area of the Bering Strait, which separates Siberia from Alaska, through most of the Tertiary (the geological era between 65–1.77 Ma – see Figure 1.18a–c later); this region was emergent during periods of low sea-level. Also, there were land connections through Greenland until the Mid-Tertiary. The southern boundary is formed on the one hand by the hot deserts, and on the other by the great physiographic divide of the Himalayas.

Table 1.2   Completed Table 1.1.

	Nearctic	Palaearctic	Ethiopian	Oriental	Neotropical	Australian
hemisphere	N	N	N and S	N	S	S
special geographical features, e.g. mountains, rivers, lakes	N–S mountain chains (Rockies), large lakes, large rivers	E–W mountain chains to S, large rivers	highest average altitude of all, very large lakes, large rivers	Himalayas to N, large rivers	Andes as N–S mountain chain, large rivers	no large lakes or rivers
climate	arctic, temperate	arctic, temperate	tropical, Mediterranean	tropical	tropical, temperate	tropical, Mediterranean
land connections with other regions	Neotropical	Oriental, Ethiopian	Palaearctic	Palaearctic	Nearctic	none
vegetation zones	tundra, taiga, deciduous forest, steppe	tundra, taiga, deciduous forest, steppe	tropical forest, savannah, desert, chaparral	tropical forest, some savannah, desert	tropical forest, savannah, desert	tropical forest, savannah, much desert
special groups of mammals	three families of peculiar rodents, pronghorn 'antelopes', one marsupial	two obscure rodents	giraffe and okapi, hippos, very varied antelopes, monkeys and apes	monkeys and apes, tree shrews, tarsiers, colugos, many gliding mammals	many peculiar forms include sloth, armadillo, vampire bats, many rodents of guinea-pig family, some marsupials	prototherians, marsupials, very few native placentals (bats and rodents)
special groups of birds	wild turkeys	hedge sparrows	ostrich, secretary birds, touracos and others	varied pheasants	rhea, toucan	emu, cassowary, birds of paradise, many pigeons
reptiles and amphibians	many reptiles, many amphibians	few reptiles, many amphibians	many reptiles, many frogs	many reptiles, especially venomous snakes, many frogs	many reptiles, many frogs	moderately varied reptiles, few amphibians
freshwater fishes	varied fishes	many cyprinid fishes	very varied fishes	very varied fishes	very varied fishes	few fishes

Many of the species of tundra are common to both the Eurasian and American Arctic. The northern coniferous forests in both regions are composed of closely related species of pine, spruce, larch and fir, and the common tree genera of the European temperate deciduous forests, such as oak, elm, ash, beech, lime and hazel, are represented by closely related species in North America. Similarly, the vertebrate faunas have many genera and species common to both areas, particularly toward the Arctic: brown and polar bears, reindeer and caribou, elk and moose, and wolf.

Despite these similarities, it is important to note that both the flora and fauna of North America are much richer in species and diversity than those of Europe and western Asia. North American vertebrate faunas have many more species. For example, there are many species of reptiles in North America but few in Europe. The freshwater fish fauna comprises about 600 species in North America, whereas in northern Europe there are less than 100. Similarly, the deciduous forests of north-west Europe typically contain six species per hectare, whereas those of the south-eastern United States may contain as many as 30 species. This is due in part to the southerly position of North American deciduous forests compared to those in Europe, in line with the important trend toward increased species diversity at lower latitudes, but there is another reason for these differences, to which we will shall return later.

The **Neotropical** region at present has a land connection with the Nearctic but this connection is relatively recent, being formed very late in the Tertiary, though there was briefly a previous connection in the Early Tertiary. There were earlier links with both Antarctica and Africa, which will become clearer in Section 1.3.1. There are many peculiar groups of mammals and birds in the Neotropical fauna which are best explained as having evolved when South America was isolated from other continents. One odd feature of the tropical forest of the Neotropical region is the number of mammal species which have prehensile tails in contrast to their relatives elsewhere; examples include the kinkajou (Figure 1.6) which is the only carnivore with a prehensile tail, the tree porcupines, and the spider monkeys. There are also three families of marsupial mammals. Land bridges with the Nearctic led to the immigration of carnivores from the north and these probably caused the extinction of many peculiar animals such as the giant sloths. In the other direction, one species of the marsupial opossums and an armadillo have been able to spread northwards into the Nearctic. Neotropical rainforests include the most species-rich plant communities recorded on Earth, characterized in particular by trees belonging to the families Bombacaceae (Kapok family) and Lecythidaceae (Brazil nut family), and epiphytic herbs such as bromeliads, whereas areas with strongly seasonal and arid climates are characterized by Cactaceae (cacti), which have also managed to spread northwards into North America.

Figure 1.6   The kinkajou *Potos flavus* ($\times$ 0.15).

The **Ethiopian** and **Oriental** regions are both connected by land with the Palaearctic. You can see in Figures 1.4 and 1.17 that the boundary between the Ethiopian and Palaearctic regions does not coincide with a plate boundary. The Sahara desert appears to act as a much more effective barrier to the dispersal of animals than the Mediterranean Sea. Some authorities include the Arabian peninsula in the Ethiopian region: others include it in the Palaearctic. Both the Ethiopian and Oriental regions are basically tropical and have mammalian faunas with a number of closely

Figure 1.7 Screw-pine *Pandanus* sp (× 0.015).

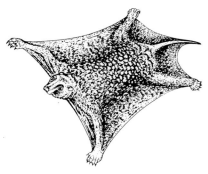

Figure 1.8 Colugo or flying lemur *Cynocephalus variegatus* (× 0.15).

related taxa or even species in common, e.g. lions, rhinoceroses, elephants, bush-babies and apes. Many plant families such as the screw-pines Panadanaceae (Figure 1.7) and the bananas Musaceae show a similar pattern, so that botanists regard both areas as belonging to a single Palaeotropical Floral Kingdom. There is evidence that the Ethiopian region was colonized from the north but has been isolated at intervals, during which the fauna diversified. Animals now characteristic of tropical Africa, such as hippopotamuses, lions, hyaenas and certain species of elephant and rhinoceros, lived in Europe, including the British Isles, as recently as the last interglacial period only 120 000 years ago. Some also occurred in North Africa until historic times. Part of the marked difference between the Palaearctic and Ethiopian regions now is the result of the extinction of species in the former following climatic changes, or perhaps of extermination by prehistoric hunters.

The Oriental region is separated from the Palaearctic by the huge barrier of the Himalayas which very effectively limits north–south faunal movements. The forest fauna of south-east Asia is remarkable in including many gliders such as the colugo *Cynocephalus variegatus* (Figure 1.8), several different families of flying squirrels, a flying lizard, a flying frog and even a flying snake. By contrast, the forest fauna of Africa shows no special sort of adaptation to flying. The most spectacular terrestrial faunal development in Africa is probably the wealth of antelopes – members of the artiodactyl (even-toed) family Bovidae – on the savannahs; these grasslands are characteristic of the plateaux which occupy much of the Ethiopian region. In the African lakes, there is an enormous diversity of fishes, especially of the perch-like family Cichlidae.

The **Australian** region has a vertebrate fauna which is poor in numbers of species but which has a very high proportion of unique forms, particularly of marsupial mammals; these include kangaroos, wallabies, wombats, koala, opossums and the two prototherian mammals (monotremes), the duck-billed platypus and the hedgehog-like echidna or spiny anteater. Many of these occupy niches which in other regions are occupied by placental mammals, and the convergent evolution that has taken place is very striking (Figure 1.9). Some rodents and bats in this region show affinities with the fauna of the Oriental region and some marsupials with those of the Neotropical region. The flora too has a very large number of endemic genera and families, and also shows interesting links with the Neotropical region. The interface between the Oriental and Australian regions is the East Indies, a volcanic area which is tectonically very unstable, so that islands may be uplifted or may sink below the ocean surface. The continent of Australia has been isolated from other land masses since the beginning of the Tertiary Era (i.e. for at least 60 Ma), and much of its bird fauna and the few placental mammals, the rodents and bats, probably arrived by crossing the sea from the north, either by flying or swimming.

After examining aspects of the geological and palaeogeographical history of the Earth, we shall return in a later Section to analyse these regional biota in more detail. However, certain plant and animal taxa (usually at the family or generic level) have distributions which transgress the boundaries between these regions. These distributional anomalies may provide a number of clues regarding the biogeographical and evolutionary history of faunas and floras.

PLACENTALS   MARSUPIALS

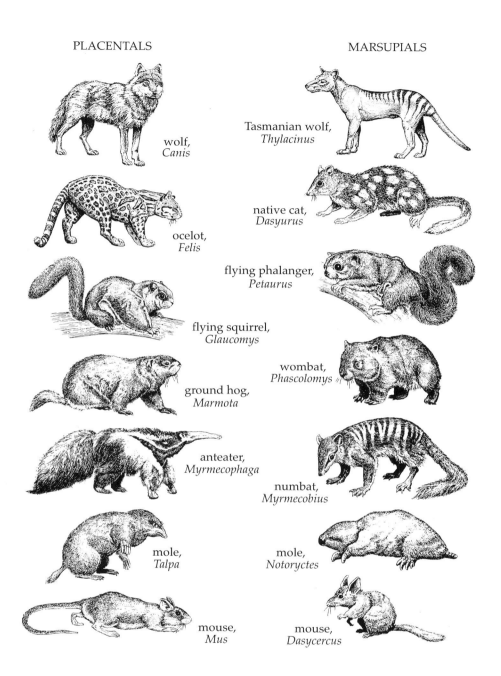

wolf,
Canis

Tasmanian wolf,
Thylacinus

ocelot,
Felis

native cat,
Dasyurus

flying phalanger,
Petaurus

flying squirrel,
Glaucomys

ground hog,
Marmota

wombat,
Phascolomys

anteater,
Myrmecophaga

numbat,
Myrmecobius

mole,
Talpa

mole,
Notoryctes

mouse,
Mus

mouse,
Dasycercus

Figure 1.9   Convergent evolution between placental mammals and Australian marsupial mammals. Note: drawn at different scales.

1.2.2   Types of biogeographical distribution

Very few species have attained anything approaching a worldwide **cosmopolitan** distribution. Those that have done so include humans *Homo sapiens*, rats, mice, lice and the parasites which accompany human civilization. A few plants with broad climatic tolerances and extremely good dispersal mechanisms such as the bracken fern *Pteridium aquilinum* and common reed *Phragmites australis* are widespread in both tropical and temperate regions, and, amongst higher taxonomic groups of angiosperms, the grass family Poaceae and the daisy family Asteraceae occur from equatorial regions to bleak polar landscapes (Figure 1.10).

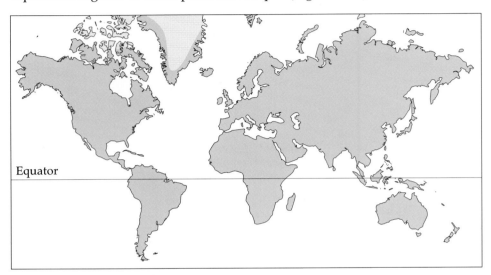

Figure 1.10 Global distribution of the daisy family Asteraceae.

More interesting are those taxa which possess **disjunct distributions**, that is, they occur in two or more widely separated areas. The tulip tree *Liriodendron* (Figure 1.11a) has a disjunct distribution, with two present-day species *L. tulipifera* in North America and *L. chinense* in China. Fossils of *Liriodendron*, however, may be found in Tertiary sediments across Europe, clearly indicating that this genus was previously much more widespread. The closely related genus *Magnolia* shows a similar distribution pattern (Figure 1.11b) with several species in eastern North America and others in China and also Japan. Amongst vertebrates, tapirs occur in south-east Asia but also in South America.

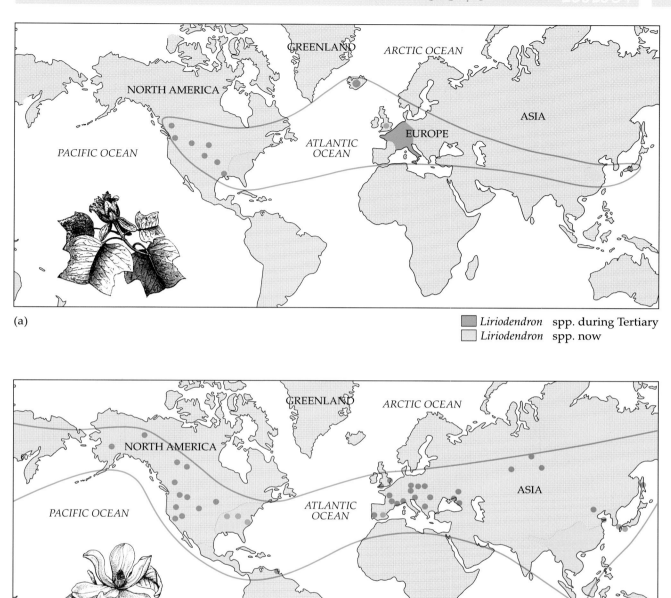

(a)

Liriodendron spp. during Tertiary
Liriodendron spp. now

(b)

Magnolia spp. during Tertiary
Magnolia spp. now

Figure 1.11 Modern and fossil distribution of (a) tulip trees *Liriodendron* and (b) *Magnolia* species.

Symphonia globulifera

Figure 1.12 Distribution of *Symphonia globulifera* and other species of *Symphonia*.

Of particular and unusual interest is the distribution of the genus *Symphonia* (Guttiferae). These are swamp forest trees (Figure 1.12), but the same species *S. globulifera* occurs in both West Africa and South America, with a long fossil record in both areas, so that it cannot have been spread by human activity alone. Other species occur in East Africa and Madagascar. We will return to consider the history of these disjunctions later in Section 1.3.2.

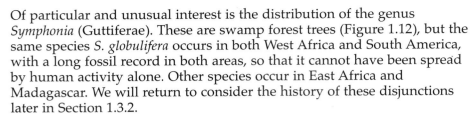
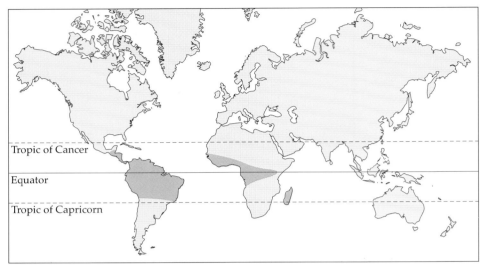

Many taxa have only a single and often very restricted area of distribution, and these are termed **endemics.** Such distributions may reflect the last refuge of a formerly widespread species, such as that of *Ginkgo biloba* (the ginkgo or maidenhair tree) which today occurs naturally in only a few localities in China, but was formerly widespread across the Northern Hemisphere (Figure 1.13). At the other extreme, a single area of distribution may reflect a newly evolved species. Oceanic islands are often

Figure 1.13 Relict distribution of the endemic gymnosperm, maidenhair tree *Ginkgo biloba*, together with fossil occurrences of this genus.

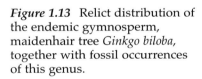

Ginkgo biloba (× 0.1)

KEY

Jurassic and Cretaceous fossil area

Early and Mid-Tertiary fossil area

Late Tertiary (Pliocene) fossil area

rich in such taxa, closely related species evolving on adjacent islands, such as Darwin's finches in the Galapagos, and the analogous succulent plant genus *Aeonium* (Crassulaceae) in the Canary Islands (Figure 1.14).

1.2.3 Dispersal and vicariance

Two different mechanisms have been invoked to account for discontinuous and disjunct distributions of both plants and animals: **dispersal** and **vicariance**. In the past, some biogeographers insisted that such distributions could best be explained by long-distance dispersal of organisms, across water bodies, or along former land bridges, whilst others argued that they related to range retraction from a previously continuous distribution, and/or the subsequent creation of natural barriers, which now prevent mixing between the two populations. The latter view is called **vicariance biogeography**. **Vicariant species** are closely related species occurring in different geographical areas.

Many plants and animals possess special mechanisms which allow dispersal away from their points of birth or origin, as part of their natural life cycle (Book 2, Chapter 1). The ability of species, including those which may not have any obvious special mechanisms, to spread to new areas is well demonstrated by the colonization of volcanic islands.

The Krakatoa islands of Indonesia lie in the Sunda Straits between Sumatra and Java, which are 35 and 45 km away respectively. In 1883, the main island of Rakuta, an ancient volcano, suffered what was one of the most violent eruptions of modern times, reducing that island to less than half its original size and destroying all the luxuriant vegetation and animal life that had previously inhabited it and the two smaller adjacent islands, leaving a sterile unstable surface of lava and volcanic ejecta. Recolonization, presumably from Sumatra and Java, was rapid. Already in 1886 there was a luxuriant growth of ferns, with much of the ground surface covered by a thin layer of cyanobacteria.

❑ Why should ferns be pioneer colonists?

■ They are dispersed by very small wind-borne spores.

The islands have been visited by many scientific expeditions so the history of plant colonization is reasonably well-known (Table 1.3).

Figure 1.14 *Aeonium arborescens* (Crassulaceae)(× 0.12), an endemic succulent plant from the Canary Islands.

Table 1.3 The number of vascular plant species recorded on the Krakatoa islands at different times since 1886. Data for 1979 relate only to the main island, Rakuta.

	1886	1897	1908	1928	1934	1979	Total known to have occurred
total no. of plant species	26	64	115	214	271	196	387
no. of littoral species	10	30	60	68	70	75	–
no. of ferns	11	12	9	38	55	41	83

In 1934, it was estimated that 41% of the plants were probably wind dispersed, 28% had floated in from the sea, including many of the littoral species (i.e. those of the beach or shoreline), a further 25% had been carried in by animals, predominantly by birds and the rest perhaps by human activities.

❑ Why should such a high proportion of the records be for littoral species?

■ Transport by sea currents is a major method of seed dispersal, but also beaches are a major feeding ground for birds, so seeds either defecated or carried attached to feet or feathers could easily arrive there. Finally, these are the areas most accessible to visiting botanists and so littoral plant species are likely to be well recorded.

What can also be noted from these figures is that colonization does not always lead to successful establishment. Many plants have appeared and disappeared either because of successional changes (which will be discussed in more detail in Chapter 3), or simply because their numbers did not become large enough to establish viable populations.

The faunas and floras of mid-ocean volcanic islands, such as Tristan da Cunha and Ascension Island in the South Atlantic and the Hawaiian and many other islands in the Pacific, demonstrate how, under favourable conditions and probably at intervals over long periods of time, a range of organisms, but particularly plants and insects, can disperse and establish themselves over ranges of not just hundreds but thousands of kilometres of inhospitable ocean. It should, however, also be remembered that ancient islands may also provide refugia for relict taxa, which have now become extinct in the more competitive environments of the continents.

It is clearly much easier to make a convincing case for dispersal events when considering island rather than continental biota. Explaining disjunct distributions in terms of vicariance events requires evidence of a different kind. First of all, as with *Liriodendron* and *Ginkgo*, it is useful to have a well-dated fossil record to show a former wider distribution of taxa. Such records might equally suggest, of course, that dispersal had been taking place. Vicariance explanations are more probable if a number of different species from different kinds of habitats show similar disjunct distribution ranges. However, since both mechanisms clearly have operated in the past, to explain and distinguish the causes of modern distribution patterns requires a detailed understanding of geological and palaeoclimatic history, as well as of the evolutionary history of the taxa concerned.

1.2.4 Species richness and diversity

Looking at a different kind of biogeographical pattern, European explorer-naturalists of the 18th and 19th centuries were astonished at the richness and diversity of tropical faunas and floras. Most terrestrial ecosystems show a clear trend towards increased **diversity** at lower latitudes in terms of their structural complexity, as well as in the actual number of species present. Habitat complexity, which affects the potential number of niches available, is particularly important. This can be reflected in the variety of small-scale physical habitats or in the structure of living communities. For example, temperate woodland is often stratified into canopy, shrub, herb and ground layer communities, each accompanied by its dependent fauna. In tropical forest, stratification tends to be even more complex with up to three layers within the canopy, whilst the presence of lianas and abundant epiphytes provides a range of additional niches. This is reflected in **species richness**. Thus, one hectare of tropical rainforest in Panama may contain over 90 species of large trees, and Amazonian rainforests sometimes more than twice as many, whilst further north the most diverse temperate forests in the USA – the Great Smoky Mountains of Tennessee – have only 30 species per hectare. Forests in Panama have 70 mammal species but beech–maple forest in the Great Smoky Mountains only 31. In the far north there are fewer forest mammals still, with only 15 or 16 species in Alaska. Such a trend is also clearly illustrated by comparing the number of native species of various different taxa in the British Isles and the Malay Peninsula (Table 1.4). The same pattern of a reduction in species richness away from the tropics exists for flowering plants as a whole, in both the Northern and Southern Hemispheres (Figure 1.15), when a large number of widely separated areas are considered.

Table 1.4 Some comparisons between the number of species in the British Isles and the Malay Peninsula.

	British Isles	**Malay Peninsula**
angiosperms	1300	8000
trees	25	2000
butterflies	60	1000

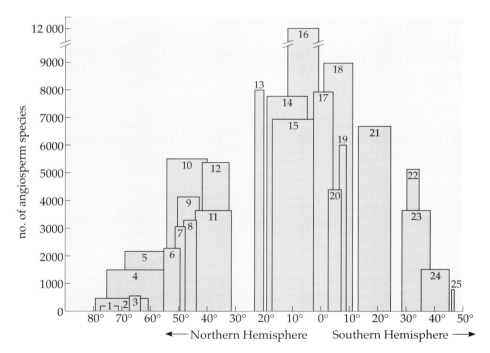

Figure 1.15 Number of species of angiosperms in the floras of different parts of the world, plotted against latitude. 1 Novaya Zemlya; 2 Greenland; 3 Iceland; 4 Yakutia (Siberia); 5 Sweden; 6 Poland; 7 Czechoslovakia; 8 Romania; 9 France; 10 Kazakhstan; 11 Japan; 12 California; 13 Cuba; 14 Philippines; 15 river basins of Niger and Volta; 16 Venezuela; 17 Gabon; 18 New Guinea; 19 Java; 20 Central Tanzania; 21 Madagascar; 22 Cape Peninsula; 23 New South Wales; 24 New Zealand; 25 Prince Edward Island, Indian Ocean.

Similar trends may be found in mountain areas, but there diversity usually decreases with altitude, and likewise, more obviously, from forested areas, through savannah or steppe ecosystems to deserts, but in this case the parallel gradient is not one of temperature but of seasonality and precipitation.

Most widely distributed families of both plants and animals show a clear trend towards increased species richness approaching the equatorial regions, correlating with global climatic gradients. The distribution of bat species (Figure 1.16) shows a more or less steady increase in species richness towards the Equator in both the New World and in Asia and Australia, but in Africa bat diversity is greatest in the savannah regions, low, as might be expected, in the Saharan and Arabian deserts, but, more surprisingly, low in the equatorial rainforests of Central and West Africa.

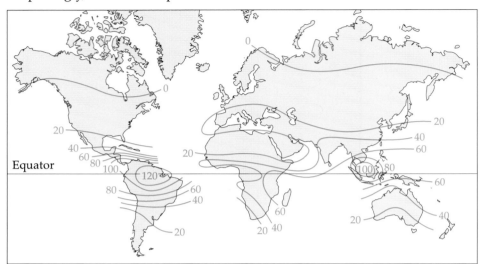

Figure 1.16 Global distribution and species richness of bats.

A variety of hypotheses have been suggested to account for these latitudinal gradients in species richness, and these will be discussed in detail in the next Chapter. Briefly, the hypotheses fall into two linked types: (i) those which explain the difference between tropical and temperate zone richness on the grounds of historical events – you will have a better understanding of the background to the historical hypotheses when you have finished reading this Chapter – and (ii) those which explain such contrasts on the grounds of differences in the abiotic and biotic environment. Even in temperate regions there can be strong variations in diversity between apparently similar vegetation types. For example, the traditional sheep-grazed grasslands of chalk and limestone areas can actually be extremely rich in both grass and broad-leaved herb species, whilst otherwise similar grasslands on acid soils, dominated of course by different species of grasses, are clearly quite species poor.

Summary of Section 1.2

From the study of the distribution of organisms on a regional or worldwide scale, the land surface of the world can be divided into biogeographical regions – **Floral Kingdoms** and **Faunal Regions** – characterized by distinctive assemblages of plants and animals. These assemblages, or rather the distribution patterns of the families, genera and species of plants and animals which comprise them, can be explained to some extent in terms of climatic and environmental factors, which provide natural barriers to migration, but also in terms of geological history, evolution and extinction. Few species other than humans and their associates have really widespread distributions. **Endemic** species that occur in single localities or restricted areas may be the last survivors of once widespread taxa or newly evolved ones. Some plant and animal taxa show disjunct distribution patterns with related species in widely separated areas. Attempts have been made to explain these in terms of **dispersal** and/or **vicariance** hypotheses. Other global biogeographical patterns of decreasing **species richness** and, concurrently, lower habitat and niche **diversity** that are clearly correlated with increases in latitude, altitude and aridity, are also introduced in this Chapter for further discussion in the next one.

Question 1.1   *(Objectives 1.1 & 1.2)*

For each of the biogeographical regions A–F below, select from list 1–10 the items which are characteristic of that region.

Regions

A Oriental; B Australian; C Neotropical; D Nearctic; E Ethiopian;
F Palaearctic.

Characteristics

1   There is a land connection with the Ethiopian region.
2   There is a high proportion of endemic species which are marsupials.
3   The climate zones are mainly temperate and polar.
4   There is a land connection with the Palaearctic region.
5   There are many and varied hoofed animals on the savannahs.
6   The region is entirely surrounded by seas.
7   Many of the forest animals are gliders.
8   There is a land connection with the Nearctic region.
9   The climatic zones are mainly tropical and subtropical.
10   There are many endemic species of lake fishes.

Question 1.2   *(Objectives 1.1, 1.3 & 1.4)*

Briefly outline two different scenarios which might lead to the natural occurrence of endemic species of plants or animals on oceanic or offshore islands.

1.3   Long-term biogeographical changes

1.3.1   Continental drift and plate tectonics

The suggestion that the continents were not fixed but moved, or drifted, across the surface of the Earth was first proposed by Alfred Wegener in 1915, but initially the idea of **continental drift** gained little acceptance by geologists, although it was regarded more favourably by biologists, because it provided explanations both for some present-day distribution patterns and for paradoxes in the fossil record. Only in the 1960s, as part of the broader **theory of plate tectonics**, did continental drift gain general acceptance. There are several aspects of this theory which help to explain the historical ecology of living groups of plants and animals.

According to the theory, the Earth's surface is divided into eight major, and several minor, rigid **lithospheric** or **tectonic plates** (Figure 1.17).

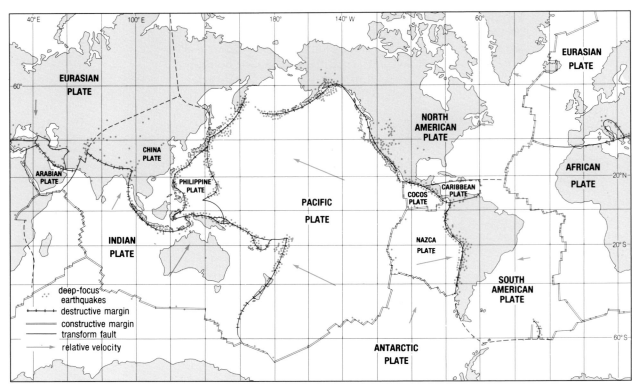

Figure 1.17 Distribution of the major lithospheric plates showing constructive and destructive margins and present-day directions of plate movement.

❑ Do continents and oceans occur on separate plates?

■ No, Some plates consist only of oceanic crust which is dense and basaltic in composition, but others are formed of continents, where the crust is less dense but thicker, fused to areas of oceanic crust.

However, the two kinds of crust have very different histories. Whereas continents are more or less permanent features of the Earth's surface, oceanic crust is being created by upwelling of basaltic magma along constructive plate margins (mid-ocean ridges) and subducted and melted along destructive plate margins, so ocean basins come and go over geological time.

❑ What is the nearest constructive plate margin to the British Isles? What evidence is there for magmatic activity in that region?

■ The Mid-Atlantic Ridge, a submerged mountain chain, that has vents, fissures and underwater volcanoes which pour out huge amounts of magma. Iceland, which lies astride this ridge, was formed by particularly massive basaltic lava flows and continues to be volcanically very active.

Furthermore, the convectional forces in the Earth's mantle below the crust involved in this process are also causing the lithospheric plates to 'drift' across the surface of the planet.

Figure 1.18 traces the relative positions of the Earth's major land masses over the past 245 Ma.

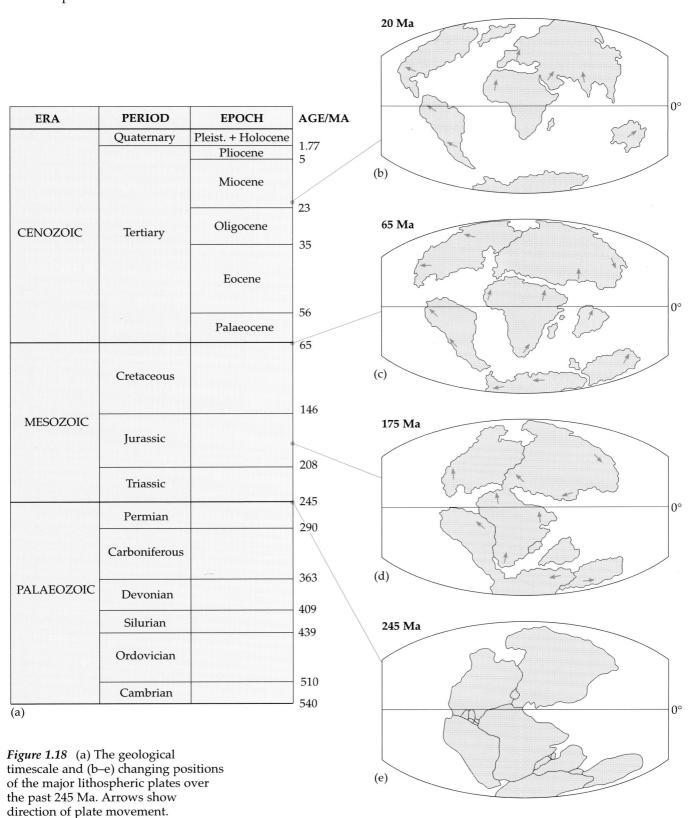

ERA	PERIOD	EPOCH	AGE/MA
CENOZOIC	Quaternary	Pleist. + Holocene	1.77
	Tertiary	Pliocene	5
		Miocene	23
		Oligocene	35
		Eocene	56
		Palaeocene	65
MESOZOIC	Cretaceous		146
	Jurassic		208
	Triassic		245
PALAEOZOIC	Permian		290
	Carboniferous		363
	Devonian		409
	Silurian		439
	Ordovician		510
	Cambrian		540

(a)

20 Ma

0°

(b)

65 Ma

0°

(c)

175 Ma

0°

(d)

245 Ma

0°

(e)

Figure 1.18 (a) The geological timescale and (b–e) changing positions of the major lithospheric plates over the past 245 Ma. Arrows show direction of plate movement.

❑   What would have been the likely general ecological and evolutionary consequences for organisms occupying a land mass, e.g. India, drifting northwards across tropical latitudes during that time?

■   India is likely to have travelled across both arid and humid tropical zones, which have ecologically very different environments. Natural selection towards different physiological behaviour and life forms will have been intense, and there may have been high extinction and high speciation rates at different times.

Another of the results of plate tectonics is that large land masses may split up and drift apart, thus subdividing populations. Alternatively, wherever plates come together, **mountain-building** occurs. At destructive plate margins where ocean crust is subducted below continents, volcanic activity may create huge mountain ranges such as the Andes in South America. Where two oceanic plates collide, volcanic activity may create volcanic arcs such as the Japanese islands and the Philippines, and where two continents collide massive mountain ranges such as the Himalayas and the Alps arise as one plate overrides the other and intense buckling takes place.

This mountain building not only produces many new habitats, but also has major climatic effects on adjacent areas. For example, before India collided with south Asia in the Early Tertiary and likewise Africa with Europe, there was a long east–west subtropical ocean named the **Tethys** whose northern shores stretched from what is now the Mediterranean right across to China (Figure 1.18c, d). Evidence from fossil plants shows that this whole area supported a lush flora, including palms and other subtropical and tropical families. Once continental collision had taken place, after the basin of the Tethys had been subducted beneath the Eurasian plate, the formation of the Himalayas and subsidiary mountain ranges produced a deep rain-shadow which led to the aridification of much of south-west and central Asia.

The process of break up and reassembly of continents also has effects on sea-level , since mid-ocean ridge activity is accompanied by upward bulging of the ocean floor, displacing seawater and raising global sea-level, whereas when the continents were mostly fused together to form a single (and later two) supercontinent(s) (Figure 1.18e), there was little constructive plate margin activity and sea-levels were low. Highest global sea-levels occurred during the Cretaceous (when there were also no polar ice-caps), and have shown an overall fall since that time.

❑   What effect is this fall likely to have had on continental and marine organisms?

■   As sea-level falls, land masses separated by shallow marine straits will be joined and populations of plants and animals can migrate across the land bridges. On the other hand, such lowering of sea-level is likely to affect marine organisms in the opposite way, isolating populations and in time perhaps resulting in divergent evolution and speciation.

1.3.2 Plate tectonics and the distribution of organisms

Although biogeography concerns the distributions of all organisms, most attention has been paid to the distributions exhibited by angiosperms, mammals and birds. These groups have radiated over approximately the same period, over the past 100 Ma, and especially over the past 65 Ma, during the Tertiary Period, since the demise of dinosaurs.

As can be seen from Figure 1.18, this 100 Ma period has also been characterized by two additional trends; on the one hand, the tectonic plates which bear the continents (having come together in an earlier geological epoch), have during this interval mostly split and drifted apart, or 'disassembled', although a few have drifted together, and collided, resulting in the building of mountain ranges and volcanic island arcs (e.g. the Himalayan range, and the Japanese Archipelago). At the same time, especially since the Middle Eocene (50 Ma ago), there has been a steady decline in global temperatures, culminating in the Ice Age of the Quaternary Period. These trends have had some very important consequences with respect to the distribution of animals and plants over the surface of the Earth. First, the movement of continental land masses through different climatic zones not only promoted extinction and evolutionary changes but also encouraged the process of dispersal; secondly, the splitting up of continents has resulted in many taxa, which formerly had continuous ranges, now being widely separated by newly formed oceans; and thirdly, the successive trend for more strongly zoned and latitudinally differentiated climates has resulted in the present ranges of species being much reduced compared to times of previous more equable climates.

Plant families such as the Arecaceae (palms – Figure 1.1) and others, like the Myristicaceae (nutmegs), are widespread in each of the three tropical regions, though separated by major oceans.

❑   How might such distributions have become established?

■   On the one hand, they may be a result of the successful dispersal of species to a new area, as a result of range expansion across water bodies or along former land bridges. However, both of these families possess large fruits which are generally poorly adapted to dispersal across water bodies, though a few palms do spread for short distances in that way. Alternatively, they may have previously had a continuous distribution when continents were united before the formation of deep ocean basins split up their former range. This would then be a vicariant distribution.

It is easy to make hypotheses of this kind, but not always possible to find evidence to test them. In the case of palms, they fortunately have a good fossil record in the form of fossil pollen grains which can be identified with certainty because of their shape and pattern, and more rarely fossil fruits occur. Pollen analysis of ancient sediments is an important technique which will be discussed in detail later in this Chapter. The fossil evidence shows that palms were one of the earliest angiosperm families that can be clearly recognized. They were already abundant throughout the tropics by Late Cretaceous and Early Tertiary times, which supports the vicariance hypothesis. Different genera have subsequently evolved in each of the major tropical plant kingdoms. Fossil fruits of the palm genus *Nipa* (Figure 1.19), now living in Malaysia, can be found in the Eocene London Clay of southern Britain, which suggests that the range of the family has actually contracted.

Figure 1.19 The palm *Nipa* growing along a river bank in Borneo.

❑ From the foregoing discussion, suggest at least three contributory factors to the disappearance of palms from north-west Europe since the Eocene.

■ The factors you could have recognized include, first, whereas palms are physiologically adapted to tropical and subtropical climates, that part of the Eurasian plate on which the present British Isles sits has drifted at least 10° northwards in latitude into a much more temperate climatic belt. Secondly, global climate has cooled considerably since the Eocene leading to more strongly zoned climates. Thirdly, the closure of the Tethys removed the warming influence of that ocean; this and the resulting aridification of climate destroyed the continuous mild coastal belt along which subtropical flora could migrate.

If you compare Figures 1.4 and 1.17, you can confirm that in many areas plate boundaries correspond to those of the regions and kingdoms.

❑ Which major land mass has been isolated longest from contact with other continents, and how is this reflected in its biota?

■ Australia. In Jurassic times (180 Ma ago) all the major southern land masses were clustered together as the supercontinent known as **Gondwanaland**. As it broke up, one of the segments that drifted apart was Australia (about 60 Ma ago), carrying with it a fauna including monotremes and marsupials but no placental mammals. These have evolved into the present highly endemic and characteristic mammalian fauna of Australia. Radiation of angiosperm floras took place in the Cretaceous, before the major radiation of placental mammals, and, as a result, the Australian flora, though largely endemic, does show links with both the floras of southern South America and South Africa.

The genus *Nothofagus* (the southern beeches) are forest trees of South
America, New Zealand, parts of Australia and the islands of New
Caledonia and New Guinea (Figure 1.20a). Clearly, this is a highly disjunct
distribution pattern. However, there is also a good fossil record for the
pollen of these trees for the Late Cretaceous (80 Ma ago) (Figure 1.20b).

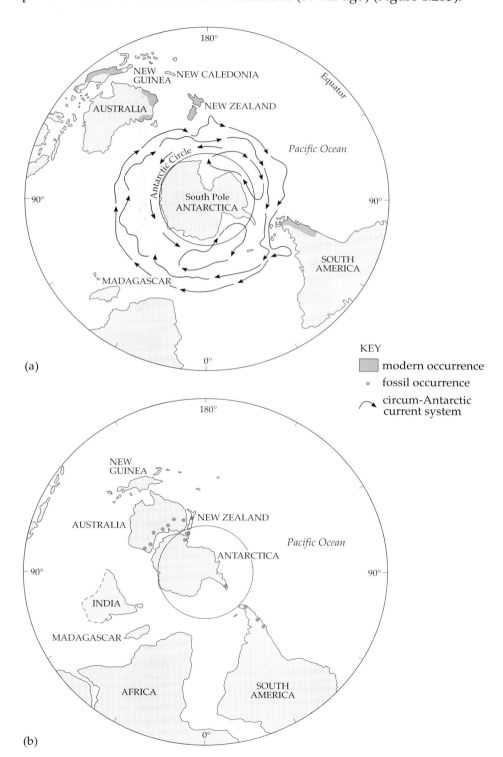

KEY

■ modern occurrence

· fossil occurrence

↷ circum-Antarctic
current system

Figure 1.20 (a) Distribution of
living species of the southern
beeches *Nothofagus*. (b)
Distribution of the southern
continents and of fossil
Nothofagus pollen records for the
Late Cretaceous (80 Ma ago).

❑ How would you interpret the present distribution pattern?

■ The fossil record, which also shows that these trees once grew on Antarctica, before it was glaciated, suggest evidence for vicariance events. Australia, Antarctica and South America remained in close proximity until the beginning of the Tertiary. The pollen record demonstrates that *Nothofagus* was in place in all three of these areas before that time, but it was absent from Africa and India which by 80 Ma ago were already far to the north.

Examine Figure 1.18b and c, and note what was happening to the northern margin of the Indian plate during the Late Cretaceous and Tertiary. In the Eocene, the Indian land mass collided with Asia, following the complete subduction of the oceanic crust flooring the Tethys in that area. Further east, in the middle Miocene, the area of the plate north of Australia began to collide with the plate carrying land masses that now form Malaysia, Sumatra, Borneo, Java and smaller islands ('Sundaland'), much of the area being strongly volcanic. The boundary between these two plates now corresponds to **Wallace's Line** (Figure 1.21), one of the world's most marked faunal boundaries, named after Alfred Russell Wallace, the pioneer of evolutionary studies who collaborated with Darwin. To the west of this line the fauna is essentially Asiatic, with monkeys, tigers and birds typical of south-east Asia. To the east, some islands have been colonized by a few Asian species, but otherwise the fauna is predominantly Australian in aspect, particularly the bird fauna and marsupials, e.g. phalangers (Figure 1.9). This region of faunal intermixing is known as '**Wallacea**' and its eastern limit referred to as **Weber's Line** (Figure 1.21).

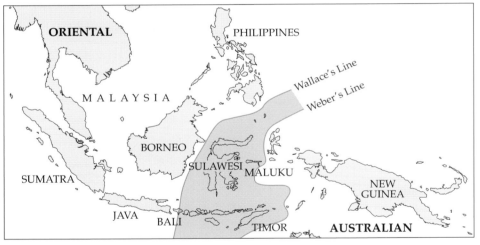

Figure 1.21 South-east Asia and the East Indies showing the position of Wallace's and Weber's Lines. The area between – 'Wallacea' – is shaded. Sulawesi and Maluku are referred to respectively as Celebes and the Mollucas in older literature.

Floristically, this boundary is more difficult to differentiate, but a recent taxonomic assessment of the family Arecaceae in the Far East clearly illustrates its importance; the distribution of palm genera which are found on both sides of Wallace's Line can be divided into three groups (Table 1.5): (i) Sundanese genera, with some species crossing to the east; (ii) Australasian genera with species crossing to the west; and (iii) widespread genera whose dispersal into both regions probably pre-dates the plate collision. The Arecaceae thus demonstrate a slight tendency for greater dispersal to the east. There is no evidence for a massive eastward invasion, as suggested by many biogeographers.

Table 1.5   Distribution of non-endemic Arecaceae to the east and west of Wallace's Line.

	Total no. of genera	Total no. of species in each area:		
		Sundaland	Sulawesi	Maluku/ New Guinea
Asian genera with immigrants to the east	7	181	18	4
Australasian genera with immigrants to the west	5	3	4	28
widespread genera	6	193	31	105

Return at this point to consider the disjunct distribution patterns of two of the taxa that were first illustrated in Section 1.2.2. The evidence concerning *Liriodendron* (Figure 1.11a) certainly suggests a pattern of vicariance. It has a widespread fossil record which in some places goes back to the Early Tertiary or even the Late Cretaceous and spans at least some of the intervening areas between its two present centres of occurrence.

❑   What geological events might be invoked to explain the restriction of its range and the present isolation of the two living species?

■   First, the opening of the North Atlantic commencing about 70 Ma ago would have separated the American and European populations. Likewise, the closure of Tethys and the aridification of Central Asia following the collision of India with the Asian mainland in the Eocene would have separated European and East Asian populations. Aridification of the central United States probably restricted its range, too. It is known from fossil evidence that *Liriodendron* flourished in the relatively mild conditions throughout the Tertiary but disappeared at the beginning of the Quaternary. The possible reasons for this will be considered shortly.

Turning to *Symphonia* (Figure 1.12), a vicariance explanation would also seem possible. There are fossil pollen records back through the Tertiary in both West Africa and several parts of South America. The two tropical areas of distribution would be neatly juxtaposed before Africa and South America split and drifted apart, but the opening of the South Atlantic occurred in the Mid-Cretaceous, at least 30 Ma earlier than the North Atlantic, when angiosperms were only just beginning their initial radiation. Furthermore, the very good pollen record, whilst clearly showing the appearance of this tree in West Africa during the Eocene, suggests that it was totally absent in South America until the Early Miocene, when it spread rapidly. This suggests a successful random or 'sweepstake' episode of dispersal at that time across the Atlantic. Dispersal events may be rare, but given the length of geological time, there have been many opportunities for such events to take place.

❑   What biological effects might the joining of two long-separate land masses have?

■ Organisms occupying similar niches or which had undergone convergent evolution would be brought into competition, either leading to further niche subdivision or diversification and to extinctions of less successful competitors.

In particular, the introduction of new predators can have a very drastic effect under these circumstances. When North and South America became joined in the Late Pliocene, the South American mammal fauna was severely reduced in diversity by the introduction of North American predators such as bears, large cats including the puma *Felis concolor* and the extinct sabre-tooth *Smilodon*, and smaller carnivores. This destruction of the large vertebrate fauna not only of South America, but also of North America, was only surpassed after another hunter, *Homo sapiens*, entered North America across the Bering Strait about 12 000 years ago at another time of low sea-level, towards the end of the last glacial period, which created a land bridge from Siberia across to Alaska. There is still much debate as to whether human hunting activities or rapid climatic change which also happened at that time (or a combination of both) was responsible for this latest wave of extinctions.

1.3.3 Palaeoclimate

During the course of geological history, there have been long-term oscillations in the global climate of the Earth's surface, over timespans of tens to a hundred Ma. Back in the Carboniferous and Permian, 220–300 Ma ago, a massive ice age affected the southern continents, but during the Mid-Cretaceous, 100 Ma ago, climates were much warmer than at present with no ice-caps and forests extending up into the polar regions. The Earth's climate was in a **greenhouse mode**. It was still warm in the Early Tertiary (Figure 1.22) with moist multi-storied forests of 'tropical' aspect (interpreted from the representation of tree species with large entire leaves and the occurrence in the fossil record of families like palms now confined to tropical and subtropical areas) extending as far north as latitudes of 60°, though the desert belts still occurred farther south. At that time there were few barriers to dispersal across the Northern Hemisphere (Figure 1.18b), with the result that many taxa of plants and animals were able to develop very wide distributions. Since the Middle Eocene, global climates have undergone intermittent decline (Figure 1.22). There were sharp falls in temperature at the end of the Eocene, the Mid-Miocene and the Mid-Pliocene. Already, the first glaciers appeared in Antarctica in the Oligocene with more ice cover in the Miocene. This climatic deterioration marks the transition from a **greenhouse** to an **icehouse mode** (see Section 1.4) which about 2.7 Ma ago saw the onset of massive and geologically rapid cyclical climatic oscillations marking the beginning of the Quaternary Ice Age.

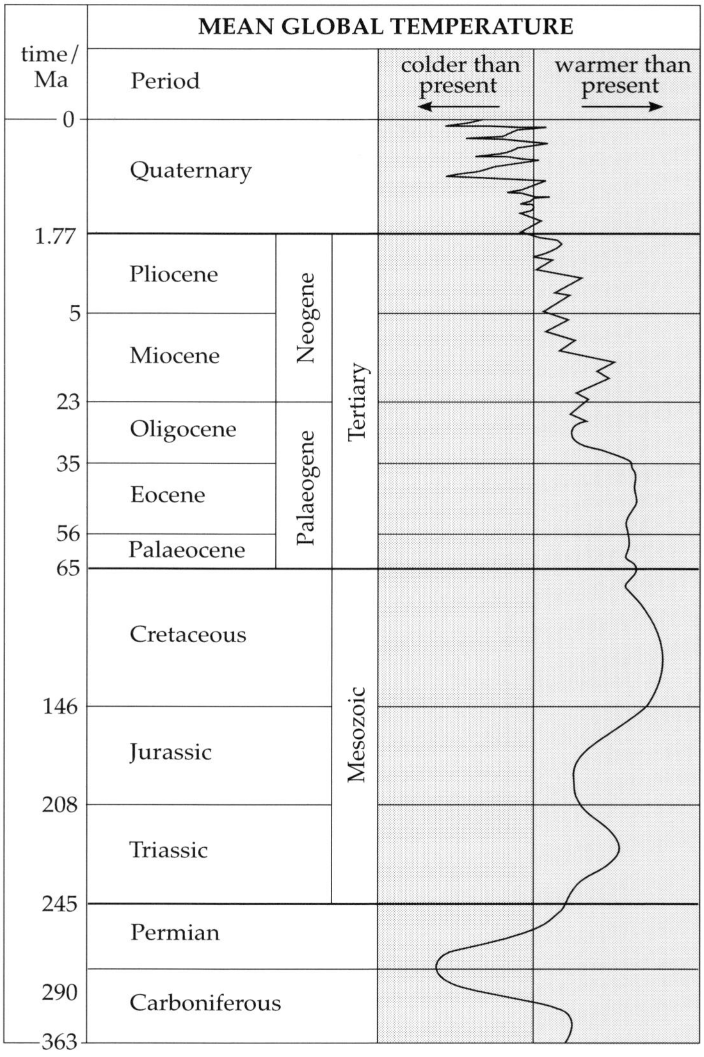

MEAN GLOBAL TEMPERATURE					
time/ Ma	Period			colder than present ←	warmer than present →

Figure 1.22 Changes in the Earth's mean global surface temperature over the past 363 Ma (note that the time axis is not drawn to scale). Temperature changes for the Quaternary are simplified here; see Figure 1.24 later.

Summary of Section 1.3

The **theory of plate tectonics** explains the interrelationships of various geological processes that have had long term evolutionary and environmental effects on the world's biota. The fact of **continental drift** is now well established, and past movements of **lithospheric plates** and continental land masses can be mapped. Like arks, continents carried their biota across latitudinal climatic belts, resulting in species richness and diversity changes and in evolutionary and extinction pressures. Continental collisions, accompanying the subduction of oceans like the Tethys, provided opportunities for faunal and floral exchange, but also resulted in the creation of barriers to dispersal such as the formation of mountain ranges, like the Himalayas and the Alps. The splitting of continents and the formation of new oceans such as the Atlantic resulted in the subdivision and isolation of populations of land faunas and floras, providing a mechanism for vicariance events. Continental movements and **mountain-building** also led to changes in oceanic and atmospheric circulation patterns which had major effects on regional climates, again leading to evolutionary pressures and extinction of taxa. Sea-level changes associated with the activity of constructive plate margins created land bridges again bringing separated faunas and floras into contact and competition, often resulting in extinctions, but also stimulating dispersal. Alternatively, the flooding of land bridges caused populations to split, perhaps leading to evolutionary as well as spatial separation of species and the development of vicariant taxa. It is in the light of these geological processes and their effects on evolution, extinction, dispersal and isolation and vicariance events on species populations that modern and fossil patterns of distribution of organisms also need to be considered.

Question 1.3   (Objectives 1.3–1.5)

A range of organisms, including 11 species of flowering plants and certain lizards and snakes, have disjunct distributions on the islands of the western Mediterranean (Figure 1.23a). These islands include the Balearics – Mallorca, Minorca etc. – Corsica, Sardinia and even some of the smaller islands very close to the French and Italian coasts. Most of these species are endemics, not found on the mainland. They are sometimes represented by subspecies or closely related 'sibling species' on different islands. Geological research has shown that the islands are associated with microplates, small tectonic plates which have significantly changed position during the Late Tertiary. Figure 1.23b shows the suggested position of the islands about 12 Ma ago and their present position, which they may have reached about 6.5 Ma ago. If the present endemism of the special group of plants and reptiles on these islands is to be explained in terms of plate tectonics, what observations can you now make about the origin and subsequent history of these species?

Figure 1.23 (a) Distribution of *Urtica atrovirens* (a nettle) and *Ptilostemon casabonae* (a thistle-like herb) in the islands of the western Mediterranean. (b) The position of Corsica and Sardinia (i) about 12 Ma ago (present coastline shown for reference) and (ii) from about 6.5 Ma ago to the present, showing the effect of microtectonic plate rotation.

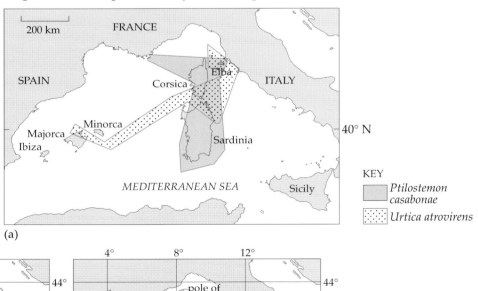

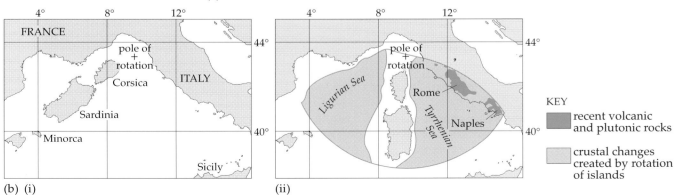

Question 1.4   (Objectives 1.4 & 1.5)

Ginkgo is a genus of gymnosperm trees, widespread in the Jurassic and Cretaceous, but now represented only by a single species *Ginkgo biloba* which has been cultivated in China and Japan for centuries and more recently in Europe and North America. Only recently have possible native sites for the tree been located in China. The fossil record of this tree is shown in Figure 1.13. The tree was widespread and abundant during the Jurassic, when it probably occurred right across the Northern Hemisphere (i.e. it was also present in the areas of its Tertiary distribution and probably in eastern North America where there is simply a dearth of information about Jurassic floras). What factors discussed so far in this Chapter might in part have contributed to the contraction of its range (a) towards the end of the Cretaceous and (b) during the Tertiary?

1.4   Quaternary biogeographical changes

1.4.1   The Quaternary Ice Age

Over the past 2.5 million years, another series of geological events, operating on a much shorter timescale than continental drift, have produced almost as great topographic, climatic and ecological effects. The **Quaternary** is the name given to the most recent geological period which extends to the present day. Though of much shorter duration (so far) than any of the preceding geological periods, its claim to special treatment rests on two grounds. First, it is the period during which hominids and ultimately our own species *Homo sapiens* have evolved, with humans eventually expanding their range into every continent. Secondly, it has been a period when the Earth's climate has become subject to extraordinary cyclic fluctuations.

During the Quaternary, the Earth has shifted fully into its alternative climatic regime, the **icehouse mode**, when global climates on average have been substantially colder than at present. The causes of such changes are not fully understood, but are generally thought to be related to plate tectonics and the changing configuration of continental land masses with the consequent reorganization of the atmospheric and oceanic circulation systems that distribute heat around the surface of the globe. Probably throughout the Earth's history, there have been small cyclic climatic changes related to changes in different parameters that affect the position of the Earth in relation to the Sun such as the variation from elliptic to nearly circular of the Earth's orbit – a 100 000-year cycle – and of the angle of tilt of the Earth's axis – a 41 000-year cycle. Somehow, the effects of these orbital changes have become greatly amplified during the Quaternary, and probably during previous ice ages, so that they have provided the 'pacemaker' for a succession of so-called **glacial–interglacial cycles**, though this is an inadequate term for climatic changes that affect the whole globe and not just areas where glaciation intermittently takes place.

Some of the major climatic patterns and how they affected ecosystems in Europe may be very briefly summarized (Figure 1.24). A sudden fall in mean global temperature at about 2.6 Ma initiated the first of the many cyclic climatic oscillations of the Quaternary Ice Age. It had an immediate effect on the forest flora and also fauna of Europe, which until then had a much higher diversity than today and more closely resembled those of North America and East Asia. Many warm temperate tree genera became extinct, including the tulip tree *Liriodendron* (Figure 1.11a), its close relative *Magnolia* (Figure 1.11b), swamp cypress *Taxodium* and the giant redwood *Sequoia*. The next 1.5 Ma was characterized by rather regular oscillations, with a frequency of about 41 000 years, between cold-climate and temperate stages. During the cold stages, glaciers spread out into some lowland areas, but probably not very extensively. More significantly in the Northern Hemisphere a fauna and flora gradually evolved well adapted to the harsh treeless environments that became so widespread. During the temperate stages, forests in Europe were largely dominated by genera such as oak *Quercus*, elm *Ulmus* and hornbeam *Carpinus* which still play that role today, though a few exotic trees (i.e. taxa no longer native in Europe) persisted.

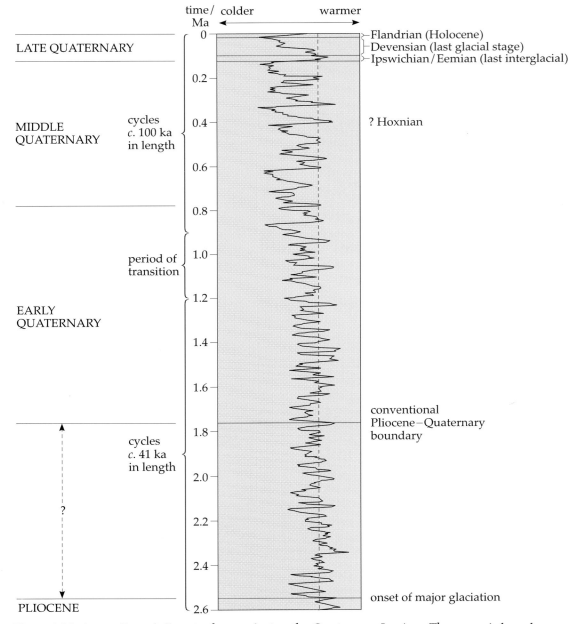

Figure 1.24 An outline of climatic change during the Quaternary Ice Age. The curve is based on isotopic data from deep ocean cores, which largely reflect the amount of seawater locked up as ice in the great ice-sheets. Conventionally, the Quaternary begins at about 1.77 Ma, but many authorities cite the lower boundary at about 2.6 Ma.

About 800 000 years ago both the length and intensity of these cycles increased, with a pattern of roughly 100 000-year cycles. These are the typical glacial–interglacial cycles of the Middle and Late Quaternary. The warm, fully temperate parts of these cycles are called temperate or 'interglacial' stages. In north-west Europe, **interglacial stages** are characterized by the presence of temperate deciduous forest and also by a rise in sea-level to approximately that of today. Shorter periods of warming during these cycles are called **interstadials**, but these are either too short or too cool to allow the return of temperate forest vegetation, though boreal forest, dominated by conifers, may spread. During the glacial stages, sea-levels were low, so that Britain and Ireland, for example, would have been part of the main European land mass, with the bed of the North Sea and much of the English Channel being dry land, except where invaded by glacier ice.

Looking at long climatic records covering this period, it becomes obvious that at present we ourselves exist in the equivalent of an interglacial stage, which has only lasted so far about 10 000 years, shorter than most of the more recent interglacial stages. This present stage is now usually referred to as the **Flandrian**, at least in Europe, but otherwise the old term **Holocene** (or even 'Recent' or 'Post-glacial') is still used, coined when it was assumed that the Quaternary Ice Age was over and done with and not part of ongoing geological history.

During the **cold** (or **'glacial'**) **stages** of this recent part of the Quaternary, ice-sheets have spread out repeatedly (from centres in mountain areas rather than from polar regions) to cover large areas of North America, northern Europe and north-west Asia (Figure 1.25). Smaller glaciers and ice-caps also developed or expanded in mountainous regions of both Northern and Southern Hemispheres, of course causing major shifts in the altitude of vegetation belts.

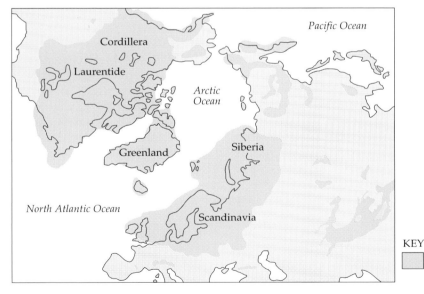

KEY

☐ ice-sheets and large ice-caps

Figure 1.25 Maximum extent of ice-sheets in the Northern Hemisphere during the Quaternary Ice Age.

In Britain, ice-caps and glaciers occupied the mountains of Scotland, Wales and the Lake District, which still show the geomorphological effects of glaciation, but during most of the major glacial stages ice streams from these centres also invaded the lowlands, where they coalesced to form an ice-sheet that itself then accumulated snow and built up to a thickness of hundreds of metres. The most extensive development of the British ice-sheet, about 400 000 years ago, brought the ice front almost to the latitude of London and in fact diverted the River Thames to its present course. The last major glaciation, approximately 30 000–18 000 years ago, did not come so far south but still reached the English Midlands and north Norfolk.

In areas where there was simply not enough precipitation, in the form of snow, to create glaciers, **permafrost** conditions prevailed, with the ground becoming frozen, often to a depth of many metres, and only the surface layers thawing out during the summer. Such conditions are generally unfavourable for the growth of trees, particularly when permafrost is actively developing. Forests do occur over permafrost today in parts of North America and Siberia, but the permafrost under these conditions is probably largely a relic, simply never having thawed since the last glacial period. Permafrost conditions supporting tundra or steppe-tundra are believed to have been the predominant natural environment over most of northern and central Europe during at least the past one million years. Forested conditions, such as we now enjoy, are the exception rather than the rule.

As a result of the growth of huge ice-sheets and glaciers, global sea-levels fell during the cold stages, but returned to approximately their present height when melting took place. Thus, during the cold stages – and, critically, for short periods after the climate began warming again but before all the ice had melted – land bridges developed between land masses that are at present separated, such as Britain, Ireland and the European mainland, and even between continents such as Asia and North America across the Bering Strait, where humans were able to cross into the New World about 12 000 years ago and then rapidly colonize both North and South America. These sea-level changes affect tropical areas in exactly the same way. Thus migration of faunas and floras could take place more easily. During warm stages, when sea-levels rise, the same principle is true for marine faunas, of course.

A major cause of local climate change during the climatic cycles of the Quaternary has been redistribution of heat and consequently precipitation as a result of changes in the pattern of oceanic and atmospheric currents. For example, the Gulf Stream–North Atlantic Drift system of ocean surface-water currents (Book 1, Chapter 4), which brings mild conditions to the Atlantic coasts of north-west Europe, is suppressed during the glacial stages, and instead southward currents bring pack-ice to those shores and this has a substantial refrigerating effect. These circulatory changes have affected not only the higher and middle latitudes, with the very prominent waxing and waning of ice-sheets, but also tropical latitudes, markedly altering the climatic regimes and boundaries of different ecosystems there. Effects of the Quaternary Ice Age on tropical environments are discussed later in Section 1.4.8.

1.4.2   Palaeoecology and the Quaternary fossil record

Clearly, such drastic and relatively rapid changes in climate must have had an enormous effect on the distribution of individual organisms and particularly on that of the whole ecosystems of which they were part. The study of past environments and their faunas and floras is called **palaeoecology**.

In marine environments, particularly the deep ocean, burial by sediments ensures that the remains of many groups of organisms are preserved as fossils. Continents are predominantly regions of erosion rather than deposition, and there are relatively few environments where preservation of fossils is likely to take place, and then only under favourable circumstances. In most but not quite all cases, fossilization only takes place in waterlogged environments.

❑ What kind of environments on a continent like Europe are most likely to produce fossiliferous sediments that could be preserved, at least for a short while, as part of the geological record?

■ Under present conditions, the main sites where sediment deposition is taking place are lakes, peat bogs and river floodplains, but the amount of time represented by their deposits may vary from a few hundred to a few thousand years and only very rarely cover long periods of the Quaternary. Sediments within very damp caves may also preserve some kinds of fossils, particularly vertebrate bones.

One of the great advantages in carrying out palaeoecological studies on Quaternary deposits, at least in Europe, is that so many fossil remains can be recognized as belonging to actual species still living somewhere in the Northern Hemisphere, so that it is possible to use knowledge of their present-day ecology to interpret in some detail what conditions were like at particular times in the distant past.

There are certain exceptions to this, which have apparently only become extinct within the past 120 000 years or much less, such as the mammoth and woolly rhinoceros of glacial times, straight-tusked elephant and at least one other species of rhinoceros found in interglacial sediments and large carnivores such as cave bear and cave lion, which differed slightly from their modern relatives.

❑ Since these animals had all survived through several glacial–interglacial cycles, can you make any suggestions as to why they should all have died out comparatively recently in geological terms?

mammoth   *Mammuthus primigenius* (× 0.015)

■ These are all large animals. Europe now has very few native large mammal species. Although it cannot be proved, many experts believe that hunting by early modern humans who expanded into Eurasia about 120 000 years ago, probably eventually wiped out these species. It has recently been discovered that the last mammoths survived on Wrangel Island off north-east Siberia until only 3700 years ago – very much later than was generally believed – when their disappearance coincided with the first human settlement. Nevertheless, other specialists believe that the complex climatic changes at the end of the last glacial stage played the critical role.

The fossil record, where it is well dated, will of course give important information about the biogeography of individual taxa and how their distribution patterns have changed during the climatic cycles of the Quaternary, but even where fossils occur in abundance the information they can provide may be limited. For example, in lake sediments the shells of freshwater molluscs, the fruits and seeds of aquatic plants and, more rarely bones of fish and amphibians, are all likely to be encountered. These may give information about temperature regime and trophic status of the lake at different times, as well as the nature of its biota, but say comparatively little about environmental conditions in the surrounding area. Large assemblages of mammalian bones, usually associated with the former floodplain deposits of rivers, may give some picture of the terrestrial environment, but in this respect the most important fossils are virtually invisible to the naked eye. These are the fossilized walls of pollen grains and spores, which, though preserved in lacustrine or bog sediments, in fact represent the products of vegetation not just in or around the margins of a lake or bog but of the entire surrounding countryside. The study of fossil pollen grains and spores, which is one of the most important and informative research techniques in palaeoecology, is called **pollen analysis** or **palynology**.

1.4.3 Pollen analysis

Pollen analysis or palynology is a technique that can be applied to sediments such as lake deposits, bog and fen peat accumulations or sometimes even marine deposits in order to study vegetational history, the changes in major vegetation types in an area over hundreds or thousands of years or even longer timespans. The technique depends on two general properties of the pollen grains of flowering plants and conifers and also of the spores of pteridophytes such as ferns, lycopods and horsetails.

The first characteristic is that pollen and spores are produced *in vast quantities*, and in a large number of species are dispersed by wind. This is true of most of our forest trees, which are essentially wind pollinated, bearing their anthers on exposed cones or catkins, and also of almost all grasses and of a large number of species of herbs and shrubs, though many others rely on insect pollination. Anyone who suffers from hay fever will realize that pollen gets virtually everywhere as a rain of minute particles. Pollen grains vary greatly in their structure, as can be observed under a high-power microscope. Usually they have one or more apertures (pores or furrows) and can have a very complicated wall structure. They vary in size from about 15 to 60 μm. Some of the commoner types are illustrated in Figure 1.26. Some can be identified to species level, most to genus level and almost all to family level. This means that it is possible to lay out a 'pollen trap' – a very simple version might be a microscope slide smeared with vaseline or glycerine – and then identify and count representative samples of the *pollen assemblages* in the air. With sophisticated traps, collecting pollen throughout the flowering season, it is possible, making allowances for the differing pollen productivity of various species of trees, shrubs and herbs, to relate these pollen assemblages to the vegetation types that are producing them. Thus, for example, alder and pine produce about ten times as much pollen as oak and beech from the equivalent-sized tree, and, although lime is a heavy pollen producer, it is primarily insect pollinated, and so only some of its pollen is dispersed by wind.

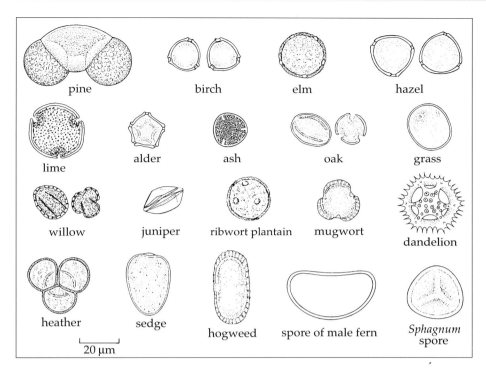

pine   birch   elm   hazel

lime   alder   ash   oak   grass

willow   juniper   ribwort plantain   mugwort   dandelion

heather   sedge   hogweed   spore of male fern   *Sphagnum* spore

20 μm

Figure 1.26 Drawings of various types of pollen grains and spores, showing their characteristic structures and surface patterns.

The second point is that because pollen grains and spores contain living contents vital to the reproduction and survival of their species, this has to be protected from desiccation and fungal and bacterial attack. Almost all land plants have evolved a complex layered structure to spore or pollen grain walls. Part of the outer wall is usually composed of a layer of a chemically almost inert protein called **sporopollenin**. Though rapidly destroyed in soils or on exposed surfaces, this protein is resistant to most agents of decay if it is protected from oxidation under waterlogged or anaerobic environmental conditions. Thus, pollen assemblages that fall on lake floors or on the wet surface of bogs may be preserved as fossil assemblages within the accumulating sediment. Naturally, the living protoplasm breaks down and is destroyed, but at least the sporopollenin wall generally survives and this retains the characteristic patterned structures that allow identification of the grains.

To investigate the vegetational history of an area, a borehole is put down through a peat bog or the bottom of a lake, so that a sediment core is retrieved. Sampling, say at every 10 cm down the core, provides a stratigraphic record covering the period during which those sediments were deposited. If the deposits are rich in organic matter, it may even be possible to use a technique called **radiocarbon dating** to ascertain the absolute age of different levels, but this method can only be applied to material up to about 40 000 years old. It is now known that radiocarbon dates do not correspond precisely with calendar years; older dates underestimate somewhat, but not greatly, the true age. In this Chapter, we use the term 'years BP' (BP = before present), to indicate ages based on uncorrected radiocarbon dates. In the laboratory, a sample of about 1 cm^3 of sediment from each level is processed using sieving and chemical treatments that remove as much of the surrounding matrix as possible but leave intact the fossil pollen grains, which can eventually be mounted on a microscope slide.

Some idea of the magnitude of pollen deposition and preservation in organic sediments can be gained from estimates that a mud sample from an American lake core deposited at the end of the last glacial stage contained about 20 000 pollen grains per cm^3, and a sample dating from the present temperate stage about 650 000 grains per cm^3.

Once the grains have been identified and a sufficient number counted under a high-power microscope, the counts are expressed (statistically) in the form of a **pollen diagram**. Usually, for every level the count for each taxon is expressed as its percentage of the total number of pollen grains of all land plants counted from that sample. Pollen diagrams published before the 1970s often use the percentage of total tree pollen (excluding that of hazel) as their statistical basis. The plots for each level are plotted in stratigraphical order, with the oldest at the base of the diagram and the youngest at the top.

As laid out in the pollen diagram, the **pollen curves** for each taxon show its *relative* increase or decrease in importance over time (Figure 1.27). Thus a pollen diagram for a forested landscape might show how the forest composition changed over a few thousand years, taking into account differences in pollen productivity of the different tree species. At any rate it will allow almost direct interpretation of the major vegetational types and their long-term past changes around the site sampled. A good knowledge of modern plant ecology will allow the pollen analyst to interpret the diagram to recognize the presence of different forest types on different soils in the neighbourhood, as well as evidence for areas of heathland or marsh or grasslands.

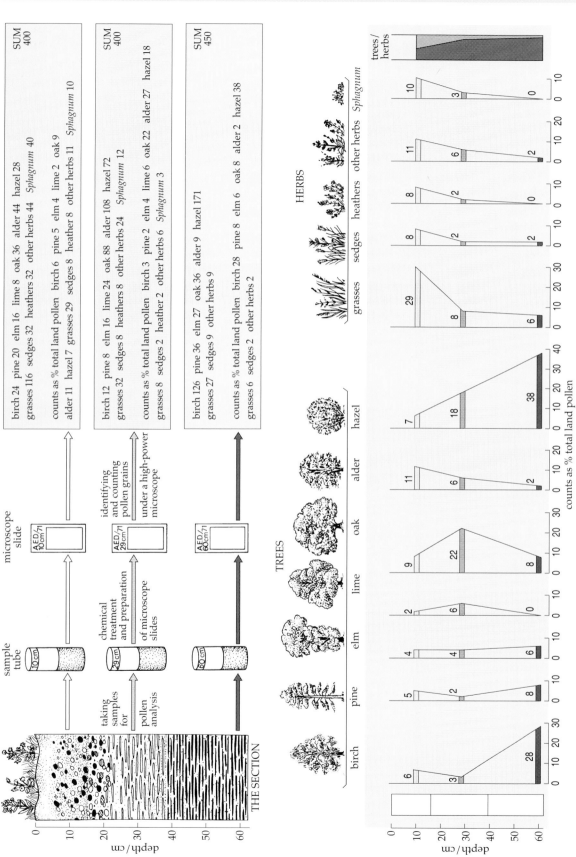

Figure 1.27 Stages in the preparation of a pollen diagram. Note that the spores of *Sphagnum* moss are not included in the percentage base, although their frequency is calculated in the same way.

1.4.4 Interglacial vegetational history – a case study

Figure 1.28 shows a simplified pollen diagram from a sequence of
sediments from a long-vanished lake in southern England (at Marks Tey,
Essex) that were laid down spanning the full duration of a warm
interglacial stage about 400 000 years ago – the Hoxnian Interglacial (Figure
1.24). The interglacial itself probably lasted about 17–20 000 years. The
diagram shows only the curves for the major tree genera and a few other
taxa; those for many other minor herbs and shrubs are omitted. Most of the
trees are still common in British forests and woodland today (see Box 1.1).
Species no longer native include silver fir *Abies*, spruce *Picea*, both
widespread in continental Europe, and wingnut *Pterocarya* which now
grows in the Caucasus Mountains to the east of the Black Sea. The
summary column in the diagrams gives an overall picture of changes
between forest and more open vegetation. Clearly, for most of the
interglacial stage the landscape was densely forested, and open habitats
would have been largely restricted to gaps where tree growth was
prevented or temporarily disrupted, disturbed ground along river
floodplains or following forest fires or storms.

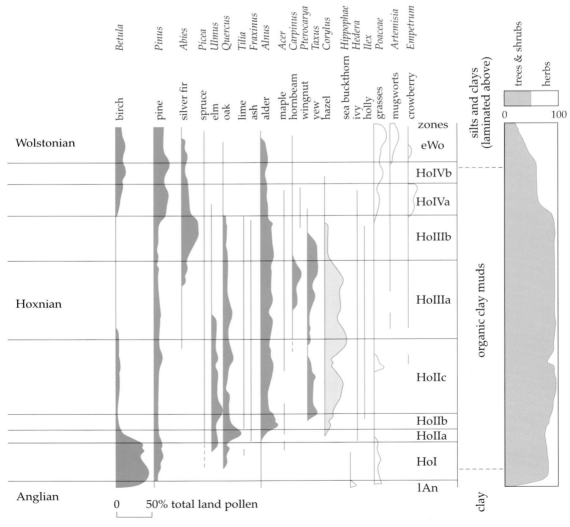

Figure 1.28 Pollen diagram from interglacial lake deposits at Marks Tey, Essex.
(Turner, 1970.)

Box 1.1   Important forest trees and shrubs in Britain

Alder
: Common alder *Alnus glutinosa* is a medium-sized tree of river banks and fen woodlands.

Ash
: Common ash *Fraxinus excelsior* is an abundant tree of deciduous woodland on limestone and neutral soils.

Beech
: Beech *Fagus sylvatica* is a large, stately tree, casting a dense shade. In Britain, native in SE England on chalk and mildly acid soils, but widely planted elsewhere.

Birch
: Silver birch *Betula pendula* is a slender tree, abundant on light soils such as on heaths and moorland, but also occurring as a pioneer tree in clearings in deciduous woodland. Downy birch *Betula pubescens* occurs on similar soils, often on wetter ground and in particular it forms open woodland in the north of Scotland.

Elm
: Elms *Ulmus* spp. are a taxonomically complex group, widely planted. Wych elm *U. glabra* is a widespread tree of woods, hedges and streamsides, tending to prefer damp soils.

Maple
: Field maple *Acer campestre* is common in deciduous woodland on limestone and clay soils in southern and central England. The related sycamore *Acer pseudoplatanus*, though much more widespread is, in fact, an introduced species.

Hazel
: Hazel *Corylus avellana* is a common under-shrub of woodland on limestone, neutral and mildly acid soils, rarely occurring as a canopy-forming tree.

Hornbeam
: Hornbeam *Carpinus betulus* is now often dominant as a coppiced shrub in oakwoods, or it may itself form a dense canopy on sandy and clayey soils, but is confined to south-east England.

Lime
: Small-leaved lime *Tilia cordata* is a now a rather local tree of deciduous woodland in England and Wales. It casts a deep shade and tends to dominate. Probably much commoner formerly since limes occupied the richest and most fertile soils. Large-leaved lime *Tilia platyphyllos* is a rare tree on base-rich soils. The small populations of lime in northern England almost never set fruit.

Oak
: Oaks are dominant in many areas of deciduous woodland, partly because they have been conserved for their excellent timber. English oak *Quercus robur* occurs principally on basic and neutral soils and the closely related sessile oak *Quercus petraea* largely replaces it on lighter, acid soils.

Pine
: Scots pine *Pinus sylvestris* is native in Britain only in the west and central Highlands of Scotland, where it is the dominant tree. Widely planted elsewhere.

Silver fir	Silver fir *Abies alba* is not a native British tree, but occurs in central and southern Europe, generally in mountain areas. Occasionally planted in Britain.
Spruce	Norway spruce *Picea abies* is also not a native tree now in Britain, though widespread in northern continental Europe, particularly in mountain areas. Widely planted for timber and as Christmas trees.
Willow	There are numerous species of willows and the related sallows, all *Salix* spp., which grow beside rivers, in fens and in damp woodland.
Wingnut	Wingnut *Pterocarya fraxinifolia* is no longer native in western Europe but still grows in the Caucasus Mountains, east of the Black Sea, where it occurs on very damp soils. It is sometimes planted in Britain.
Yew	Yew *Taxus baccata* is the only large gymnosperm tree in deciduous woodland, widespread on chalk in southern England, sometimes colonizing abandoned open downland, and more scattered farther north.
Holly	Holly *Ilex aquifolium* is a small evergreen tree or shrub occurring throughout the British Isles.
Ivy	Ivy *Hedera helix* is not technically a shrub but a woody climber prominent in many British woodlands.
Juniper	Juniper *Juniperus communis* is a local shrub of moorland, open pine woodland and chalk downland.
Sea buckthorn	Sea buckthorn *Hippophae rhamnoides* is a spiny shrub of sand dunes in Britain, also occurring on river gravels in central Europe.

Notice that the pollen diagram in Figure 1.28 has been split up into sections by horizontal lines. The pollen assemblages have thus been artificially divided up into blocks called **pollen zones**.

❑   What purposes does this zonation serve?

■   (i) It simplifies discussion of the diagram.

(ii) It delimits sections with relatively homogeneous pollen assemblages, and emphasizes levels where marked changes occur.

(iii) It makes it easier to compare this pollen diagram with those from other sites.

Very often, the zone numbers (or letters) are prefixed with initials that designate the site or, as in this case (Ho), a group of sites. Again this helps when comparing different sites.

The zone boundaries are placed at horizons at which, according to their pollen curves, particular trees either immigrated into the region or substantially increased their importance in the vegetation or else declined abruptly or even disappeared. It is clear that a vegetational succession took place, a topic to which Chapter 3 will be devoted.

Examine the pollen diagram carefully and answer the following questions:

❑ Which trees dominated the vegetation during zone HoI? Where would vegetation of this kind occur naturally today?

■ Birch and pine which, growing in the absence of temperate trees, are characteristic of the boreal forests of Scandinavia and Russia, extending up into the subarctic.

(Note, however, that they are pioneer species, both with wind-dispersed seeds, which in some types of temperate woodland, if they are also present, tend to quickly occupy clearings or gaps in the forest, later being shaded out by the dominant deciduous trees. The question unanswered here is whether at this early stage in the interglacial succession they indicate a cool climate or are simply quick-migrating pioneer species moving in after climatic amelioration but before the immigration of oak.)

❑ In zone HoIIa, oaks were clearly the dominant trees in the forest, but the expansion of alder (and to a lesser extent hazel) at the beginning of zone HoIIb, led to a fall in oak pollen percentages. Today, common alder (believed to be the same species represented at Marks Tey) is a tree of wet woodland and riversides. It is a more plentiful pollen producer than oak. How would you explain its expansion in ecological terms?

■ Alder was already present in zone HoIIa, so its expansion must be a response to environmental change. It would not replace oak species on dry slopes, so flat ground and river floodplains must have become much wetter. The expansion of alder therefore suggests a climatic change involving an increase in annual rainfall. The high pollen productivity of alder over-emphasizes the decline of oak in the pollen diagram, because of the method of calculation.

❑ Which were the trees that particularly expanded in zones HoIIIa and HoIIIb? What was their impact on elm, oak and hazel which together with ash (a low pollen producer) are the commonest native forest trees over much of Britain today?

■ Hornbeam, yew, silver fir and also wingnut are the trees which expanded in the later part of the interglacial succession. A fall in the oak and elm curves coincided with the expansion of hornbeam and re-expansion of yew. Later, hazel and these latter two trees successively virtually disappeared as silver fir expanded. The replacement of oak and its companion species by hornbeam and/or silver fir is a characteristic of many interglacial pollen diagrams across Europe. There is ongoing debate as to whether this relates to the gradual leaching and maturation of soils during the course of interglacials or to a gradual transition to a more 'continental' climate with cooler winters and warmer summers, or to other factors.

❑ Which features suggest a major climatic change at the beginning of zone HoIVa?

■ The onset of zone HoIVa seems to have marked the point where temperate tree species virtually ceased to be important elements in the forest. Pine and birch began to re-expand but the developing boreal forest was opening out, with grasses becoming increasingly important. Crowberry (*Empetrum*), a plant of wet coastal heaths and also acid moorland on mountains, suddenly became abundant. These developments must be interpreted as a return to much cooler, wetter conditions. However, it is the increase of herbaceous pollen and the expansion of mugwort *Artemisia* after the end of zone HoIVb that indicates the beginning of the development of steppe-tundra under cold-climate periglacial conditions.

This pollen diagram has been examined in some detail because it provides evidence of a natural vegetational succession and transitions between ecosystems as a result of climatic change in the complete absence of the effects of modern humans and their activities which now have such a far-reaching effect on all ecosystems in Europe and most other parts of the Earth's surface.

It also illustrates a series of substages characteristic of most interglacial stages in which different ecosystems develop in succession. To provide a general summary (Figure 1.29):

- Climatic amelioration at the end of a glacial stage, the treeless **late-glacial**, permitted the immigration and expansion of boreal forest trees (zone I, the **pre-temperate substage**) forming an increasingly dense woodland cover.

- Arrival and quite rapid spread of oak and/or elm species marked the onset of zone II, the **early-temperate substage**, with a succession of broad-leaved deciduous trees immigrating and expanding to form a dense forest cover. Differences between species in the times of arrival and expansion, particularly between different interglacial periods, are ascribed to such factors as speed of migration, distance from refugia where these temperate species survived the intervening harsh glacial conditions, and climatic factors.

- During zone III, the **late-temperate substage**, the early-temperate forest trees were gradually replaced by late-immigrating species, perhaps as a result of soil maturation or climatic change, but certainly greatly changing the nature of the forest. These trees are principally hornbeam *Carpinus* and silver fir *Abies*, but in this diagram wingnut *Pterocarya* might be included and in Flandrian diagrams beech *Fagus*.

- Zone IV, the **post-temperate substage**, saw the disappearance of temperate forest and its replacement by increasingly open boreal forest or woodland with the development of heathland or cold grassland steppe.

- Ultimately, **early-glacial** conditions returned with the breakdown of woodland vegetation as a result of falling temperatures and the spread of freeze–thaw activity and perhaps permafrost, so that bog and tundra developed over a landscape with greatly impeded drainage.

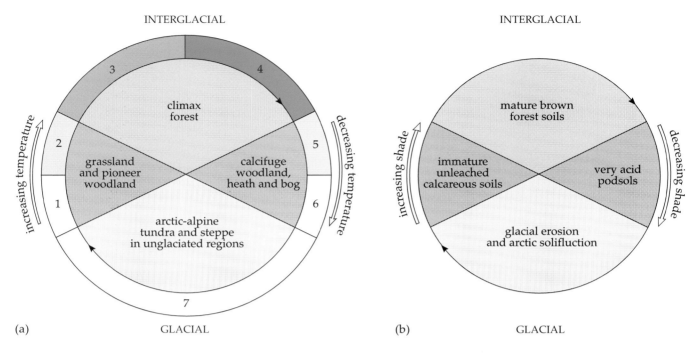

KEY

1   late-glacial
2   pre-temperate substage   5   post-temperate substage
3   early-temperate substage   6   early-glacial
4   late-temperate substage   7   pleniglacial (full glacial)

Figure 1.29 Diagrammatic summary of a glacial–interglacial cycle and the characteristic successional development of vegetation and soils during interglacial stages. Note that the cold-climate parts of such cycles are, in fact, very much longer than the temperate parts and are much more complex than shown here, being interrupted by phases of interstadial warming.

Interglacial faunas, as known from fossil assemblages of different taxa, consist largely of taxa still found (though sometimes now very rare) in forested environments today. For example, amongst the larger vertebrates from the last two major interglacial stages are various deer (including roe, fallow deer and elk), wood bison, fox, badger, wild boar, beaver, bear, as well as a few extinct taxa, straight-tusked elephant *Palaeoloxodon antiquus*, two extinct rhinoceros species and a large beaver *Trogontherium*.

1.4.5 Glacial stage environments

During the glacial stages, most of northern Europe was covered intermittently by ice-sheets or was in the grip of deep permafrost. Pollen analysis on thin deposits formed in temporary pools shows that the vegetation was treeless. Plant macrofossils reveal a curious mixture of species from the point of view of their modern ecology. Many of these indicate openness and instability of both soils and plant cover. Some species now occur in the Arctic tundra or else on rocky slopes and cliffs in mountain areas (Figure 1.30), but others today live in disturbed habitats, on river banks or even as weeds of human cultivation or waysides. Their common feature is that they are shade intolerant. Plant communities were nevertheless diverse with some much richer grassland and tall herb communities and clearly a great deal of bog, because of the impeded drainage caused by underlying permafrost. Although trees were absent, dwarf shrubs included dwarf willows, crowberry and perhaps sometimes juniper in some communities. The modern distribution patterns of many of the species present do not overlap and they now apparently have different climatic requirements, which has confused some attempts to reconstruct past climate by simply using present-day plant communities as analogues. However, it is necessary to remember that there *are* no modern analogues to the tundra-like environments of the middle latitudes during the Quaternary Ice Age, which, for example, had quite different seasonal patterns and day-length variations to present-day arctic or alpine environments.

mossy cyphel (*Cherleria sedoides*)
(×1)

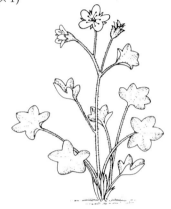

brook saxifrage (*Saxifraga rivularis*)
(×1)

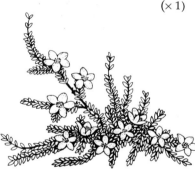

purple saxifrage (*Saxifraga oppositifolia*)
(×1)

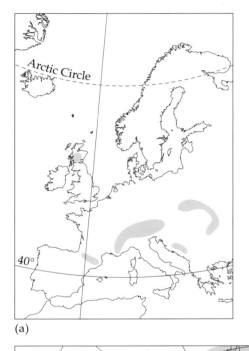

(a)

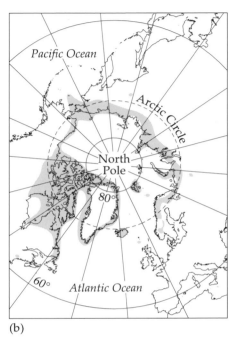

(b)

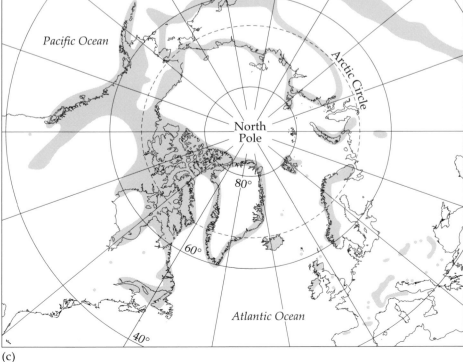

(c)

Figure 1.30 Modern world distribution maps of (a) mossy cyphel *Cherleria sedoides*, (b) brook saxifrage *Saxifraga rivularis* and (c) purple saxifrage *Saxifraga oppositifolia*. All are found in the British Isles today, but otherwise they show alpine, arctic and arctic–alpine distribution patterns respectively. Fossil remains of all three have been found in deposits in southern Britain, dating from the last glacial stage.

These environments also had a distinctive mammalian fauna. Mammoth and woolly rhinoceros have already been mentioned, but musk-ox, reindeer, and at times bison and saiga antelope also roamed the north European plain from Britain and France to southern Russia and beyond, together with small mammals such as lemming, ground squirrel and arctic hare. Carnivores included the extinct cave lion and cave bear, but also wolf, wolverine and ermine. Polar bear has on occasion been found as a fossil in Britain. Most of the species that survive occur now in the arctic regions or in the arid steppe lands of Siberia and central Asia. These areas must be regarded as refugia into which such species have been driven, partly by climatic factors, but also by human activities, until the next phase of global cooling restores at least some of them to their position as the characteristic fauna of most of Eurasia during the Quaternary.

Discussion of modern refugia for plants and animals that were particularly adapted to cold-stage conditions immediately raises the question as to where the refugia were for temperate species of plants and animals in Europe during the glacial stages. It used to be assumed that as climate changed vegetation belts migrated as a unit together with their fauna.

❑   What kind of evidence suggests that this is not the case?

■   Pollen diagrams, such as that from Marks Tey, show that during the interglacial periods, and likewise the Flandrian, the temperate forest trees arrived in Britain at different times and indeed in a different sequence. In other words, different species have been behaving in an individual fashion in response to climatic change and other environmental factors.

There are important implications here, when considering the nature of communities. For example, the interglacial oak-dominated forests of zone HoIIa clearly had a different species composition from those later in the interglacial and from oak forest growing in the region today. This would be true not only for the trees, but also for the herbaceous species which are poorly recorded in the pollen record and also, of course, for the animal communities, which we have hardly considered. In historical terms, communities derive from *available* species. Given the instability of ecosystems during the Quaternary, the composition of communities will depend not only on physical factors like climate and soils and on competitive interactions, but also on the survival of taxa in **refugia** during unfavourable climatic intervals, and on rates of migration from those refugia into new territories when climates become more suitable for individual species.

Summary of Sections 1.4.1 to 1.4.5

During the Mid-Tertiary, the Earth's climate passed from a greenhouse mode into an **icehouse mode** which culminated in the **Quaternary** Ice Age. This began about 2.6 Ma ago, the initial cooling causing extinction of many temperate plant genera in Europe which still survive in other regions of the Northern Hemisphere. The Quaternary is characterized by a highly unstable climate, and in temperate latitudes, such as that of north-west Europe, by long cold or glacial stages alternating with shorter temperate or interglacial stages, accompanying the growth and melting respectively of huge ice-sheets over North America and Eurasia and associated oscillations of sea-level. We live in the **Flandrian,** the latest **interglacial stage**. These **glacial–interglacial cycles** also affect atmospheric and oceanic circulation patterns. During interglacial stages, the climate of western Europe is greatly influenced by the warm Gulf Stream–North Atlantic Drift current system, which is suppressed during the glacial stages.

Palaeoecology is the study of past environments and their faunas and floras. Ideally, such studies require a clear and well-dated stratigraphic record with good fossil preservation. Reconstruction of Quaternary palaeoenvironments is helped by the fact that most taxa found as fossils are still extant. Important fossil material includes vertebrate bones, molluscs, plant fruits and seeds but above all the distinctive fossilized walls of pollen and spores, which survive in great abundance in waterlain or waterlogged sediments.

The technique of **pollen analysis** is particularly important in the reconstruction of past vegetation and, by inference, climate. It is based on the following premises:

- Plants produce and disperse pollen grains in vast numbers. Pollen grains can be identified as belonging to species or groups of species.
- Pollen and spores deposited in wet environments may become incorporated in accumulating sediments and fossilized. Assemblages of different kinds of pollen grains reflect the local and regional vegetation at the time of deposition.
- Proportional counts of pollen assemblages from different depths in lake and peat deposits can be displayed as pollen diagrams, and changes in pollen curves can then be interpreted in terms of vegetational change.
- Organic deposits laid down over the past 40 000 years are young enough for **radiocarbon dating** to be applied, providing a timescale for vegetational changes during the Flandrian period and much of the Devensian (last glacial) period.

A **pollen diagram** from a sequence of ancient lake deposits provides an example of a complete vegetational succession through a temperate interglacial stage, which is believed to be virtually unaffected by human disturbance. The **pollen zones** provide evidence for the following substages:

(i)   A **late-glacial substage** suggesting an open, treeless landscape, though with some willow and sea-buckthorn scrub.

(ii) A **pre-temperate substage** in which boreal woodland, and eventually forest, becomes established, dominated by birch and pine.

(iii) An **early-temperate substage** during which a succession of broad-leaved deciduous tree taxa immigrate and expand, oak, elm, hazel and alder being particularly important.

(iv) A **late-temperate substage** in which late-immigrating temperate trees, particularly hornbeam and silver fir, immigrate and soon largely replace most of the early temperate deciduous trees.

(v)   A **post-temperate substage,** showing a return to dominance of boreal forest trees and at the same time the development and spread of heathland and grassland.

(vi) An **early-glacial substage** in which forest declines and open communities, perhaps steppe tundra, expand probably as soils are disrupted by freeze–thaw processes.

An important observation is that temperate tree species immigrate and expand their populations at different times and not as a community. This suggests that communities are to some extent defined by historical chance.

Pollen and plant macrofossil evidence can also be used to reconstruct the tundra-like communities of the glacial stages, and in particular the biogeographical and historical status of plants with arctic–alpine distribution patterns now found in British mountains. However, the plant communities of the glacial stage consist not only of species presently found in cold-climate arctic and alpine regions, but also species that are now weeds or plants of waste ground, with very different geographical distributions today. This emphasizes that these plant communities have no modern analogue. The cold-stage mammal faunas were also very distinctive, contrasting strongly with the forest faunas of the interglacial stages.

Question 1.5 *(Objective 1.7)*

What effects do you think the presence of large ice-sheets might have on oceanic islands farther south in the Atlantic Ocean and their fauna? Suggest two or three hypothetical examples.

Question 1.6 *(Objective 1.1)*

What role do (a) spores, (b) pollen and (c) seeds play in the dispersal of plants?

Question 1.7 *(Objective 1.8)*

Suppose that a further pollen sample is prepared and counted from a depth of 45 cm in the sediment sequence shown in Figure 1.27. The pollen analyst's count sheet shows the following totals for grains of each taxon: birch 10, pine 5, elm 65, lime 45, oak 130, alder 160, hazel 70, grasses 5, other herbs 10.

Calculate the percentage values for these taxa, based on the sum of total land pollen. You should then draw these percentages in as lines on the pollen diagram in Figure 1.27 at the appropriate horizon, since this information will be used further in Question 1.15.

Question 1.8 *(Objectives 1.6 & 1.9)*

At the beginning of interglacial periods, birches are almost always the first deciduous trees to immigrate and multiply to form a fairly closed woodland. However, it is known from other climatic indicators that climate warms up very rapidly at this time, so that both summer and winter mean temperatures would be more than adequate for oaks (and other fully temperate deciduous trees) to thrive. Suggest three factors (not necessarily of equal importance) which would encourage the appearance of birches rather than oaks at this critical period in the interglacial vegetational development.

Question 1.9   (Objectives 1.6 & 1.12)

In the early years of the 20th century, there were fierce debates about the history of plant and animal species found on mountains in Britain which had arctic and or alpine distribution patterns. One school of thought claimed that since highland Britain had been entirely glaciated during the glacial periods, these species must have arrived by various dispersal methods (such as transport by birds for plant seeds), from arctic or alpine areas during the post-glacial period. Others claimed that they must have survived through the glacial periods on nunataks, 'islands' of unglaciated rock that protrude above the level of large ice-sheets. What would your explanation now be, and what evidence would you produce to back it up?

1.4.6 Southern Europe

Pollen diagrams from many places in northern Europe suggest that for long periods during the glacial stages the whole region north of the Alps was virtually treeless. During the course of these glacial stages, there were occasional short interstadial intervals when climate warmed up, often with quite high mean summer temperatures. At these times, tree birches, pine and sometimes spruce arrived and formed open woodland, but there were almost no temperate deciduous tree species. This led people to believe that the area where mixed oak forest trees survived must be around the Mediterranean, and, for a while, it was assumed (though without any firm evidence) that a zone of temperate deciduous woodland persisted there during the glacial stages.

A small number of sites have been found in central France, Italy and Greece where sedimentation in lakes has been continuous throughout the last glacial period and sometimes for much longer. The evidence from the French sites confirms that deciduous forest trees were absent there virtually throughout the last glacial stage, though small stands of pine may have persisted.

More important are sites in Italy, where lakes have persisted in ancient volcanic craters near Rome. At Valle di Castiglione, where such a lake still existed but was finally drained in the 19th century, it was possible to put down a borehole in the centre of the lake basin to a depth of 88 m. The sediments are estimated to represent more than the past 250 000 years. In this part of Italy today, the vegetation shows a strong altitudinal zonation. At low altitudes near the coast, the vegetation is typically of *Mediterranean* aspect, even though the burning and clearance of forests means that scrub communities such as maquis and garrigue (Book 1, Section 3.4.1) predominate. The tree and shrub species include evergreen oak *Quercus ilex*, olive *Olea*, *Phillyrea* and *Cistus*. Inland, in the foothills of the Apennine mountain range, the *submontane* forests contain most of the tree species found in British woodlands, together with additional species. These include deciduous oaks, elm, lime, maple, hazel, hornbeam and sweet chestnut. Today, most of the woodland around the site of Valle di Castiglione has been cleared, but, under undisturbed conditions it would be surrounded by this kind of submontane forest, but close to the Mediterranean forest zone. The montane forests in the higher part of the Apennines contain beech, fir and spruce.

The pollen diagram from the deep core at Valle di Castiglione shows that very great changes in vegetation have taken place in the neighbourhood, as indeed over the whole of the Mediterranean area, during the past 250 000 years. It is a very detailed and complex record, so that here in Figure 1.31 a condensed pollen diagram is presented in which the curves for tree pollen are combined into three ecological categories, based on the vegetation zones described above. The fourth curve is that for herbs, but it is labelled xeric (i.e. dry) vegetation because its principal constituents are not only grass pollen but pollen of mugwort species *Artemisia* and chenopods Chenopodiaceae. The latter two taxa are believed to represent a group of herb species adapted to growing under quite arid steppe conditions.

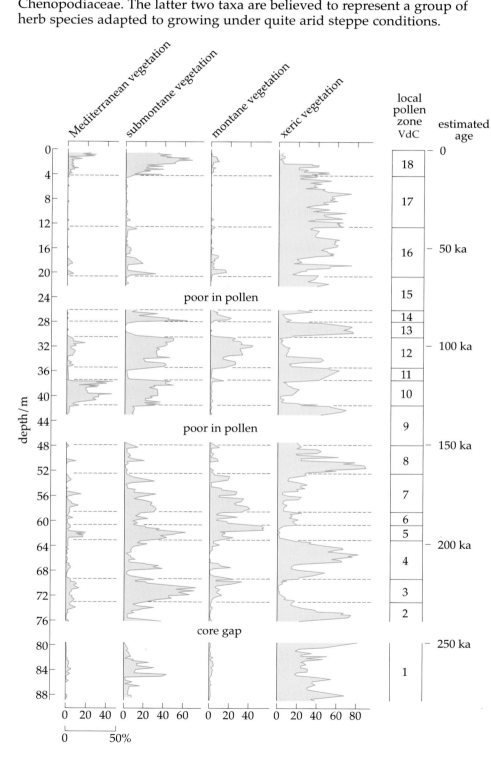

Figure 1.31 Summary pollen diagram from lake deposits at Valle di Castiglione, Italy, showing four main groups of vegetation types (Mediterranean, submontane, montane and xeric). (Follieri, Magri and Sadori, 1988.)

❑ On the basis of the pollen record, can you subdivide the different pollen assemblages recorded over the past 130 000 years into three different groups? How would you characterize each of these assemblages in terms of their composition (i.e. contributions from different vegetation types)? Use the zone numbers to describe the different time periods when particular assemblages predominated.

■ Zones VdC-18 and 10 have the highest percentages of Mediterranean-type pollen; the assemblages VdC-11, 13 and 15–17 are dominated by pollen of xeric vegetation; zones VdC-12 and 14 possess pollen assemblages predominantly of submontane and montane forest type.

Zone VdC-18, when clearly both Mediterranean and submontane forest have been growing close to the site, largely represents the Flandrian or Holocene, together with a short warm oscillation marking the end of the last glacial stage. The other period with vegetation closely resembling this is Zone VdC10, which must represent the last interglacial stage (130–115 000 years ago). Stronger development of the Mediterranean vegetation at that time suggests that climate may even have been warmer then than today. Periods of forest vegetation in which montane forest trees were more abundant than today, and the Mediterranean element sparser or absent, occurred in Zones VdC-12 and 14, so overall climate must have been cooler then, though probably with quite high rainfall, as in the more mountainous areas of Italy today. The most striking feature is the rapid shifts to xeric vegetation and apparent virtual elimination of trees first in Zones VdC-11 and 13, and then for much longer during Zones VdC-15–17. This indicates development of some kind of virtually treeless 'steppe' vegetation, certainly under very dry and probably rather cold conditions (though warm steppes can occur). Furthermore, this 'steppe' vegetation has actually dominated the area for a rather longer period than forest during the past 130 000 years.

Comparing these ancient pollen assemblages with those from modern vegetation, we have quite good analogues for the forested periods, but not for the cold-stage vegetation. Some of the cold, arid semi-deserts of Central Asia and the bleak treeless mountain plateaus of Iran carry plant communities in which either *Artemisia* species or chenopods are frequent, but together with other taxa which seem never to have reached Europe. This example again shows that vegetational communities, even of the quite recent past, may, at least in their species composition though not necessarily in their life forms, be different from any existing vegetation types. This situation means that, whereas we may look at communities and ecosystems in terms of their species composition and the complex interactions, in fact their nature depends fundamentally on the history of individual populations in a rapidly changing world.

1.4.7 Temperate refugia

We have seen that during the Quaternary there have been immense changes in populations and distribution of virtually the whole fauna and flora of Europe. The same could certainly be said of many other temperate areas of the world, but also about some tropical and subtropical environments, as we shall see in Section 1.4.8. In these changes, the key unit is the population, including its size, its mobility and its adaptability, as well as its interrelationships with other taxa.

❑ At times of climatic deterioration, e.g. at the end of an interglacial stage, what would you expect to happen to the populations of deciduous trees (and their progeny) in the forests of north-west Europe, and also the populations of animals dependent on them?

■ The parent trees will obviously die, and they are unlikely to leave any progeny. Even though they have the capacity for seed dispersal, as shown by the arrival of their forebears, all available niches are likely to be occupied. Almost all tree species found in northern Europe also occur in southern Europe. The same will be true of most of the invertebrate fauna. Larger mammals, birds and some migratory insects may be able to move to more favourable climatic areas.

The death of existing species in the vegetation will enable boreal trees, and later, as these fail, heath and tundra dwarf shrubs and herbs to move in, together with a cool-climate invertebrate and vertebrate fauna.

It therefore seems that southern Europe should contain the refugia in which populations of the many different species of plants and animals adapted to temperate deciduous forest and related ecosystems can survive whenever adverse conditions of the long glacial stages of the Quaternary return.

❑ To what extent does the Valle di Castiglione pollen diagram (which is indeed similar to diagrams covering this period in other parts of the Mediterranean area) support this hypothesis?

■ In fact, it suggests that most of the area was as unfavourable to forest growth as the periglacial steppe-tundra of northern Europe. The one feature suggesting that refugia might be not too distant is the relatively rapid appearance of temperate tree taxa in the pollen diagram even when minor ameliorations of climate, i.e. interstadials, took place.

One further possibility needs to be addressed. Pollen diagrams calculated on a percentage basis can overemphasize the importance of taxa which simply produce abundant pollen. Where the rate of accumulation of sediment is constant and the volume of sediment counted is known exactly, it is possible to prepare pollen diagrams that also show changes in the concentration of the pollen of different taxa through time. This is effectively a measure of the *absolute* abundance of plants in the vegetation and can in turn be interpreted in terms of plant productivity over time. The pollen concentration diagram from Valle di Castiglione (Figure 1.32) has also been simplified to show the curves for tree pollen and non-tree pollen. These obviously suggest that trees were enormously productive during the peaks of the temperate stages and major interstadials, but again that tree pollen (with the exception of a very small curve for pine) was virtually absent throughout much of the last cold stage.

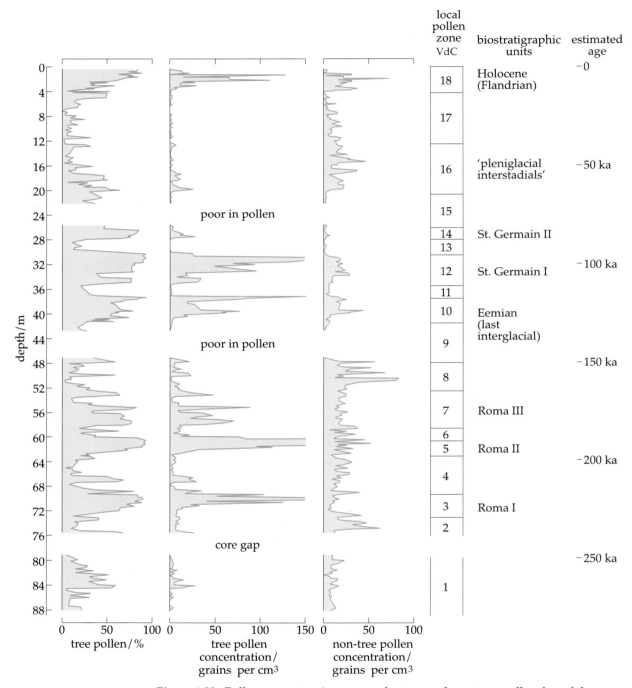

Figure 1.32 Pollen concentration curves for tree and non-tree pollen from lake deposits at Valle di Castiglione, Italy. (Follieri, Magri and Narcisi, 1990.)

❑ Compare the percentage and concentration pollen curves for xeric vegetation and non-tree pollen in Figures 1.31 and 1.32. Virtually the same taxa are represented. How can the differences between them in the two diagrams be explained?

■ During the forested zones, the pollen productivity of herbaceous species is still as high or higher than their productivity during the open-vegetation, cooler/drier climate zones. In fact, the high percentage curves for xeric vegetation species primarily indicate the absence of trees and actually represent a rather sparse vegetation cover and one that would have had a limited capacity to carry any great faunal diversity.

The problem, therefore, remains as to whereabouts the refugia for temperate forest and woodland species of both fauna and flora were during successive glacial stages of the Quaternary in Europe, allowing them to spread out during both interglacials and the temporary warming of interstadial intervals. Current opinion suggests that temperate deciduous trees might have survived in scattered sheltered places, such as gorges and cliffs in the mountains of Greece, Italy and Spain, or in small areas of riverine forest, but this is inevitably speculation, as such sites are unlikely to leave a fossil record. The difficulties of survival are compounded by geographical factors which probably account for the much greater diversity of temperate forest species in eastern Asia and in North America than in Europe (Section 1.2.1). In Europe, physiographical barriers to migration are presented by east–west-trending mountain ranges, such as the Alps, the Pyrenees and the Carpathians, and also by the Mediterranean Sea itself. These are thought to be responsible for the great number of extinctions, particularly at the beginning of the Quaternary, when cold-climate conditions first expanded. They have certainly helped to prevent the persistence of any real belts of deciduous forest vegetation. By contrast, in North America, and in China and Japan, mountain ranges trend north–south. In Europe, the Tertiary forests had nowhere to migrate in the face of deteriorating climate, whereas in North America and eastern Asia there were no such barriers to their southward dispersal to favourable niches in which to take refuge and the possibility of altitudinal changes in mountain vegetation zones, to an extent not possible in Europe.

1.4.8   Tropical refugia

Until about 1970, it was believed that tropical ecosystems were more diverse than temperate ones because of the supposed stability of tropical environments, and that the tropics remained relatively free from disturbance, while higher latitudes were affected by long periods of cooling during the Quaternary Ice Age. Palynological studies of Late Quaternary lake deposits from tropical mountains from each of the three tropical regions subsequently demonstrated that the tropics also experienced major changes with respect to their vegetation, as temperate regions became invaded by ice-sheets.

Vegetation changes in the low latitude tropics are of two types – those relating to temperature change, and those relating to changes of moisture availability. As a result of temperature fluctuations, lowland, montane and tropicalpine vegetation established itself at different altitudes at different times. During glacial periods, tropicalpine and montane vegetation became much more widespread, whereas lowland vegetation was pushed down to lower altitudes compared to its present distribution. During interglacial periods, montane vegetation became restricted to higher altitude settings, and lowland vegetation expanded its areas of distribution.

A good example of a pollen diagram depicting vegetational change as a result of past temperature changes is presented in Figure 1.33. This has been produced by studying pollen and spore assemblages from a radiocarbon-dated lake deposit from the Colombian Andes, and provides a continuous record of vegetational history from the mid-part of the last glacial to historical times. The lake is at 2580 m altitude and the natural vegetation at this level is Andean (tropical montane) forest.

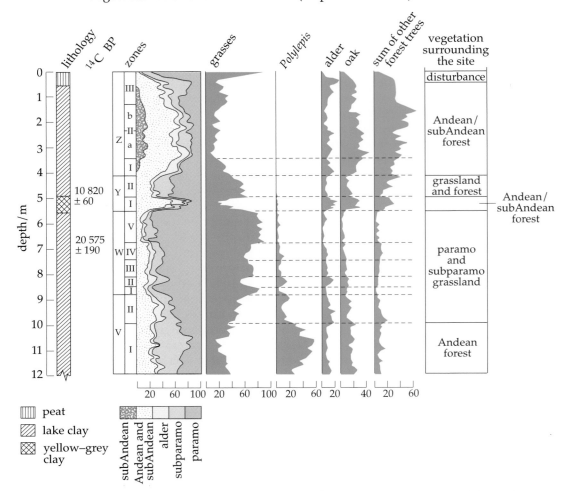

Figure 1.33 Pollen diagram from Laguna de Fuquerne, Colombia (2580 m), showing interpreted vegetation changes (after Flenley, 1979 and van Geel & van der Hammen, 1973)

Assemblages from the upper 4 m of the profile are dominated by oak *Quercus* and alder *Alnus* pollen, together with that of other forest elements, whereas from 4 m to 5.5 m forest elements alternate with pollen of grasses. The section from 5.5 m to 8.5 m contains abundant grass (Poaceae) pollen, suggesting that from 10 800 to before 20 000 years BP, unforested Paramo (tropicalpine grassland), surrounded the site. Pollen of the shrub *Polylepis*, which characterizes the upper part of the Andean forest, is common within the basal section of the profile, and suggests that the area surrounding the lake was vegetated by *Polylepis* forest at the period when the deepest sediments examined were deposited.

The vegetational succession from this pollen profile suggests an initial period with conditions a little cooler than at present, followed by much colder conditions during deposition of the 8.5–5.5 m interval. There were rapid temperature fluctuations at about 10 000 years BP, after which temperatures were more or less comparable to those of the present day. The maximum of grass pollen in the topmost sample relates to human activity.

Evidence for such vegetation change over the past 30 000 years or so is now widely available from each of the tropical regions of South America, Africa and the Far East, and also from different altitudes. When the timing of vegetation changes at different altitudes is compared, it becomes clear that changing temperatures have affected tropical vegetation at low altitudes as well as in the mountains. Figure 1.34 presents a summary of vegetation change over the past 35 000 years for the Far East (New Guinea and Indonesia), and shows variations in the position of the main vegetational boundaries with time. It is clear that, at the same time as montane forests were depressed in the tropical mountains, the upper boundary of tropical lowland rainforest was also being depressed.

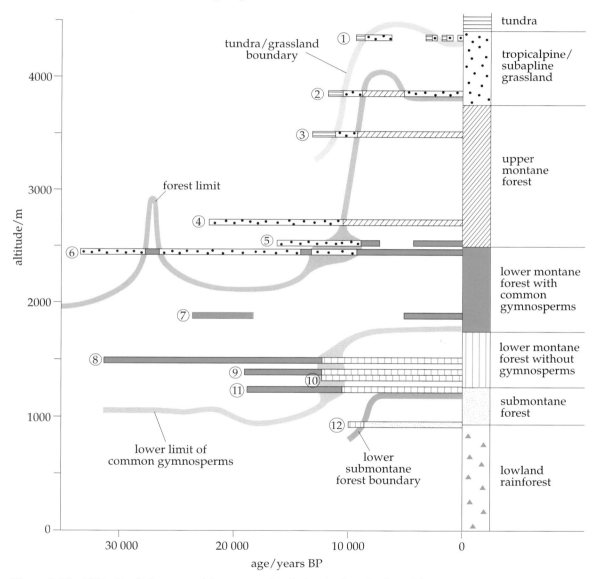

Figure 1.34 Altitudinal changes of the vegetation belts during the Late Pleistocene in New Guinea, Sumatra and West Java, as interpreted from palynological evidence. The horizontal bars represent sites for which there is a pollen record and changes in the nature of the vegetation at those sites through time. Sites 1–6 are in New Guinea and sites 7–12 are in Sumatra and West Java. The present-day height of the tundra/grassland boundary varies greatly according to local conditions such as aspect, and no doubt did so in the past. (After Morley & Flenley, 1987).

The above simplified examples may give the impression that tropical vegetation behaves in a uniform manner, but this is not the case. Detailed palynological studies by Walker and Flenley (1979) from New Guinea demonstrate that montane vegetation types did not simply migrate up and down mountain slopes as climates changed, but that species reacted in a wholly individualistic manner, with species being recruited from adjacent vegetation types as climatic changes created opportunities for new vegetation types to become established.

Changes of moisture availability are thought mainly to have been most pronounced in the lowlands, and resulted in the expansion and subsequent contraction of rainforests, monsoon forests and savannah. During warmer, interglacial periods, tropical rainforests are believed to exhibit their greatest distribution, whereas during glacial stages, there was an equivalent expansion of savannah and monsoon forests as climates became not only cooler, but also drier (e.g. Flenley, 1979). This is clearly illustrated by fluctuations of forest pollen and grass pollen from lake deposits at several localities in West Africa and South America, and also the occurrence of fossil faunas with many savannah species in areas which would naturally bear forest vegetation today, such as the Mid-Pleistocene faunas of central Java which include grazing ungulates and an early species of hominid, *Homo erectus*.

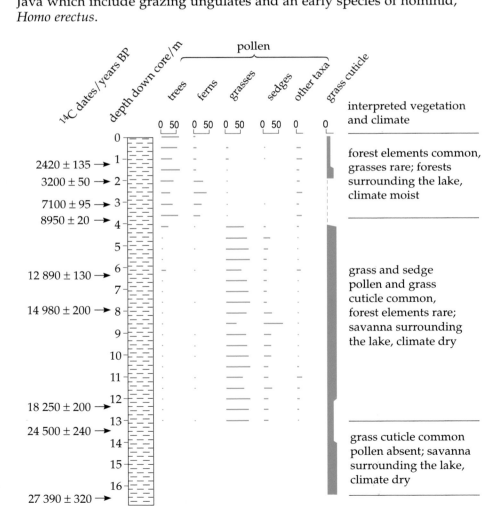

Figure 1.35 Fossil pollen and grass cuticle evidence for changes in the forest-savannah boundary at Lake Bosumtwi, Ghana over the past 27 000 years. (After Talbot *et al.*, 1984.)

A highly simplified example of a palynological profile from a low altitude site in Ghana, West Africa which reflects such change is presented in Figure 1.35. This diagram shows that prior to 9000 years BP, the area surrounding the volcanic Bosumtwi Lake in Ghana bore savannah, whereas after 9000 years BP, the lake was surrounded by forest. This diagram also demonstrates that the savannah was subject to frequent burning, since the remains of burned grass cuticle is abundant in those lake sediments, in which grass pollen is also abundant.

In fact, during the early Flandrian/Holocene, until about 5000–6000 BP, many lakes in subtropical Africa had considerably higher water levels and in many cases, such as that of Lake Chad on the borders of the Sahara, were very much more extensive than today. Indeed, the aridity of the Sahara was much reduced at that time, with large areas supporting not only savannah-type grassland but also great herds of typical African grazing mammals, as well as human settlements. This wetter climate of the tropics and subtropics in the earlier part of the present interglacial stage seems to have been brought about by an intensification and northward displacement of the monsoonal circulation.

The above diagrams clearly demonstrate that 'glacial' climates were both cooler and drier at low latitudes. What effect did these changes have on the distribution of lowland rainforest, which contains the greatest diversity of both plant and animal life of all global ecosystems? Lower sea-levels would have created some additional areas for such forests, but nevertheless, the expansion of savannah and monsoon climates during 'glacial' phases resulted in a substantial reduction of the areal extent of moist tropical forests. It thus appears that, in the present interglacial, rainforests are or have been as extensive, or nearly so, as at any time in the Late Quaternary, and that at glacial maxima, rainforests contracted and only persisted where conditions remained favourable for them, as patches surrounded by tropical seasonal forests. In subsequent interglacials, the rainforests expanded out of these patches, which have become termed **Pleistocene refugia**.

The concept of Pleistocene refugia very convincingly explains many distributional anomalies in equatorial Africa, with refugia formerly occurring in Eastern Zaire, Cameroon–Gabon and Upper Guinea (Figure 1.36). The concept was originally proposed to explain distribution patterns of birds, by Moreau (1966), although it equally well explains many distribution patterns within rainforest plants. Using similar reasoning, a complex pattern of refugia has been proposed for South America on the basis of the overlap of centres of endemism for both plant and animal groups (Figure 1.37). Whether the Pleistocene refuge theory truly applies in South America is currently undergoing hot debate; much of the original evidence for formerly drier climates in the Amazon came from geomorphological evidence, and this is currently being disputed. Also, it has proved difficult to find suitable sites which effectively illustrate the character of dry-land vegetation during 'glacial' periods using palynology. In south-east Asia, centres of endemism cannot be so clearly differentiated, but it is thought that since a major proportion of the region is currently submerged, the 'glacial' refugia may coincide with the present-day land areas.

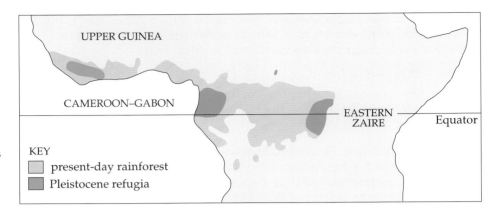

Figure 1.36 Areas of high species richness and distribution of tropical rainforest in Africa. (Whitmore, 1994.)

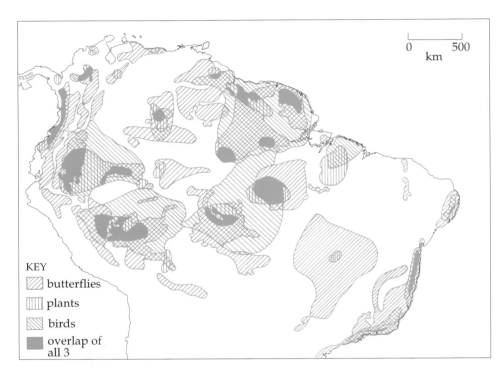

Figure 1.37 Pleistocene refugia in South American rainforests, based on overlap of centres of endemism of butterflies, plants and birds. (Whitmore and Prance, 1987.)

Summary of Sections 1.4.6 to 1.4.8

Deep, very ancient lake basins occur at a number of sites in southern Europe, often formed originally as volcanic craters. Their sediment sequences and resulting pollen diagrams may cover tens, or even hundreds, of thousands of years, recording long successions of vegetational change through both glacial and interglacial stages. The long pollen sequence from Valle di Castiglione in Italy records forested interglacial and interstadial intervals, but, during the colder parts of the glacial periods, the Mediterranean area was apparently covered by steppe vegetation and deciduous temperate trees were virtually absent. Since all temperate tree populations in northern Europe probably became extinct at the end of each interglacial, the question is raised as to where these tree taxa survived the extremes of the glacial stages before reoccupying northern Europe during each successive interglacial period, particularly in the light of natural east–west barriers to migration in Europe such as the main mountain ranges and the Mediterranean Sea.

Whereas it was once believed that conditions in the tropics were very stable during the Quaternary Ice Age, unlike temperate latitudes, it has now been well established by pollen analytical studies and other observations that the tropics also underwent major vegetational changes during that time. Some clearly relate to changes in temperature, others to changes in precipitation. Temperature changes caused altitudinal changes in vegetation belts, for example in the South American Andes and in south-east Asia, though species reacted individually to changing climate. Changes in precipitation, associated with changing patterns of monsoon climates, can be associated with expansion and contraction of rainforest, savannah and desert boundaries. Distribution patterns of refugia, centres of endemism and high species richness in tropical rainforest have been used to try to map the pattern of reduced areas to which rainforests may have contracted during the last glacial stage, when climate is believed to have been both cooler and drier in the tropics.

Question 1.10   (Objective 1.6)

As climate ameliorates at the end of glacial stages, individual species of the temperate fauna and flora migrated from their per-glacial refugia (i.e. the refugia in which they survived through the glacial stages) to recolonize northern Europe, displacing the faunas and flora of the steppe–tundra that had been forming the dominant ecosystem there. What analogous processes do you think were happening in northern Europe at the end of interglacial periods, as climate deteriorated?

Question 1.11   (Objectives 1.7 & 1.9)

Note the statement earlier that, as demonstrated in New Guinea, montane vegetation types did not simply migrate up and down mountain slopes as climates changed, but that species reacted in a wholly individualistic manner. Can you find anything in Figure 1.34 that supports this statement?

1.5   Flandrian environmental changes

The Flandrian, the past 10 000 years of geological time, is best regarded as just the latest of a long series of Quaternary interglacial stages. Nevertheless, it has many claims to be different and distinct. As a time period, it has been the subject of much more numerous and detailed investigations of its palaeoecology. It is also the period during which human activities, such as agriculture and pastoralism, completely changed the face of the landscape in most of Europe and many other parts of the world (see Book 5). In this case, we return to look at Britain.

The first real climatic amelioration that heralded the end of the last glacial stage, the Devensian (Figure 1.2.4), occurred at about 13 500 years BP, perhaps a little earlier in terms of absolute chronology, but the uncorrected radiocarbon timescale is used throughout this Section. This amelioration coincided with the retreat of the polar front in the North Atlantic and the temporary re-establishment of warm-water circulation along the coasts of western Europe. Biologically its effects included a great increase in biological productivity in some of the pre-existing environments, such as lakes and grasslands, and also the initiation of rapid waves of migration by both plants and animals. The first trees to reach Britain, were, as in previous interglacial periods (Figure 1.28), tree birches, with juniper beginning to flower and set fruit more vigorously. Pine probably also reached southern England. Many species of beetles, some demanding higher summer temperatures than today, also migrated into Britain, as shown by an abundant fossil record. This amelioration, the **Late-glacial Interstadial**, was however a false dawn. Already by 11 000 years BP ice-caps were forming in the Scottish Highlands and permafrost returning to the rest of Britain. After several hundred years of exceedingly severe conditions, a period known as the **Loch Lomond Stadial**, amelioration began anew and a new succession of immigration and expansion of forest trees began. Once again, pollen analysis is used to present a basic framework for the environmental changes that have taken place during the past 10 000 years, with the added advantage that this is a timescale over which radiocarbon dating can be quite readily applied to organic materials such as wood, peat and bone to give a more precise determination of age.

The rise in sea-level associated with Late-glacial and Flandrian warming depended not on the melting of the British or Scandinavian ice-sheets, but on that of the very much larger 'Laurentide' ice-sheet that covered North America; this meant that sea-levels did not reach their maximum level until after 8000 years BP. In the Late-glacial then, and during the earliest part of the Flandrian, the land connection , particularly across the North Sea, allowed migration of temperate plants and animals, and also human groups, over this land bridge into Britain, and – for a more restricted period – even into Ireland.

1.5.1   Blelham Tarn

Blelham Tarn is a small lowland lake in the English Lake District, that first formed in an enclosed depression of glacial origin. It is one of many sites where pollen analysis has provided a detailed local record of vegetational change for the Flandrian stage in Britain. This technique was applied to c. 4.4 m of sediments, cored below 2 m of water. Since the pollen diagram for this site (Figure 1.38) was originally published in 1970, it was drawn up using the sum of total tree pollen – excluding hazel, which was counted as a shrub. This means that the percentages shown, particularly for hazel *Corylus* and for the grasses and other herb taxa, are greater than they would be if they had been presented as in the interglacial pollen diagram from Marks Tey. The zones into which the pollen diagram has been divided represent arbitrary subdivisions of the local vegetational succession, but one which has been shown to be paralleled by similar changes over much of southern Britain, though there are small local differences in tree dominance and times of expansion in different regions.

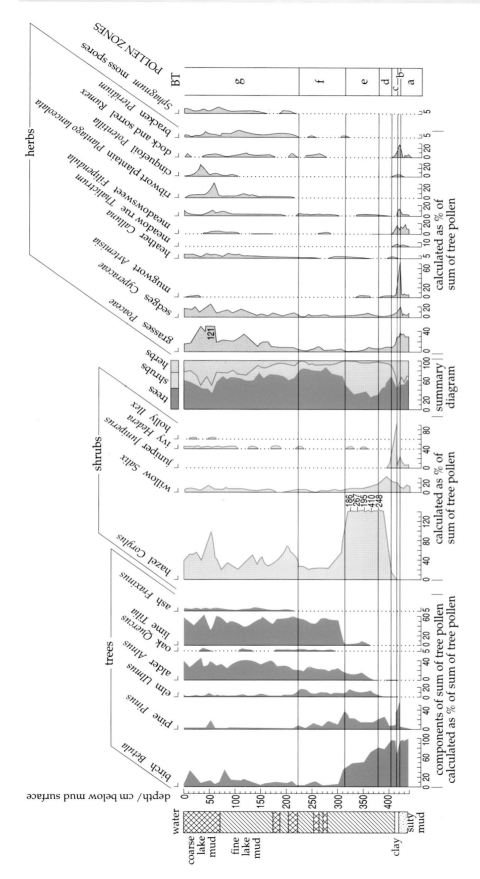

Figure 1.38 Simplified pollen diagram from Late-glacial and Flandrian deposits at Blelham Tarn, English Lake District. Note that the percentages are based on the sum of the tree pollen, excluding hazel, not on that of total land pollen. (After Evans, 1970.)

Table 1.6   Important changes between the different zones in the Blelham Tarn pollen diagram (Figure 1.38).

	Zone	Dominant pollen types	General trends	Zone boundary	Pollen types increasing in frequency at zone boundaries	Pollen types decreasing in frequency at zone boundaries
Flandrian	BTg					
				BTf-BTg		
	BTf					
				BTe-BTf		
	BTe					
				BTd-BTe		
	BTd					
				BTc-BTd		
	BTc	birch, juniper, willow	trees increasing at expense of herbs			grass, sedge, mugwort and other herbs, pine
				BTb-BTc	willow, juniper, birch	
Devensian (Late-glacial)	BTb	grass, sedge, mugwort and other herbs; pine	herbs dominant			
				BTa-BTb	sedge, mugwort and other herbs, pine	birch, juniper
	BTa	birch, juniper, grass with other herbs	trees and shrubs both important			

Complete Table 1.6 by noting what you consider to be the important changes in the Blelham Tarn pollen diagram that take place from zone to zone. List only those pollen types (not necessarily the most abundant) which you feel are significant in this respect. Begin with the oldest levels at the bottom of the diagram and work upwards; some data have already been added. When this is completed, the next step is interpretation in terms of vegetational and climatic change. Both the information in Box 1.1 and the interpretation already made of the Marks Tey pollen diagram, will help you to make a tentative assessment of these changes in note form, but clearly there are parts of this diagram which are very different from the interglacial one.

❑ Suggest two or three features in which the Blelham Tarn pollen diagram differs from that from Marks Tey, particularly with regard to the early and late zones of the sequences.

■ There are several, partly related features that might have caught your attention. In fact, these are features of (Devensian) Late-glacial and Flandrian pollen diagrams from most of Britain, and not just of purely local significance:

(i)   The Marks Tey diagram shows a simple progression from open vegetational conditions to forest at the beginning of the interglacial. The basal part of the diagram at Blelham Tarn, though only covering a short depth of sediment, suggests an oscillation between forested and open conditions. Actually, Zone BTa represents part of the Late-glacial Interstadial mentioned earlier in Section 1.5.

(ii)   The very high values for hazel at Blelham which in the Flandrian immigrated and expanded before most other temperate forest trees.

(iii)   At Blelham there is no sign of late-immigrating temperate trees such as hornbeam or silver fir, which played such an important role during the late-temperate substage of the interglacial at Marks Tey, nor is there any evidence for a regression towards boreal forest dominated by pine and birch, though the rise of the heather pollen curve does suggest the spread of moorland.

(iv)   The progressive and substantial rise in the pollen curves of grasses and other herbs during zone BTg, in what is otherwise a period of temperate forest dominance, clearly has no counterpart at Marks Tey.

Points (iii) and (iv) must raise the question of how far along a typical interglacial cycle of the kind represented in an idealized form by Figure 1.28 the Flandrian 'interglacial' might have reached.

1.5.2   Late-glacial and Flandrian vegetational history

Our rather condensed interpretation of the Late-glacial and Flandrian vegetational history of the Blelham Tarn area is presented as Table 1.7. Like all interpretations, it is hypothetical, and there are many areas of doubt. Check it carefully from your own analysis of the Blelham Tarn pollen diagram (your completed Table 1.6) and interpretational notes; follow our argument and decide whether you agree with them. In this particular borehole, the sediments have not been subjected to radiocarbon dating, since they contain too much redeposited calcium carbonate from older rocks, but nearby sites in Cumbria, where the pollen diagrams are similar, have yielded dates for zone boundaries which have been appended to Table 1.7.

Table 1.7 Suggested important changes between the different zones in the Blelham Tarn pollen diagram.

Zone	Dominant pollen types	General trends	Zone boundary	Pollen types increasing in frequency at zone boundaries	Pollen types decreasing in frequency at zone boundaries	Approx. age/radio carbon yr BP*
BTg	oak alder hazel; increasingly grass, sedges and herbs	trees declining, herbs increasing				
			BTf-BTg	ash, ribwort plantain, grasses & other herbs, hazel	elm, pine	5000
BTf	oak, elm, alder	trees dominant, low shrubs and herbs				
			Bte-BTf	alder, lime	birch, pine, hazel, willow	7500
BTe	hazel, birch, pine, oak, elm	shrubs (hazel) dominant, shrubs very low				
			BTd-BTe	elm, oak	birch	9000
BTd	birch, pine, hazel, willow	shrubs (hazel) increasing at expense of herbs				
			BTc-BTd	hazel, pine	birch, juniper, herbs	9600
BTc	birch, juniper, willow	trees increasing at expense of herbs				
			BTb-BTc	birch, willow juniper	grass, sedge mugwort & other herbs, pine	10 000
BTb	grass, sedge, mugwort and other herbs; pine	herbs dominant				
			BTa-BTb	sedge, mugwort & other herbs, pine†	birch, juniper	
BTa	birch, juniper, grass with other herbs	trees and shrubs both important				
						12 000

Left-margin groupings: **Flandrian** spans zones BTg to BTc; **Devensian (Late Glacial)** spans zones BTb to BTa.

* Dates in this column obtained from other sites in Cumbria, not from Blelham Tarn.

† High pine values in zone III are ascribed to redeposited fossil pine pollen at this site, not to living trees.

The Late-glacial zones (BTa–b)

Late-glacial deposits are poorly represented in the core from Blelham Tarn, though found in nearby boreholes. In fact, the vegetational succession of the Late-glacial period is rather more complex than described here. The earliest part of the Late-glacial vegetational succession has not been recorded at Blelham Tarn. After the melting of the ice-sheet of the main phase of the last glaciation, cores elsewhere give evidence for a treeless open vegetation dominated by grasses and sedges. Many of the other species present, for example dwarf birch *Betula nana* and dwarf willows such as *Salix herbacea*, are now found in tundra vegetation in the Arctic or in high mountain areas. About 13 500 years BP, as mentioned earlier, climate ameliorated, though at first the landscape was virtually treeless, except for willows and juniper, but soon tree birches immigrated.

Zone BTa: This represents a time when tree birches had spread into the area and juniper was flowering freely. The vegetation probably consisted of a mosaic of open birch woodland, scrub and grassland. In fact, this represents the latter part of the Late-glacial Interstadial, when mean annual temperatures were already declining again.

Zone BTb: This zone, spanning the time period between 11 000 and 10 200 BP, shows a return to open vegetation during the Loch Lomond Stadial, with tree birches completely disappearing, indicating a climatic reversal and, indeed, a rigorous cold climate.

The Flandrian

Zone BTc: The vegetational development was closely similar to that of zone BTa and followed a similar climatic amelioration. Juniper scrub was succeeded and replaced by the spread of birch woods, at first interspersed with herb-rich meadows. Willows flourished on wet, poorly drained soils.

Zone BTd: Hazel and later pine immigrated. Earlier records of pine pollen can probably be accounted for by long-distance wind transport. Hazelwoods began to spread at the expense of birch, which could not regenerate under the shade of hazel. This woodland became dense and the closing of the tree canopy excluded many herbs and grasses from the forest floor. Elm appears to have immigrated at the end of this zone.

Zone BTe: Pine forest was important during this zone, but elm and oak were spreading rapidly. Elm grows best on rich loamy soils that retain moisture but are not waterlogged, oaks are a little more tolerant of poor soils, but pine and birch may well have retained their dominance on poorer acid soils. Hazel was clearly widespread and could flourish under the canopy of all these other trees. During this zone there is the first evidence for the immigration into the region of alder – a tree of damp soils, swampy woodland and streamsides, where it can compete with willow.

Zone BTf: The beginning of this zone is characterized by a sudden spread of alder in many parts of Britain. This is taken to indicate the onset of wetter climatic conditions with increased rainfall over western Europe, rather than just local successional changes. A mixed deciduous forest, with oak particularly important (mixed-oak forest), gradually replaced pine and birch. As this forest grew denser, hazel was less able to flower in the shade than it had been in more open woodland. Lime entered the forest during this zone, but the low pollen percentages probably do not represent its true frequency, as it is mainly an insect- rather than wind-pollinated tree. Lime was actually the dominant forest tree in some areas of southern England during this time.

Zone BTg: The boundary between this and the previous zone is marked by a sharp decline in the frequency of elm pollen. It led into a period of small but significant forest changes; this was accompanied by a steady increase in herbaceous plants such as grasses and plantain, which indicates the return of open ground habitats. Significantly, the first grains of cereal pollen are found at this horizon. There is also evidence – in the increasing heather *Calluna* and *Sphagnum* moss curves – of the spread of moorland and bog communities.

This analysis raises two further questions. The first is: were climatic conditions at any stage of the Flandrian warmer than at present? This is of particular interest when we are faced at present with the prospect of global warming. The second question relates to the role of human activities in the vegetational changes recorded during the Flandrian, and is considered in Section 1.5.3.

You will appreciate how hard it is to quantify either changes in average or seasonal temperatures or precipitation from this kind of pollen evidence, though estimates can be made using certain indicator species like holly and mistletoe, when data covering a wide area are reviewed. In general, there are too many variables controlling the distribution of vegetation types.

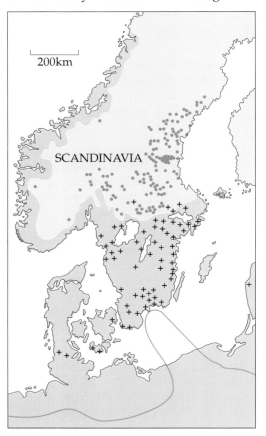

Figure 1.39 Fossil Flandrian occurrences of hazel *Corylus avellana* and water chestnut *Trapa natans* in western Scandinavia. There is also one Flandrian record (from East Yorkshire) of this plant having occurred in Britain at this time.

KEY

+ fossil post-glacial occurrence of *Trapa natans*

— northern limit of present distribution of *Trapa natans*

▢ northern limit of occurrence of *Corylus avellana*

∴ fossil occurrence of *Corylus avellana*

Nevertheless, occasionally, the fossil occurrence of individual species, whose present-day climatic tolerances are well known, can give the possibility of a direct comparison between today's conditions and those of particular periods of the past, especially if that evidence is of fossil fruits or seeds, which imply presence actually on the site. Thus, there is good evidence that between 8000 and 5000 BP, mean summer temperatures over most of Europe were at least 2 °C warmer than today. For example, at this time, both hazel and the water chestnut *Trapa natans*, an aquatic plant not now found in Britain, are known to have occurred much further north in Scandinavia than at present (Figure 1.39). Similarly, ripe fruits of the saw-sedge *Mariscus* and the floating duckweeds *Lemna* spp. have been found fossilized in sediments of these zones, in places where today their reproduction is almost entirely vegetative, and they only set fruit during abnormally warm summers. This interval of climatic warming is generally referred to as the **thermal maximum** or, more ambiguously, the climatic optimum of the Flandrian (Figure 1.40).

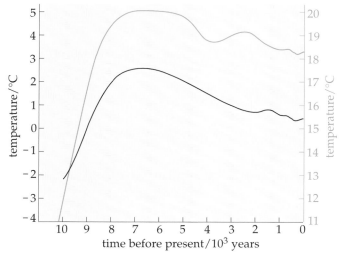

Figure 1.40 Estimated average summer (green) and winter (black) temperatures (±1 °C) for southern England over the past 10 000 years.

Although we have been concentrating on vegetational evidence, animal fossils also tell a similar story.

❑ Consider evidence of the former distribution of the European pond tortoise *Emys orbicularis* (Figure 1.41). This is a useful climatic indicator. Why?

■ A specific and indeed essential function – breeding – appears to be closely linked with high summer temperatures. The present mean July temperature of East Anglia is about 16.5 °C.

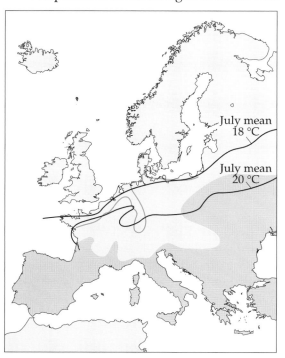

July mean 18 °C

July mean 20 °C

KEY

▨ distribution of breeding populations

— northern limit of non-breeding animals

Figure 1.41 Modern distribution of the European pond tortoise *Emys orbicularis*. The isotherms shown are mean July temperatures corrected to sea-level. The 20 °C July isotherm for France, uncorrected for altitude, largely follows the northern limit for breeding populations. There are abundant records of breeding animals from mid-Flandrian to Flandrian deposits in Denmark and a single record of the animal from Flandrian deposits in East Anglia.

One particular group of animals – beetles – are particularly good environmental and climatic indicators. First, they are well preserved, although in disarticulated fragments, in many freshwater sediments. (However, their identification and ecological interpretation require even more specialist knowledge than does pollen.) Secondly, many beetles, being flying insects, are very mobile and migrate much faster than trees.

1.5.3 Early human impacts during the Flandrian

There is good evidence for human occupation of western Europe, including Britain, for at least 500 000 years. These early humans were hunter-gatherers, who were versatile enough to flourish under both interglacial and cold climate conditions. Their presence is most commonly recognized from stone tools, which have been used to define the cultural stages of the **Palaeolithic** ('the Old Stone Age'). The Lower and Middle Palaeolithic cultures are associated with the ancestral *Homo heidelbergensis* and forms of early modern humans, particularly *Homo sapiens neanderthalensis* (Neanderthals). About 100 000 years BP, humans virtually indistinguishable from ourselves (*Homo sapiens sapiens*) had spread into the Near East and by 30 000 years BP appear to have replaced the Neanderthals in Europe, initiating Upper Palaeolithic cultures. Their cave art and bone sculptures remind us that they had the same basic talents and intelligence as ourselves.

The end of the last glacial stage and disappearance of the open plains of steppe and tundra also saw the end of the large herds of grazing mammals – reindeer, mammoth, steppe bison – on which these hunter-gatherers largely depended in Europe. Indeed, as ecosystems changed rapidly and populations dwindled, hunting by humans perhaps contributed to the extinction of large mammals – herbivores such as mammoth and woolly rhinoceros, and predators such as cave lion and cave bear – not only in Europe but also in North America and elsewhere.

In Europe, archaeological evidence shows that human populations from the beginning of the Flandrian were concentrated in river valleys and on coasts, where fishing became important, as well as the development of new techniques for hunting and trapping animals in the now dense forest environments. Hunting was assisted by domesticated dogs. These new cultures are classified as **Mesolithic** ('Middle Stone Age'). There has been quite a lot of debate as to whether the presence of Mesolithic settlements had impacts on their environment which can be detected in pollen diagrams. Certainly there were small vegetational changes in some areas, which can be associated with charcoal horizons in the sediments, and have been interpreted as the burning of vegetation to retain or encourage open areas which would attract large herbivores, particularly red deer – essentially an early management strategy.

The practices of agriculture and pastoralism had evolved in south-west Asia by 10 000 BP, spreading to south-east Europe by 8000 BP and gradually westwards over the next three millennia. These early farmers brought with them cereals, sheep and goats, not native to Europe, and also domesticated cattle and pigs. They also made pottery and manufactured distinctive ground stone tools. The earliest **Neolithic** ('New Stone Age') farmers eventually reached Britain and Ireland by sea, probably about 5500–5000 BP and their cultural influence spread also amongst the existing population, including the development of elaborate funerary monuments, long barrows, and ceremonial centres such as the earliest henges and stone circles. There was thus a considerable cultural revolution at this time.

❑   What changes in the Blelham Tarn pollen take place or begin at about this time, which might have some relationship to human activities?

■   The zone BTf/BTg boundary at about 5000 BP marks a fall in tree pollen percentages and the gradual increase of herb pollen types, particularly, you might note, of grasses and ribwort plantain. There is also an increase in bracken spores at this level.

Today's agricultural practices and the extent of arable and pasture land are clearly reflected in modern pollen spectra with high values for grasses, including cereals, and for herbs, particularly weeds. The uppermost samples of the pollen diagram from Blelham Tarn have not been dated precisely, but the sediment must be very recent and the herb pollen curves, though not presented in detail, suggest that arable, pasture and moorland environments are widespread in the neighbourhood. This is indeed the case.

The earliest attempts by prehistoric people to clear forest for the cultivation of crops would have been very small and local. Significant changes in the pollen spectra may be very small, perhaps less than 2%. To detect such changes accurately, large numbers of pollen grains need to be counted from each level.

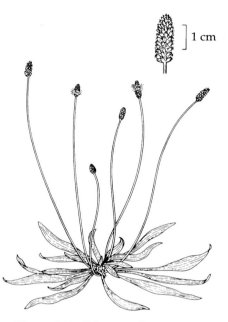

Figure 1.42 Ribwort plantain *Plantago lanceolata*.

Perhaps the most certain indicator for human disturbance of the vegetation is pollen of the ribwort plantain *Plantago lanceolata* (Figure 1.42), a plant almost absent from the forested periods of the early and mid-Flandrian and today most commonly found in habitats strongly influenced by human activities. In fact, it is often a plant of closely grazed grassland.

Two other features that you should note as occurring at about 5000 BP are the sudden **elm decline** and, from Figure 1.40, that the thermal maximum came to an end at this time and a gentle climatic deterioration set in.

Examine the section of the pollen diagram from Barfield Tarn, Cumbria, which covers the same zone boundary you have just been considering (Figure 1.43). Evidence of three episodes of forest clearance has been picked out.

❑   Before reading on, list the major features of these episodes.

■   *Episode 1*, which has been dated to about 5350 years BP, shows very little change in the tree-pollen curves, but there is a small, temporary but well-marked increase in plantain, dock and other herb pollen types for the first time.

Episode 2 does suggest changes in the forest composition. Oak and elm curves decline sharply; those for birch and hazel gradually increase. After the elm decline, herb pollen types – particularly grasses, ribwort plantain and weeds such as docks, composites and chenopods – all show a period of increase. There is pollen of cereals and an increase in spores of bracken for the first time. Sedimentary changes in the tarn suggest that these disturbances were occurring within the catchment area. Soil inwashing, due perhaps to cultivation or tree felling, is indicated by the increase in the mineral component, which eventually almost entirely replaces the organic component

Episode 3 is characterized by the expansion of many herb pollen curves on a larger scale, and is the beginning of a permanent increase in the proportion of herb pollen within the total pollen sum.

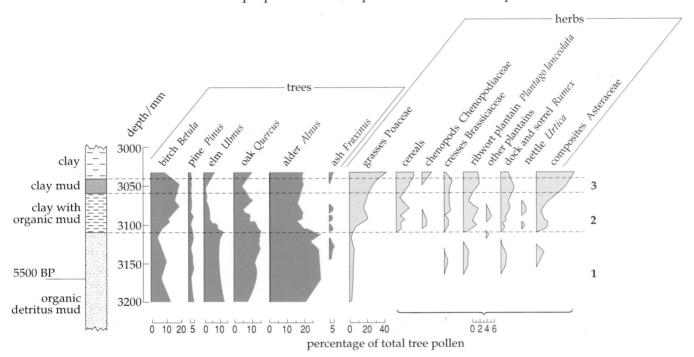

Figure 1.43 Simplified pollen diagram from Barfield Tarn, Cumbria, showing a series of forest clearance phases. The horizontal percentage scales vary for different groups of plants.

The evidence from this and many other similar pollen diagrams suggests that people first actively felled trees to create clearings in the forest during Neolithic times. These clearings were small and were occupied only for a few years, after which the forest regenerated and the Neolithic farmers – living a wide-ranging nomadic existence as many primitive agricultural peoples do today – moved on to make new clearings elsewhere. Such small clearance episodes are generally called **landnam** phases.

In Denmark, experiments to test this interpretation showed that Neolithic stone axes can easily be used to chop down considerable areas of natural forest (Figure 1.44), and the timber and brushwood can be burned. Burning was found to be necessary for the successful growth of cereals, as the ash acted as fertilizer for the otherwise infertile forest soil. Even by the second year, soil fertility and the productivity of cereals sown in the clearings were reduced (Figure 1.45). However, the area could have been used to graze cattle on the regenerating vegetation for several years after crop production failed, thus prolonging the signature in the pollen records. In the burned area, many weeds appeared which were previously absent from the forest. Prominent amongst them were plantains and composites (dandelions, sowthistles, groundsel, etc.). The pollen of these weeds occurs in pollen diagrams at the same levels as the forest clearance phases. There was rapid colonization of the Danish clearings by bracken whose spores also increase in the clearance phases in pollen diagrams. Where the slender trunks of hazel had merely been razed to the ground, new growth sprouted readily from the cut stumps and flowered within a few years. Birch also regenerated swiftly from seed. The other forest trees regenerated more slowly, but eventually grew up and eliminated the open-ground herbs and weeds.

Figure 1.44 An actual Neolithic stone axe, hafted with a modern wooden handle, is used to fell a tree during the Danish clearance experiment.

Figure 1.45 Cereals being cultivated in a clearing during the Danish experiment.

Both the Danish experiments and radiocarbon dating of such clearance phases in pollen diagrams suggest that such a regeneration cycle lasts less than 50 years. It is also probable that animals, such as cattle and sheep, were set to graze in the clearings after cropping. This would add some fertilizer in the form of dung, and delay the regrowth of woody vegetation through trampling and browsing.

The permanent decline of elm pollen has been dated to around 5000 BP in many pollen diagrams. It is one of the few pollen zone horizons that is broadly synchronous over much of Britain. It often appears to be closely associated with human clearance activities. There has been controversy about its precise interpretation. Explanations put forward include (a) decline in soil fertility, preventing regeneration after clearance (elm is one of the most nutrient-demanding of forest trees); (b) the lopping of elm branches to provide fodder for grazing animals, known to be an old rural practice in remote parts of Europe. However, the enormous number of elm trees that must have been affected not only in Britain but across much of north-west Europe makes a primary human cause most unlikely. Human populations were small and a large area was involved over at most a couple of centuries, too short a time for a cultural change to spread over such a wide area and too few people to lop anything like the number of trees affected.

In the 1960s and 1970s, there was a massive outbreak of Dutch elm disease, caused by the fungus *Ceratocystis ulmi*. This fungus invades the water-conducting vessels of the tree, whose reaction is to secrete a gum that seals the vessels. However, this blocking leads to severe disruption of the water supply and the tree dies. The disease killed up to 60% of Britain's elm population. The fungus is spread by two species of bark-beetle, *Scolytus scolytus* and *S. multistriatus*. It is now believed that a similar outbreak was responsible for the Neolithic elm decline. Since injury to the tree increases susceptibility to infection, lopping by humans may have helped the spread of the disease, and similarly areas of dead or dying elm, which would probably be on rich soils, may have been selected as good sites for clearance and cultivation.

1.5.4   Early agriculture in East Anglia

A longer and more detailed record of human impacts on the environment is provided by a pollen diagram from Diss Mere, Norfolk, a small lowland lake, about 200 m in diameter, on the edge of the East Anglian Breckland (Figure 1.46). Its origin is not fully understood, but it appears to have formed at about the end of the last glacial stage. Note that the record from the lower part of the diagram, especially within zones DM1–4, is affected by small hiatuses within the sedimentary sequence, either as a result of erosion of deposits by waves or currents when the lake was shallow, or by coring problems. The upper part of the diagram, however, gives a very full record of the later half of the Flandrian, and its environmental changes in the Diss area, right up to the present day.

❑   At which level do you think there is evidence for more or less continuous human impacts on the vegetation in the neighbourhood of Diss Mere? What is the nature of the evidence, and when did the impacts occur?

■   The boundary between zones DM4 and DM5 records the elm decline. It also marks the first continuous curve for the pollen of ribwort plantain and chenopods, which may be interpreted as clearance indicators. The elm decline has been dated throughout southern Britain at or shortly before 5000 years BP. You could however argue that the first clear evidence for actual occupation of the area comes with the appearance of cereal pollen in zone DM6, which can be dated to after about 3500 years BP.

❑   What are the *main* differences in habitat change at Diss Mere and Blelham Tarn during the past 5000 years suggested by the two pollen records? You will have to take into account that the two diagrams have been drawn up on different percentage bases.

■   Clearly there was much greater forest clearance in East Anglia with major declines in oak, alder, hazel, yew and lime, particularly after zone DM6. Similarly, there is a big increase in grasses there and a great diversity of herb pollen, including agricultural indicators. In the Lake District, forests continue to be important to the surface which is more or less the present day. In fact, the herb pollen from Blelham does not include crop plants; the clearance indicators in fact suggest grazed pasture as the dominant element in the farming landscape.

At both sites, the presence of heather, and at Blelham that of *Sphagnum* moss spores, suggests a small development of heath or moorland somewhere nearby.

❑   Which pollen taxa from the Diss Mere do you recognize as belonging to crop plants? Also list any arable weeds that may be present.

■   The crops indicated include a range of cereals, probably both oats *Avena* and wheat *Triticum* (their pollen types are difficult to separate), rye *Secale cereale* and barley *Hordeum*. Hemp *Cannabis sativa*, sometimes difficult to distinguish from closely related hops, was clearly an important crop for part of the period; there are also indications of flax *Linum*, beans or tares *Vicia* and members of the cabbage family *Brassica* type (cabbage or perhaps turnip) being grown. Arable weeds include stinging nettle *Urtica* (perhaps eaten, but not deliberately sown), chenopods, cornflower *Centaurea cyanus* and poppies *Papaver*.

The abundance of grass pollen together with ribwort plantain, docks *Rumex* spp. and bracken *Pteridium aquilinum* spores suggests that meadow and open grazing land were also important.

The zonation of the upper part of the pollen diagram is based on changes in both the tree and the herbaceous pollen types. In this particular borehole, the sediments have not been subjected to radiocarbon dating, as they contain too much redeposited calcium carbonate from older rocks; but nearby sites in East Anglia, where the pollen diagrams are similar, have yielded dates for zone boundaries which can be used to date a succession of forest and agricultural changes in the Diss area, extending to the present day, so that they can, in fact, be linked to historical sources.

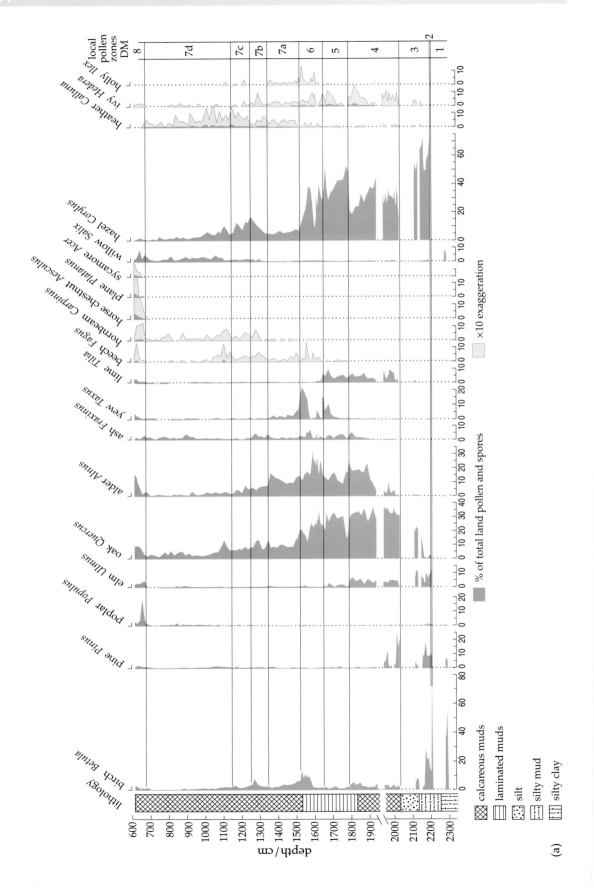

(a)

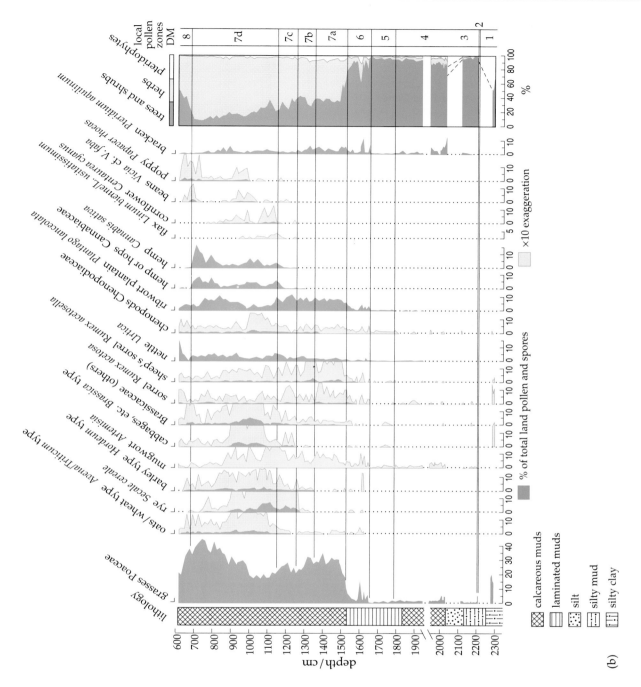

Figure 1.46 Simplified pollen diagram from Diss Mere, Norfolk: (a) trees and shrubs; (b) herbs and pteridophytes. Note that the percentage basis for this diagram is total land pollen as in the Marks Tey interglacial diagram (Figure 1.28), not tree pollen as at Blelham Tarn (Figure 1.38).

❑ Complete Table 1.8 by filling in the appropriate characteristics of the Late Flandrian pollen zones DM6–8, then examine our suggestions in the completed Table 1.9 overleaf.

Table 1.8 Characteristic pollen curve changes and approximate ages of the pollen zones at Diss Mere.

Local pollen zone	Pollen zone characteristics	Approx. age (yrs BP)
DM8	decline of	0–150
	1st appearance of	
	rise of	
DM7d	major increase of	150–1000
DM7c	increase of	1000–1500
	1st appearance of	
DM7b	declines of	1500–2000
DM7a	major increases of	2000–2500
	sharp declines of	
DM6	sharp declines of	2500–3500
	increase of	
	1st appearance of	
DM5	sharp declines of elm, oak, alder	3500–5000
	first rise of ribwort plantain & yew	
DM4	increases of alder & lime	5000–7800
	decrease of hazel	
DM3	sharp increases of hazel & elm	7800–9200
	corresponding decline of birch	
DM2	birch dominance	(?) 9200–10 100
DM1	high birch and herb pollen	before 10 000

In Neolithic and Early Bronze Age times (zone DM5), there is little definite evidence for human occupation actually close to Diss Mere, either from the pollen record or from any archaeological evidence. On the other hand, there is a good archaeological record of Neolithic settlement at other sites not very far away in Norfolk and Suffolk. You have to take into account the very small size and impact of early landnam clearances. They are only likely to be recorded in a detailed succession, as they are at Barfield Tarn (Figure 1.43), if the area of clearance and cultivation is near to the pollen sampling site. The ribwort plantain curve in the Diss Mere diagram suggests clearance was probably taking place somewhere in the neighbourhood during zone DM5, and there are even occasional traces of ribwort plantain earlier in zone DM4, but these need not necessarily be associated with human clearance, as the edge of the mere might have been grazed and trampled by wild animals. Diss Mere may have been too far away from farming sites for any cereal pollen to be recorded or the clearances might have been associated with pastoralism rather than planting crops.

In the Later Bronze Age (zone DM6), the real decline of forest began, implying that some, still small, areas were becoming permanently cleared. Cereals were being cultivated, with charred grains of barley and wheat in particular found on archaeological sites of this age. Note the fall in the pollen curve of lime *Tilia*. As noted earlier, this tree is primarily insect- rather than wind-pollinated, so that its pollen is poorly dispersed. It is believed that, although pollen curves show values of only about 10%, it was for much of the Flandrian a major or even dominant tree in the forests, particularly on the richest soils. Suggestions for its decline include clearance of the best land for agriculture and selective cutting by prehistoric settlers, who used its leaves for animal fodder and its bark for fibres. It shows a sharp decline in many pollen diagrams, but, unlike elm, the lime decline is not synchronous but occurs during Neolithic, Bronze Age or Iron Age times in different areas of lowland England.

The Iron Age (zone DM7a) marks the beginning of much more intensive forest clearance, with a great increase both of land used for agriculture and for pastoralism. By this time, Britain had been invaded by peoples who knew the technique of iron working.

❑   Can you suggest two reasons for the intensification of clearance and agriculture during the Iron Age?

■   1   Iron ploughs and axes were much more efficient, much easier to produce and made from a widely available metal.

    2   The technique of iron working not only produced these tools, but also required an abundant supply of timber for use as charcoal in the smelting process.

During the Roman period in Britain, there seems to have been comparatively little further change. In southern Britain, most of the areas of easily cleared land with fertile soil, predominantly on chalk and limestone, had already been brought into agricultural production. Areas of light sandy soils, once cleared, had largely gone over to grazed heathland, as they were of little use for regular cultivation. The Anglo-Saxons, however, are known from archaeological and historical sources to have used multiple ox teams capable of ploughing heavier clay soils, which were avoided by their predecessors. Again, the pollen diagram from Diss Mere (zone DM7c), after a brief increase in tree pollen perhaps marking some abandonment of land at the end of Roman times, provides evidence for an intensification of arable, as opposed to pastoral, land use in Saxon times, together with the cultivation of new crops – rye, flax and hemp.

Through medieval times and until the early 19th century (zone DM7d), open-field agriculture dominated the area and woodland cover was at a minimum. Cereals, flax and particularly hemp were important crops; the pollen record also includes characteristic field weeds such as cornflower and poppies, which were abundant in the absence of chemical weedkillers.

Cultivation of hemp *Cannabis sativa* was a speciality of this part of eastern England, where there are still public houses called 'The Hempsheaf'. It was an important crop in medieval and later times as one of the basic materials for the manufacture of ropes, not least for the Royal Navy. After harvest, the plants had to putrify and be 'retted' (submerged in water over winter) to release the fibres. Many small field ponds in Norfolk and Suffolk were dug not for cattle to drink from (indeed, the waters were highly poisonous) but for the retting of hemp, and fossil hemp seeds may still be found in their sediments. *Cannabis* was also used widely as a medicinal, though not as a recreational, drug at that time. Nevertheless, there are records of farmers complaining about their labourers smoking hemp seeds in their pipes and not working properly!

The uppermost pollen zone at Diss Mere (DM8) is interesting in that it records many changes over the past 150 years which are well documented from historical sources. These include the enclosure of the open fields and quite extensive planting of woodland and shelter-belts, the introduction of non-native trees, particularly horse chestnut *Aesculus hippocastaneum*, sycamore *Acer pseudoplatanus* and plane *Platanus*, as the market town of Diss grew prosperous and expanded. It also records the quite abrupt collapse of hemp farming in England around 1800, when it became cheaper to import hemp and jute from India, by then partly under British control.

Table 1.9   Pollen zone characteristics at Diss Mere related to archaeological periods.

Local pollen zone	Pollen zone characteristics	Historical period	Approx. age (yrs BP)
DM8	decline of hemp first appearance of horse chestnut & sycamore rise of elm, oak, lime, yew & other trees	late 19th–20th century	0–150
DM7d	major increase of hemp & arable weeds (e.g. cornflower)	11th–late 19th century (medieval–early modern times)	150–1000
DM7c	increase of rye and other cereal-type pollen first appearance of hemp	6th–10th century Anglo-Saxon	1000–1500
DM7b	declines of alder and yew	1st–5th century Roman	1500–2000
DM7a	major increases of grasses and other herbs sharp declines of almost all trees	c. 500–0 BC Iron Age	2000–2500
DM6	sharp declines of lime and hazel increase of grasses and other herbs first appearance of cereal type pollen	c. 1500–500 BC Later Bronze Age	2500–3500
DM5	sharp declines of elm, oak, alder first rise of ribwort plantain & yew	c. 4000–1500 BC Neolithic and Early Bronze Age	3500–5000
DM4	increases of alder & lime decrease of hazel		5000–7800
DM3	sharp increases of hazel & elm corresponding decline of birch		7800–9200
DM2	birch dominance		(?) 9200–10 100
DM1	high birch and herb pollen		before 10 000

Summary of Sections 1.5.1 to 1.5.4

The pollen diagram from Blelham Tarn covers, poorly, the Late-glacial interval and, in greater detail, the Flandrian. Major differences between this sequence and the much earlier one from Marks Tey include the occurrence and vegetational effects of the complex Late-glacial climatic oscillation preceding the substantive climatic warming, the early immigration and expansion of hazel, the **elm decline** and the effects of prehistoric peoples upon their vegetational environment. Evidence for the **thermal maximum** of the Flandrian between 8000–5000 BP is provided by evidence for the geographical spread of indicator species beyond their present thermal limits.

Palaeolithic and **Mesolithic** people were hunter-gatherers who had a limited effect on the landscape, except perhaps through fire. From **Neolithic** times onwards, pollen diagrams record evidence for both agriculture and pastoralism in Britain and other parts of north-west Europe. The earliest **landnam** clearances made little permanent impact on their densely forested environment, but more permanent clearance is evident after 1500 BC in the Later Bronze Age, with more cereal cultivation, and the clearance of forest for both agriculture and pastoralism greatly accelerated during the Iron Age after 500 BC. Anglo-Saxon settlers cleared heavy clay lands and introduced new crops such as rye, flax and hemp. Forest cover reached a minimum in medieval and early modern times, before enclosure and some replanting in the past 150 years. Some indications of land after clearance converting to heathland or moorland are recorded from both the Lake District and East Anglia.

Question 1.12   (Objectives 1.10 & 1.12)

How would you account for the presence of colonies of both species of lime *Tilia* in localities in northern England, where they are apparently unable to set seed? (Usually, colonies consist of just a few trees, often very old, on rocky and relatively inaccessible sites. These apparently very rarely produce ripe seed under present conditions and then such seeds normally fail to germinate and establish.)

Question 1.13   (Objectives 1.5 & 1.10)

In general terms, what effects would changes of sea-level in the Straits of Dover and the North Sea be likely to have had on the composition of the fauna and flora of southern Britain, both during the last glacial period and during the past 10 000 years when the climate has been at least as warm as at present?

Question 1.14   (Objectives 1.10 & 1.11)

Which combinations of pollen types would you expect to find in Late Flandrian pollen diagrams from southern Britain as evidence of (a) pastoral and (b) agricultural activities by prehistoric people?

Consider the pollen profile shown in Figure 1.27 to which you should have added the results obtained in Question 1.7. This is essentially a hypothetical rather than an actual pollen diagram; but supposing it represented a Flandrian succession, what major environmental event could be deduced to have taken place during the interval represented by 45 to 28 cm in the sediment column?

In Section 1.4.4, four substages (pre-temperate, early-temperate etc.) were recognized in the development of interglacial environments, specifically at Marks Tey (Figure 1.28), but it was stated that this scheme is applicable to most other interglacial sequences. The environments of the latest part of the Flandrian are strongly affected by human activities. Nevertheless, what evidence can you suggest for identifying which substage the Flandrian might now have reached, assuming that, in the absence of human impacts, the pattern of earlier interglacials would be followed?

1.6   Recent biogeographical changes

From prehistoric times onwards, humans have played an important role in dispersal through the introduction – both deliberate and accidental – of many species of plants and animals into new parts of the world. This process has accelerated rapidly over the past 200 years, and humans have now become the major agents of passive dispersal of animals and plants. The most obvious deliberate introductions are crop plants and domestic animals, but in addition there are those species, such as sitka spruce *Picea sitchensis*, larch *Larix* spp. and Turkey oak *Quercus cerris* associated with forestry, and many others associated with horticulture. Even recreations such as angling, field sports or foreign travel have led to the introduction of many new plants and animals into Britain.

Once a plant or animal has been introduced by human agency, it is often able to continue its spread by natural means. A striking example is the small creeping New Zealand willowherb *Epilobium nerterioides* (Figure 1.47) which was originally introduced into Britain from New Zealand as a rockery plant. It is now found in upland areas of northern England, Scotland, Wales and Ireland, where it grows profusely in damp places such as the margins of springs and the banks of streams. It would certainly be assumed to be native to Britain if the history of its introduction was not well documented. Likewise, the sweet chestnut *Castanea sativa*, probably first imported by the Romans, is widespread in woods in south-east England; and the sycamore *Acer pseudoplatanus* is now found throughout Britain and reproduces by seed as freely as any native tree, although it came originally from southern Europe and is first recorded as an introduction in the late 15th century. A more recent introduction, the common rhododendron *Rhododendron ponticum*, now occupies extensive areas of acid heathland in the west of Britain and particularly in Ireland, where many ecologists regard it as a pest species, damaging the native vegetation. By a strange twist of fate, we know from the fossil record that the same species formerly occurred in Ireland as a native plant during certain interglacial periods earlier in the Quaternary, but became extinct with the major expansion of ice-sheets over 300 000 years ago.

Figure 1.47 New Zealand willowherb *Epilobium nerterioides* (× 1).

Amongst the animals now widespread in Britain, rabbit *Oryctolagus cuniculus*, whose ecology but not its history were discussed in Book 1, Chapter 1, fallow deer *Dama dama* and pheasant *Phasianus colchicus* are believed to have been introduced by the Normans during the Middle Ages. The American grey squirrel *Sciurus carolinensis* was deliberately released in a number of localities in the late 19th century. Mink *Mustela vison*, a voracious carnivore, originally bred for its fur during the 1930s-1940s, escaped and is now a widespread pest along Britain's river banks. Similarly, coypu *Myocastor coypus* (source of the fur known as nutria) also got out and established successful breeding colonies, damaging river banks and ravaging sugar beet crops in East Anglia until a successful extermination programme in the 1980s. A number of invertebrate species have also been deliberately introduced, such as the garden snail *Helix aspersa* and the Roman snail *Helix pomatia*. In association with deliberately introduced species, there has come an extensive range of unwanted animal pests and weeds of arable fields and waste ground. Other species have come in purely by accident; for example, the woodlice *Trichorhina tomentosa* from tropical America and *Agabiformis lentus* from the eastern Mediterranean were brought in quite unintentionally by horticulturalists but can survive only in greenhouses in Britain (Sutton, 1972).

The ease with which animals and plants which could prove harmful can be so introduced is a good reason for imposing restrictions on those wishing to import plants, soil or water from abroad. An example of this is the particularly aggressive strain of the fungus *Ceratocystis ulmi*, imported with timber from Canada in about 1968, which is believed to have set off the recent and, in some areas, still current outbreak of Dutch elm disease.

Roads, railways and ships have all opened up new pathways for plant and animal dispersal. The Oxford ragwort *Senecio squalidus* escaped from the Botanic Gardens there at the end of the 18th century. Its native home is the slopes of the volcano Mount Etna in Sicily. During the 19th century, it appears to have spread along the cindery railway tracks to the sidings and goods yards of London and Bristol, and it is now common on urban waste ground throughout Britain.

Around the coasts of southern England, the New Zealand barnacle *Elminius modestus* was able to establish itself after reaching British waters on flying boats during World War II. More recently, ships have carried a Japanese seaweed *Sargassum muticum* to the south coast of Britain, where it is spreading rapidly. This has caused concern because it is displacing eel grass *Zostera*, the natural food for certain species of geese, and also because of the great length of its fronds (up to 30 m) which tend to foul ships' propellers.

Figure 1.48 Canadian pondweed
Elodea canadensis (× 0.5).

A case history that illustrates several of the points made in this Section is provided by the exotic water plant **Canadian pondweed** *Elodea canadensis* (Figure 1.48) which became naturalized in Britain during the 19th century (Simpson, 1984). The date and method of first introduction are uncertain. Possibly the plant, which is common in eastern North America, was deliberately brought in by a plant collector, or it may have arrived as fragments attached to imported timber that had been floated downriver before shipment to Britain. The first confirmed record was from Northern Ireland in 1836; but more important are records from the Grand Union Canal system at Market Harborough in Leicestershire in 1847, and from Watford, Northamptonshire in 1850 or possibly earlier. In 1848, plants cultivated in the Cambridge Botanic Garden managed to spread into the River Cam. Like many successful introduced species, the population increased explosively – at Cambridge its initial abundance was so great that it disrupted the rowing! The plant spread rapidly along canals, rivers and fen ditches and even into isolated ponds (Figure 1.49). After spectacular 'blooms' in abundance when it first appeared, the population levels decreased, so that even though it is now found virtually throughout the British Isles, it plays a relatively minor role in freshwater plant communities today. The plant is dioecious (with separate male and female plants) and male plants are extremely rare, so there is almost no setting of seed and the plants spread by the dispersal of leafy shoots which can develop roots.

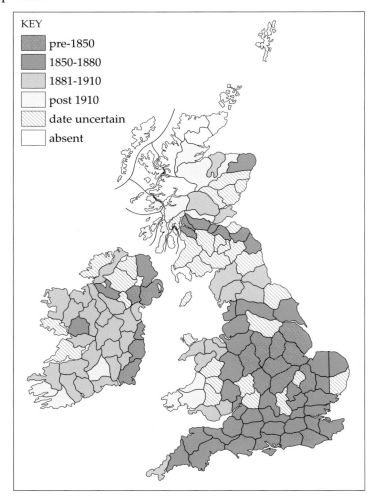

KEY

- pre-1850
- 1850-1880
- 1881-1910
- post 1910
- date uncertain
- absent

Figure 1.49 Spread of Canadian pondweed *Elodea canadensis* in Britain.

❑ List the different agents of dispersal likely to be involved in this story.

■ Initially, the introduction of this plant to Britain was due to human agency, whether accidental or deliberate. However, it has subsequently been spread, as small detached fragments of the plant, by running water, by boats, probably by water birds such as ducks which occasionally get long strands of waterweeds caught round their necks and legs, and again by the deliberate introduction of water plants into artificial ponds.

Figure 1.50 Collared dove *Streptopelia decaocto* (× 0.25).

Since 1966, a second species, *Elodea nuttalli*, also from North America, has been invading similar freshwater habitats in many parts of England. It has displaced *E. canadensis* in some localities. However, the scale of this new invasion has not as yet been comparable to the earlier one.

Looking beyond Britain to some other parts of the world, notably to comparatively isolated island groups like Hawaii and New Zealand, introduced plants and animals have had a drastic effect on the native flora and fauna, particularly of lowland areas. In New Zealand, over 500 alien species of flowering plants have become established, mostly in the past 100 years, compared with a native flora of about 2000 species; some of these, such as the bramble *Rubus fruticosus*, have invaded very large areas and are a serious ecological problem, destroying native plant communities. Hunting and shooting, introduced carnivores including cats and dogs, and egg-eating rats have wiped out most of the flightless bird species of New Zealand or confined them to offshore islands. Similarly, the lizard-like reptile *Sphenodon* has been virtually exterminated there by cats. These aspects of human impact on vulnerable ecosystems will be discussed further in Book 5.

Not all recent changes in the distribution of organisms can be clearly linked to human activities, although there may be indirect influences of which we are still unaware. In Book 2, Section 1.6.1, for example, we described the spread of both the collared dove *Streptopelia decaocto* (Figure 1.50) and Cetti's warbler *Cettia cetti* (Figure 1.51), birds which have quite recently extended their breeding range into the British Isles through natural dispersal.

Figure 1.51 Cetti's warbler *Cettia cetti* (× 0.4).

In a similar way, several rare orchids appear to have dramatically extended their range in the British Isles in recent years or even appeared there for the first time. Irish lady's tresses *Spiranthes romanzoffiana* has long been known from various sites in Ireland and the Western Isles of Scotland, but recently was also discovered growing in Devon. Dense-flowered orchid *Neotinea maculata*, a species with a largely Mediterranean distribution but also native in the west of Ireland, has appeared in the Isle of Man. Most controversially, two plants of another orchid, dwarf serapias, *Serapias parviflora*, again with a predominantly Mediterranean distribution but occurring up the west coast of France as far north as Brittany, were found in 1989 on a clifftop in Cornwall, raising arguments as to whether they had arisen from natural dispersal or were deliberately planted.

❑ Why should orchids be particularly well adapted for long-distance dispersal?

■ They possess very small dust seeds (Book 2, Section 1.6.1) which make them easily dispersed by air currents high in the atmosphere, from where they can then be washed out and deposited by rain.

Summary of Section 1.6

Occasionally, successful dispersal of a species may result in dramatic changes in distribution. Human activities are now the main cause of such events, whether through direct introductions or through changes to habitats. Some distribution changes can largely be ascribed to natural dispersal, while in others human factors have been involved.

Question 1.17   *(Objective 1.11)*

The New Zealand barnacle *Elminius modestus* was first recorded in Britain in 1945, when it was spotted in Chichester Harbour and the Thames Estuary. It is similar in anatomy and size to the British barnacles *Semibalanus balanoides* and *Chthamalus stellatus* (characteristically found on intertidal rocks of the middle shore) but it has only four shell plates, which are less strong than the six shell plates of *Balanus*. The distribution of *Elminius* around the British coasts in 1960 is shown in Figure 1.52; the numbers give the order in which colonies were noticed in new areas between 1945 and 1960. *Elminius* can live on rocks of the middle shore and slightly lower; it is a filter-feeder with a planktonic larva. Given this information, try to explain:

(a) how *Elminius* reached Britain;

(b) how *Elminius* has spread round the coasts of the British Isles;

(c) why *Elminius* has not colonized the rocks of North Cornwall (area + + + in Figure 1.52) although *Semibalanus* and *Chthamalus* live there;

(d) why *Elminius* has been able to establish itself on rocks of the Severn Estuary area (area 7 in Figure 1.52), where native barnacles also live.

Figure 1.52 The areas in which *Elminius modestus* occurred in 1960.

1.7   Semi-natural vegetation

1.7.1   Historical development and woodland classification

Pollen diagrams, such as those from Blelham Tarn and Diss Mere, show that by 5000 BP temperate deciduous forest was the dominant natural vegetation cover over the British Isles as far north as the Midland Valley of Scotland. On richer soils in southern England and the English Midlands, lime *Tilia* was probably dominant (even though its pollen percentages appear low), together with oak and elm, but on the poorer sandy soils, and towards the north and west, oak, particularly sessile oak *Quercus petraea*, was increasingly important. Wet ground and river valleys supported alder carr and swamp vegetation.

In the Scottish Highlands pine forest, dominated by Scots pine *Pinus sylvestris* ssp. *scotica*, formed the natural vegetation and farther north, in Caithness and Sutherland, open birch woodland is suggested by pollen diagrams. Only the windswept Hebrides and Northern Isles remained relatively treeless, except in sheltered valleys.

The advent of agriculture and pastoralism, as we have seen in Section 1.5, largely destroyed this natural vegetation and particularly the **wildwood**, as it has been termed. With very few exceptions, almost all woodland in Britain can be regarded as having been subject to long-term active human management, or at least interference. By the Middle Ages, forest cover had been reduced, particularly in southern Britain, to small parcels of quite intensively managed woodland and certain larger tracts of land which had been designated as royal forests (e.g. the New Forest, Sherwood Forest) and others, less extensive, in almost every county in England, though these were gradually encroached upon. By the 18th century, however, widespread replanting began to take place. Large landowners were organizing the legal enclosure of land, which involved a great extension of hedging, and were laying out parks, shelter belts and new plantations. This trend increased in the 19th century, particularly where large estates planted blocks of woodland to provide cover for game. Several very large sporting estates, for example, were developed on the otherwise thoroughly poor and unremunerative soils of the East Anglian Breckland. Some reflection of this perhaps is seen in zone DM8 of the Diss Mere pollen diagram (Figure 1.46). Only after the Second World War did the expansion of subsidized intensive agriculture result in further widespread grubbing up of woodlands or their conversion to the growth of conifers. The loss of up to 50% of so-called ancient woodland through these initiatives between 1945 and 1975 set alarm bells ringing amongst conservation organizations, particularly since Britain already has the lowest percentage of woodland cover of any country in Europe, other than Ireland.

The Nature Conservancy Council, now part of English Heritage, has recognized the following categories of woodland, based on their historical development (Kirby *et al.*, 1984) (Figure 1.53):

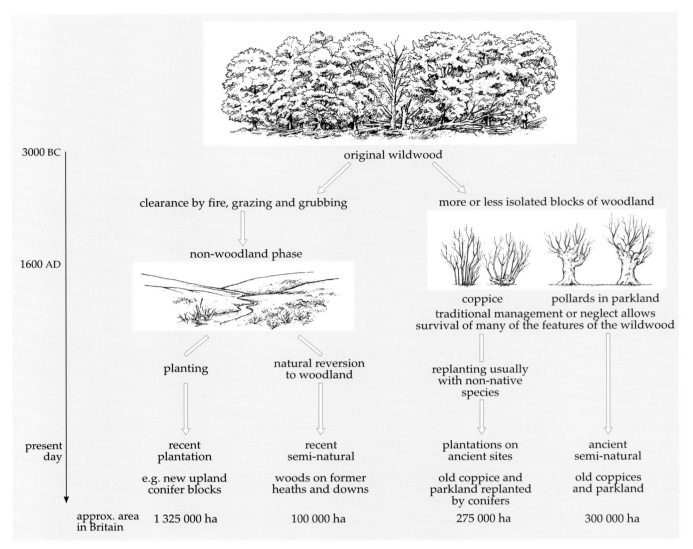

Figure 1.53 The historical development of different kinds of woodland in Britain.

1   Ancient semi-natural woodland

This is defined as woodland 'on sites which appear to have been continuously wooded since pre-1600 (probably much longer) *and* have a tree and shrub layer composed of species native to the site, derived from natural regeneration or coppice regrowth from individuals which were themselves derived from natural regeneration'. **Ancient woodland** includes:

(a)   Fragments of woodland occurring on inaccessible cliffs, in gorges etc. The antiquity (and inaccessibility) of such habitats was emphasized recently (Hampton and Kay, 1995) by the quite unexpected discovery on coastal cliffs in South Wales of two separate colonies of a small tree, service tree *Sorbus domestica*, a relative of rowan *S. aucuparia*, which had not previously been considered to be native to Britain.

(b)   Ancient high forest – mainly pine forest in Scotland, remnants of the once widespread Caledonian Forest, much of which was deliberately destroyed after the Jacobite Rebellion of 1745, also the birch woodland farther north.

(c)   Relicts of wood-pasture – ancient unenclosed woodland, once parts of medieval hunting forests, deer parks and wooded commons.

(d)   Ancient coppice woods, or woods formerly coppiced which have since grown up, identifiable today by their branching patterns.

2   Plantations on ancient sites

These occur where ancient continuously wooded sites have been completely or partially cleared and replanted with native or introduced trees. Thus, many ancient woods have been planted up with conifers in recent years.

3   Recent semi-natural woodland

This category includes **secondary woodland** which has recolonized arable land, grassland or moorland, after abandonment of cultivation or as a result of reduction of grazing or burning.

4   Recent plantations

These began with the deliberate planting of trees on open sites, either for amenity purposes, such as park landscaping or game conservation, or for commercial purposes. The latter greatly increased in some areas during the 20th century, with the establishment of the Forestry Commission and tax incentives for large landowners to 'reclaim' areas of moorland and bog. In particular, large tracts of conifers have been planted in upland areas, with a very mixed reception from both the public and environmental organizations.

❑   Suggest two factors, ultimately related to human activities, which, it has been suggested in newspaper reports in recent years, might be adversely affecting the pine forests of the Scottish Highlands.

■   (a) There are concerns about the effects of 'acid rain' (release in rainfall of atmospheric pollutants from power stations, factories, vehicle exhausts, etc.), and (b) damage to pine seedlings and the consequent prevention of regeneration possibly caused by population growth of red deer from estates primarily devoted to shooting. Since red deer in Britain have no natural predators other than humans – wolves having become extinct in Scotland about 1745 – their populations easily consume available resources, resulting not only in environmental damage but also in mass starvation for them, unless they are selectively culled over and above those shot for sport.

1.7.2   Ancient woodland and its management

From the earliest times of settlement, forests have been exploited for a wide range of products. Foremost, of course, come timber and wood, but also bast for fibre, herbs and berries for food and medicine, as well as the range of animals and their products (from antlers to honey), which are also naturally part of the forest ecosystem. The historical difference between the terms **timber** and **wood**, in this context, is important. Timber is produced from the trunks of trees and includes beams, planks, door and gate posts, whereas wood is the thinner material such as poles for fencing or light building work but also brushwood, firewood and the raw material used for charcoal ovens.

Woodland, then, may be managed for the regular and efficient production of both timber and wood, using the trees themselves as a naturally self-renewing resource. This ancient tradition of **woodmanship** is rather different from much modern forestry, where trees are planted on cleared ground and mass harvested.

The great survey of Domesday in 1086 records areas of woodland belonging to parishes and manors in many parts of England. Sometimes it is possible to identify existing woods within this survey. However, many of the records relate to 'wood for so many swine', because the King's surveyors were more interested in recording the extent of pannage, where pigs were set out in autumn to fatten on the acorn crop, than directly in the timber and wood resources of the kingdom. Nevertheless, until the 17th century or later, these blocks of woodland, some large, but many comparatively small, played a vital role as local resources for village communities, which needed to be largely self-sufficient in building materials, products such as hurdles and wood for carts, tool handles and furniture, and, of course, firewood. Alternatively, the woods might belong to the estates of great lords or religious institutions which owned property in different areas of the country and managed their resources on a grander but still carefully regulated scale. Thus, for example, in about 1330 a number of oaks of a size that would be impossible to match in one place today were felled at Chicksands in Bedfordshire and hauled to Ely, Cambridgeshire, to be cut and hoisted many metres to the roof of its Cathedral to form the 40-foot (12-m) long struts and massive uprights of the famous Octagon.

Over the years, many of these blocks of medieval woodland have survived almost intact, at least until after the Second World War, but often their shapes and extent have been altered by being partly grubbed out or by adjacent land being added to them, whether by deliberate planting or simply the abandonment of cropping and grazing. However, the original medieval boundaries are often marked by a stout outer **woodbank** and ditch, which served to keep out domestic animals that grazed in the surrounding open fields; such banks might also subdivide parts of the wood in different manorial ownership. They were probably once topped by fences or hedges and may still be marked by trees that have in the past been **pollarded**, that is trees regularly lopped at a height of 2–3 metres. In a few cases, such banks were also constructed to keep in such animals as deer or wild boar, where blocks of forest were conserved specifically for hunting or the raising of game for the table. These ditches and woodbanks are useful together with vegetational evidence (Section 1.7.3) for reconstructing the history of local woodlands. It is probable that many woodlands known to have survived from medieval times to the present have, as suggested in Figure 1.53, been continuously wooded since the period of the wildwood, but occasionally prehistoric earthworks, such as barrows and ring-ditches, deeply concealed within woodland, particularly on the Chalk Downs, suggest that early clearance and recolonization by trees even in prehistoric times have taken place.

Figure 1.54 Pollarded trees in Cambridgeshire, surviving after the hedgerow has been grubbed up.

Most ancient woodland consists of both timber trees, or **standards**, which are allowed to grow up to their natural height, and **coppice** or underwood, trees which are regularly cut down to just above ground level but respond by producing a number of young shoots. The action of repeated coppicing seems to stimulate renewed vigour, so that many **coppice stools** represent individual trees that are in fact hundreds or even thousands of years old. They are thus by far the oldest living multicellular organisms you are likely to encounter.

Figure 1.55 Mature hazel coppice with oak standards, Hayley Wood, Cambridgeshire. A multi-stemmed ash, once coppiced, has also been left to develop as a standard.

❑ What is the purpose of coppicing trees?

■ The coppice shoots grow into long, straight poles, which are harvested at the end of the coppice cycle and are valuable for fencing or building work. Brushwood and less regular shoots are all used for other purposes. Furthermore, as explained above, the vigour and longevity of the trees are increased by coppicing.

Coppice is generally cut at regular intervals of 12–20 years, though shorter cycles were customary at some periods, for example in the Middle Ages. No doubt the rotation depended partly on custom and partly on the precise usage of the crop.

Several of our woodland trees respond well to coppicing, in particular hazel *Corylus*, which is in fact seldom found as a single-stemmed tree, ash *Fraxinus* and, in south-east England hornbeam *Carpinus* and sweet chestnut *Castanea*. Where lime woods have survived, lime *Tilia* may also be coppiced. These trees, of course, are also capable of growing up as standards. The rotation of standards is much longer, perhaps 40–100 years depending on the growth and species of the individual tree. Basically, they are harvested when timber is required for a particular purpose, and, after they have been felled, a young sapling nearby is allowed to grow up to fill the gap in the mosaic of coppice and standards, rather than be cut down at the time of coppicing.

❑   What kinds of tree are unlikely to be suitable for coppicing, and why?

■   Essentially, trees that fail to produce strong shoots from cut stumps will not form good coppice. This includes almost all conifers, such as pine *Pinus* and spruce *Picea*. Oaks *Quercus*, which produce rather weak basal shoots, are rarely coppiced, except on acid soils, where other trees grow poorly; anyway, it is much more profitable to grow oak as a standard crop. Most elms *Ulmus* produce suckers from their root systems rather than shoots from cut stumps, and their wood products are generally less in demand than those of traditional coppice trees.

Particularly during the 19th century, oak was greatly favoured as a timber tree above other trees. Selection of young oaks as standards, or even planting where oak was not regenerating well, undoubtedly altered the character of some large areas of woodland in Britain, although, of course, trees like ash, hornbeam and maple, though disfavoured, would still be present as coppice and have often reasserted themselves when this management practice was relaxed or coppicing ceased.

❑   Which introduced tree, other than planted conifers or beeches, has made its mark on the composition of some British woodlands?

■   The introduced sycamore *Acer pseudoplatanus* can be a very successful invasive weed of woodland, even of ancient woodland where management has been neglected. It has often been encouraged in amenity planting and shelter belts or as hedgerow trees. In parts of northern Britain, where tree cover is sparse, its ability to establish itself rapidly has been regarded as an asset and it is widespread as isolated trees in hedges or as small copses and shelter belts.

Coppice with standards was the traditional management regime from distant times (certainly before the medieval period, when it was described in estate records in terms of its different products and through laws against the abuse of woodland) until the early part of the 20th century when a decline in its usage set in.

❑   What reasons might have caused this change in long-established woodland management patterns?

- This kind of management is labour-intensive and there has been much less demand for traditional hardwood forest products, such as roofing poles, brushwood fencing, firewood and charcoal. Also, with the First World War, came the decline of the large sporting estates, which favoured well-managed woodland as well as needing plenty of labour. Finally, the establishment of the Forestry Commission to produce sufficient timber for national needs, particularly during times of war, was an important factor. They, of course, were largely concerned to plant and grow large areas of conifers.

In some areas of the country, coppicing rotations have remained standard practice to the present day, for example in south-east England, where sweet chestnut coppice is still widespread, but there has been a moderate return to it in other areas, particularly in woodland managed by conservation organizations such as the Woodland Trust and County Naturalists' Trusts.

- ❑ Apart from trying to make obtain an economic return from the ownership of woodland, why should there be a natural history interest in continuing or reinstating traditional forest management practices?

- In woods where coppicing has ceased, some trees grow up into the canopy, but hazel stools tend to deteriorate in the absence of repeated cutting and prolonged shade and may eventually succumb to fungal diseases. Even more important, coppicing and the maintenance of broad paths (rides) within the woods to permit extraction of wood and timber, greatly increase the diversity of habitats and allow a range of herbs and insects to flourish which would otherwise disappear.

1.7.3 Ancient woodland flora and fauna

Although fragments of ancient woodland are now scattered and isolated within the British countryside, nonetheless (together with the even more scattered and threatened fragments of wetland vegetation such as fens and bogs) they provide the refugia for many species of plants and animals which were formerly widespread when Britain retained a natural vegetation cover.

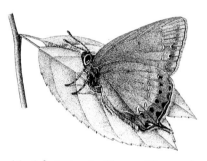

black hairstreak *Strymonidia pruni*

Both zoologists and botanists have long recognized that certain insect and plant species are virtually confined to ancient woodlands. The black hairstreak butterfly *Strymonidia pruni*, for example, is restricted to a small number of woods in the English Midlands, where it has been known for over 200 years. Plant examples include the wild service tree *Sorbus torminalis*, and particularly ground flora herbs such as herb paris *Paris quadrifolia*, lily-of-the-valley *Convallaria majalis* and the much commoner wood sorrel *Oxalis acetosella*. Some species behave differently in different areas, thus *Melampyrum pratense* is largely confined to ancient woodland in eastern England but occurs in heathland and moorland in the west.

Recent woodland and plantations, even after 200 years, tend on the other hand to be characterized by a very different ground flora, with easily dispersed taxa such as ivy *Hedera helix*, cow parsley *Anthriscus sylvestris*, sweet violet *Viola odorata* and lords and ladies *Arum maculatum*. True woodland butterflies, other than ringlet *Aphantopus hyperantus*, are rarely present. Nevertheless, some of the commoner woodland herbs, such as

wild service tree
Sorbus torminalis

dog's mercury *Mercurialis perennis* and bluebell *Hyacinthoides non-scriptus* may eventually succeed in colonizing such areas.

❑   Where could such dispersal patterns of taxa spreading from ancient to more recent woodland be best studied?

■   Where blocks of ancient woodland have been extended by later planting or the abandonment of adjacent cultivated fields. Under these circumstances, direct colonization is possible, whereas that of isolated recent woodlands is clearly more difficult.

The three species of *Primula* that grow in southern England provide interesting contrasts in terms of their dispersal patterns. The cowslip *Primula veris* is essentially a plant of grassland, more specifically of meadows, where it has declined drastically, and roadside verges, though it also occurs in woodland grassland, the rides and clearings within ancient woodland. Where grassland has been converted to secondary woodland, the plant can survive for many decades. The oxlip *Primula elatior* occurs only in eastern England, where it is virtually restricted to ancient woodland on soils derived from chalky till (glacial deposits). Its spread into directly adjacent secondary woodland has been monitored at about one metre a year, so that the chances of it spreading to isolated planted woods even on the right soil type are fairly remote. The primrose *Primula vulgaris* is a much more widespread plant, growing not only in ancient woodland, where coppicing greatly stimulates flowering, but also in hedgebanks and in open grassy places in the west of England. Where motorways cut through ancient woodland, the grassy banks may be rapidly colonized by this plant. Strangely, however, though it can be successfully naturalized in the rich soils of gardens, it seems to be very reluctant to colonize plantations naturally even after a century and, when planted, usually fails to thrive and dies out. It has, perhaps, certain specific soil requirements in terms of mineral nutrients.

1.7.4   Extinctions and conservation of isolated plant and animal populations

Throughout this Chapter, and to some extent through this whole Course, we have very often chosen flowering plants, ferns or butterflies to illustrate many of our arguments. This can be partly explained by the personal enthusiasms of Course Team authors, but particularly with regard to this Chapter it is significant that these very attractive groups of organisms have earned the attention of natural historians from the 17th century onwards, when detailed observations first began to be made and published, and herbaria and insect collections were established. Thus, we have far more detailed information about former distribution patterns for these than for any other groups of organisms. Two features stand out. The first is that some very restricted organisms have been known from precisely the same locality for several hundred years. A classic example is bloody cranesbill *Geranium sanguineum*, a local but never common plant of dunes, limestone cliffs and grassland in western and northern Britain, but in eastern England now confined to a single locality on the Devil's Dyke in Cambridgeshire, where it was first recorded by the great 17th century naturalist John Ray in 1660.

The second feature is that wherever we have reasonably detailed lists, whether of plants or butterflies and moths (Lepidoptera) from individual

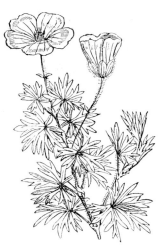

bloody cranesbill
Geranium sanguineum (× 0.7)

and still extant sites covering the past hundred years or more, a considerable proportion of species have become extinct. In some cases, it is not at all clear why these losses should have taken place, since the present habitats still seem quite suitable for the species; in other cases, changes in management, loss of particular microhabitats or documented historical events may provide possible reasons for their loss. These considerations apply not only to ancient woodlands but to wetland habitats and also to unimproved grasslands, such as chalk downland and to heaths.

❐ What particular characteristics do these habitats share in terms of their recent history?

■ They are all declining in area in the face of modern land-use changes, and they are mostly now generally reduced to isolated fragments, which makes dispersal of biota from one site to another much more difficult than previously. Thus, many of their populations of different groups of organisms are also becoming isolated, both spatially and genetically.

The concept of metapopulations may throw some light on this situation. Much of this Chapter has been chiefly concerned with the changing distribution of species populations in space and time. We have seen how natural ecosystems have become fragmented, particularly over the past 5000 years by human activities, but in fact, depending on the scale examined, all species have discontinuous distributions. What we are concerned with here is species that are so patchily distributed that they consist of populations which are spatially isolated from one another, though there may over time be some flow of individuals between them. A **metapopulation** is essentially a population which consists of a network of such smaller isolated populations.

If we consider the wildwood of 5000 years ago, many species, including the dominant forest trees, were widely distributed and must have formed more or less continuous breeding populations – so, too, may other species, such as insects of high, well-developed forest canopy or decaying timber, which are now rare. However, ancient forest has a complex mosaic structure, reflecting decay and regeneration. Where old trees have died and fallen, or areas of forest have been affected by storm or fire or flooding or perhaps by local outbreaks of fungal disease, successional changes will have been initiated on a small spatial scale. No doubt many of the herbs and invertebrates that rapidly invade cleared areas in modern woodlands and persist there for a few seasons until the trees shade out the ground, were also present in the wildwood and played a similar role in natural clearings. Populations of such species can be regarded as belonging to metapopulations, which are maintained by a high ability to disperse and colonize new sites.

Another aspect of heterogeneity with the wildwood would be local topographic or geological features, small streams and flushes, rocky outcrops and cliffs, patches of unusual soil conditions, etc., which would also support small isolated populations of plants and animals requiring special niches. In these cases, dispersal between populations might be much more irregular. There would also be a significant chance of some of these small populations becoming extinct from natural causes such as small habitat changes, disease, a spell of unusually cold or dry climate, predation or population numbers fluctuating and eventually falling below a critical threshold. Over a period of time, loss of such a population might be compensated for by recolonization following dispersal from a surviving population, or by the founding of further populations in new sites, but this is likely to be a much slower process than in the case of organisms occupying clearings in the forest.

In either of the general cases outlined above, it is possible to think of relatively well-established and/or high density **source populations** and **sink populations** (Book 2, Chapter 1), much more liable to go extinct and in the longer or shorter term maintained by occasional dispersal of seed in the case of plants or by active migration or passive dispersal in the case of juvenile or adult animals from source populations.

In some cases of metapopulations, even these categories are not really appropriate. A modern small-scale example is provided by the heath fritillary butterfly *Mellicta athalia* in southern Britain. This butterfly, now one of the rarest in Britain, was once local but widespread in woodland on sandy soils, where its principal food plant (cow-wheat *Melampyrum pratense*) grows. However, this plant really only flourishes well and reaches its full abundance in coppice clearings, where the wealth of other flowers and open sunny but sheltered conditions provide an ideal environment for the adult butterfly. A nickname for this butterfly was the 'woodman's follower' because, in the large woods which it favoured, small coppice plots were opened up at regular intervals and in different areas. Nevertheless, as after two or three years coppice stools began to grow up and render the clearing unsuitable for the butterfly, a number of individuals would successfully disperse through the forest, detect new clearings and establish new colonies and effectively new populations, whereas the parent population would effectively become extinct. In this case, the widespread abandonment of coppicing after the First World War proved fatal to the survival of this butterfly in most of its localities. It survived in just a few sites where it was on the brink of extinction, when deliberate renewal of regular coppicing in the 1980s saved it and its numbers increased considerably. Fortunately, small populations of this butterfly are also found at a few sites in south-west Britain, where it occupies two rather different habitats – on heathland, where cow-wheat also occurs, and in certain restricted types of old grassland, where the larvae feed on ribwort plantain.

heath fritillary *Mellicta athalia* on cow-wheat *Melampyrum pratense* (× 1)

❐ What *general* factors are likely to be important in the survival of such metapopulations?

■ (1) The number of populated sites; (2) the number of vacant sites suitable for colonization; (3) the rate of colonization; and (4) the rate of extinction.

Suppose the number of populated sites at time t is described as P_t and the number of vacant sites as V_t, and that populated sites become extinct at a rate x per population per time interval and vacant sites are colonized at a rate c per population per time interval, then the number of populated sites at time $t+1$ will be:

$$P_{t+1} = P_t + cP_tV_t - xP_t \tag{1.1}$$

where cP_tV_t is the number of new sites that are colonized and xP_t the number of existing sites where existing populations become extinct.

If the number of populated sites is in equilibrium $P_{t+1} = P_t$, then from Equation 1.1,

$$cP_tV_t = xP_t \qquad (1.2)$$

In which case, $V_t = \dfrac{x}{c}$ $\qquad (1.3)$

This tells us that if populations are to increase (i.e. $P_{t+1} > P_t$) the density of vacant habitats (V_t) has to exceed the relative extinction rate (x/c). If there are changes either in habitat availability or extinction rate or a failure of colonization, then a threshold may be crossed so that $V_t < x/c$ and extinction of the populations becomes likely.

Some but not all of the rarer woodland plants in the existing British flora probably had patchy distributions even 5000 years ago, and existed even then as metapopulations. Since that time, their populations have become considerably more fragmented, as have those of many species of the British woodland invertebrate fauna, such as the black hairstreak and heath fritillary butterflies. Furthermore, many of these species are now on the margins of their European distribution ranges perhaps for climatic reasons, and for them climatic deterioration has posed extra problems.

❐   In terms of Equation 1.3, what do you regard as the main problems in conserving rare species which occur in British woodlands today, essentially as metapopulations?

■   The number of populated sites has already been reduced by habitat destruction (and in many cases continues to be reduced by continuing extinction of small populations). The number of vacant sites suitable for colonization also generally continues to diminish. The rate of colonization depends crucially on dispersal and on time. There are now considerable geographical barriers (particularly large tracts of inhospitable agricultural land) which prevent many populations of rare plants and animals from spreading or reinforcing adjacent populations. Thus, the chances of achieving a successful colonization event are reduced. Finally, human activities have greatly increased the possibilities of extinction for small colonies of other taxa, often in ways that are not recognized until the damage has been done. Extinctions may take place even within carefully managed nature reserves, particularly because management for one group of species may inadvertently put at risk or actually disfavour others.

Karieva and Wennergren (1995) have discussed how the interactions of population change and the disruption of landscape patterns may be modelled, noting not only the extinction thresholds for individual species, but how, under these conditions, biodiversity and eventually the composition of communities may change. For example, the spatial disruption of communities may permanently favour species capable of rapid dispersal, whereas under undisturbed conditions slower-dispersing species would eventually have occupied particular niches. Looking to the future, they emphasize that notwithstanding the generally gloomy prognoses of these concepts for the conservation of the remnants of natural or semi-natural ecosystems, only by understanding them can constructive management plans have any hope of success.

Summary of Section 1.7

Despite the progressive destruction of the natural forest vegetation cover of the British Isles – the **wildwood** – over the past 5000 years, various categories of **ancient woodland** have survived and are characterized by distinctive species of plants and invertebrates. Ancient **coppiced** woodlands are particularly important in this respect since long-established management patterns have maintained a rich diversity of habitats and therefore species. Decline in active management of ancient woodland after the First World War and widespread grubbing up of woods after the Second World War have both had serious deleterious effects on the abundance and diversity of rarer species of the fauna and flora. This is not compensated for by the planting of **secondary deciduous woodland** or by coniferous plantations, as many of the most characteristic herbs and insects of ancient woodland only disperse very slowly or not at all into such newly created habitats.

A further problem is that even where habitats are conserved a gradual loss of the rarer species of both plants and animals occurs. Many of these only survive as small groups of isolated populations. The concept of **metapopulations** can be applied here, and the dynamics of such groups of populations can be expressed and analysed in mathematical terms. Small fluctuations in habitat availability, or rates of colonization and extinction of individual populations, are likely to have wider implications for the spread or extinction of the metapopulation itself. Clearly, such analyses are important for conservation management.

Question 1.18   (Objective 1.13)

Explain the differences between the categories ancient woodland, secondary woodland and plantations in the classification of woodland in Britain.

Question 1.19   (Objective 1.14)

Ancient pollarded trees (Figure 1.54) are found in hedgerows, on commons and in closes (small meadows adjacent to villages), on woodbanks and beside rivers (here almost always willows). What purposes might pollarding serve?

Question 1.20   (Objective 1.15)

In the light of the concept of metapopulations, what practical but controversial management strategy might conservationists need to debate in considering the future of small isolated populations of plants and animals?

Objectives for Chapter 1

After completing Chapter 1, you should be able to:

1.1 Recall and use in their context the terms shown in **bold** in the text. (*Questions 1.1, 1.2, 1.6 & 1.7*)

1.2 Discuss the basis on which biogeographical regions are defined and give examples of major differences in faunas and floras between regions. (*Question 1.1*)

1.3 Discuss the differences between the dispersal and vicariance hypotheses in biogeography and give named examples that support each hypothesis. (*Questions 1.2 & 1.3*)

1.4 Make reasoned explanations of disjunct distribution patterns. (*Questions 1.3 & 1.4*)

1.5 Use named examples to discuss how continental drift and sea-level changes may explain the modern distribution patterns of plant and animal taxa. (*Questions 1.3, 1.4 & 1.13*)

1.6 Outline the major effects of the Quaternary Ice Age on the biogeographical distribution of the fauna and flora of western Europe. (*Questions 1.8, 1.9, 1.10 & 1.16*)

1.7 Outline the major effects of the Quaternary Ice Age on the distribution of faunas and floras in tropical areas. (*Questions 1.5 & 1.11*)

1.8 Explain how pollen diagrams are constructed and zoned. (*Questions 1.15 & 1.16*)

1.9 Discuss the use of pollen diagrams for reconstructing vegetational and climatic change. (*Questions 1.8, 1.11 & 1.16*)

1.10 Outline the major changes in the vegetational cover of Britain during the Flandrian. (*Questions 1.12 & 1.14–1.16*)

1.11 Describe the increasing effects of human activities on the natural environment of Britain during the past 5000 years. (*Questions 1.14, 1.15 & 1.17*)

1.12 Discuss with reference to named examples, how the fossil record of forest trees, mountain plants and pastoral weeds in Britain helps to explain their present distribution. (*Questions 1.9 & 1.12*)

1.13 Describe the classification of woodland in Britain today and the principles on which it based. (*Questions 1.1 & 1.18*)

1.14 Discuss the historical and vegetational importance of traditional management practices regarding trees and woodland in the British countryside. (*Question 1.19*)

1.15 Explain the relevance of the concept of metapopulations to the distribution and conservation of rare species of plants and animals in semi-natural habitats, such as ancient woodland, wetlands or downland. (*Question 1.20*)

References for Chapter 1

Bell, M. and Walker, M. J. C. (1992) *Late Quaternary Environmental Change: Physical and Human Perspectives*, Longman.

Evans, G. H. (1970) Pollen and diatom analysis of Late-glacial Quaternary deposits in the Blelham basin, North Lanacashire, *New Phytologist*, **69**, 821–74.

Flenley, J. R. (1979) *The Tropical Rain Forest: A Geological History*, Butterworths.

van Geel, B. and van der Hammen, T. (1973) Upper Quaternary vegetational and climatic sequence of the Fuquene area (Eastern Cordillera, Colombia), *Palaeogeography, Palaeoclimatology, Palaeoecology*, **14**, 9–92.

Godwin, H. (1975) *The History of the British Flora*, 2nd edn, Cambridge University Press.

van der Hammen, T., Werner, J. H. and van Dommeln, H. (1974) The Pleistocene changes of vegetation and climate in tropical South America, *Journal of Biogeography*, **1**, 3–26.

Hampton, M. and Kay, Q. O. N. (1995) *Sorbus domestica* L., new to Wales and the British Isles, *Watsonia*, **20**, 379–84.

Jones, R. L. and Keen, D. H. (1993) *Pleistocene Environments in the British Isles*, Chapman & Hall.

Karieva, P. and Wennergren, U. (1995) Connecting landscape patterns to ecosystem and population processes, *Nature*, **373**, 299–302.

Kirby, K. J., Peterken, G. F., Spencer, J. W. and Walker, G. J. (1984) *Inventories of Ancient Semi-Natural Woodland*, Nature Conservancy Council.

Moreau, R. E. (1966) *The Bird Fauna of Africa and its Islands*, Academic Press, NY.

Morley, R. J. and Flenley, J. R. (1987) *Late Cainozoic Vegetational and Environmental Changes in the Malay Archipelago*, Oxford Monographs in Biogeography 4, Clarendon Press, Oxford.

Peglar, S. M., Fritz, S. C. and Birks H. J. B. (1989) Vegetation and land-use history at Diss, Norfolk, U.K., *Journal of Ecology*, **77**, 203–22.

Pennington, W. (1970) Vegetation history in North-West England, in *Studies in the Vegetational History of the British Isles*, eds D. Walker and R. G. West, Cambridge University Press.

Rackham, O. (1980) *Ancient Woodland: Its History, Vegetation and Uses in England*, Edward Arnold.

Talbot, M. R., Livingstone, D. A., Palmer, P. G., Maley, J., Melack, D. M., Delibrias, G. and Gulliksen, G. (1984) Preliminary results from sediment cores from Lake Bosumtwi, Ghana, *Palaeoecology of Africa*, **16**, 173–92.

Turner, C. (1970) The Middle Pleistocene interglacial deposits at Marks Tey, Essex, *Philosophical Transactions of the Royal Society of London*, **B257**, 373–440.

Walker, D. and Flenley J. R. (1979) Late Quaternary vegetational history of the Enga District of upland Papua, New Guinea, *Philosophical Transactions of the Royal Society of London*, **B286**, 265–344.

Whitmore, T. C. (1994) *An Introduction to Tropical Rain Forests*, Oxford University Press.

Whitmore, T. C. and Prance, G. T. (1987) *Biogeography and Quaternary History in Tropical America*, Clarendon Press, Oxford.

COMMUNITY COMPOSITION, STRUCTURE AND FUNCTION

CHAPTER 2

Prepared for the Course Team by Mike Gillman

2.1　Introduction

This Chapter builds on the biogeographical studies of Chapter 1 where global patterns of species richness were described and accounted for by processes occurring over long periods of geological time. In this Chapter, we focus in on the assemblages of species produced by these large-scale spatial and temporal processes. The aim is to describe some of the smaller scale community patterns observed across the Earth today and to try to understand the underlying ecological mechanisms. This will prepare us for Chapter 3 which considers the dynamics of communities, particularly the phenomenon of succession.

2.2　Definition and composition of ecological communities

In Book 2 we saw how the rates of birth, death and migration of individuals are used to investigate the abundance and distribution of animal and plant populations. This is the approach taken by population ecologists. However, nearly all animals and plants occur in communities (defined below) containing other species, and in some communities there may be hundreds of species. We obviously cannot hope to study the population ecology of all these species separately, let alone all the important interactions between them. Hence ecologists also need methods for describing and studying the structure and dynamics of communities in their own right. As we saw at the end of Chapter 4 of Book 2, population ecology can only take us so far in answering questions such as 'why is the world green?'.

2.2.1　Interactions and area

An **ecological community** is defined either as all individuals of any species living in the same area or as all individuals of any species which interact with each other. The first definition is convenient for sampling and follows the area-based definition of populations given in Chapter 1 of Book 2. The latter definition is more interesting as it focuses on mechanisms and allows considerations of community structure and dynamics. We have already met simple communities defined by interaction in Chapters 3 and 4 of Book 2 where we considered populations linked by competition and predation. We will use both area and interaction definitions of communities in this Book.

The range of ecological interactions was introduced in Chapter 1 of Book 1, using the $0/+/-$ notation to describe the presence or absence of an interaction and its effect on the interacting individuals. These interactions occur within and between trophic levels and are summarized in Figure 2.1.

| | | effect of species j on i | | |
		+	0	−
effect of species	+	+ +	+ 0	+ −
i on j	0	0 +	0 0	0 −
	−	− +	− 0	− −

Figure 2.1   A method of summarizing interactions between species. A species i can have a positive, negative or no effect on a second species j, and vice versa, leading to nine possible combinations of interaction.

In community analyses we will not only be interested in the sign of the interaction (e.g. +/−) but also its strength. The latter is rather difficult to measure but will be determined by factors such as how much the survival or fecundity of individuals of species j is reduced by the presence and activities of individuals of species i. Indeed, we might want to delimit our communities according to the strength of interactions, otherwise we will be left with a community which is unmanageably large and also artificial because many of the interactions are so weak. For example, let us consider the grouse described in Chapter 4 of Book 2. It interacts with its food plant (heather) and insects (as a chick) and a natural enemy (a parasitic worm). Some grouse are also preyed upon by foxes. However, there are many other species with which it may be interacting, including competitors and other natural enemies (Figure 2.2). These species in turn will have interactions with other species. Where do we draw the line around the community? At what point do the interactions become too weak? The issue of strength of interaction is discussed in Section 2.6.

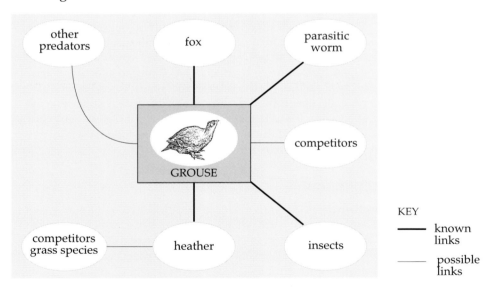

KEY
— known links
— possible links

Figure 2.2   The grouse community based on ecological interactions.

A more fundamental problem than the strength of the interaction is knowing whether species interact at all, that is, whether the interaction is zero or non-zero. We may observe some feeding interactions in the field, but identifying even a small fraction of all the feeding interactions may be an enormous task as illustrated by the complexity of the two food webs in Figure 2.3 constructed around two species. The first (Figure 2.3a) is the web derived from the feeding interactions of different ages of herring *Clupea harengus* in the North Sea (Barnes and Hughes, 1988). The second (Figure 2.3b) is based on feeding links between 44 species or species groups on the Caribbean island of St. Martin which lies between Antigua and Puerto Rico. This food web was constructed around *Anolis* lizard species from the work of Roughgarden and colleagues (Goldwasser and Roughgarden, 1993). We shall return to food webs in Section 2.5.4.

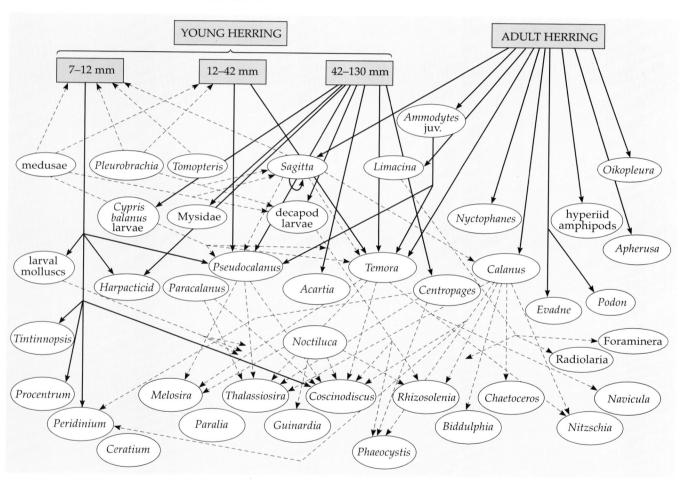

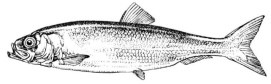

Figure 2.3   (a) The feeding relationships of the herring *Clupea harengus* in the North Sea at different stages in its life cycle. The direction of the arrows is from consumer to consumed. Bold arrows are from herring, dashed arrows are from other species or species groups.

herring

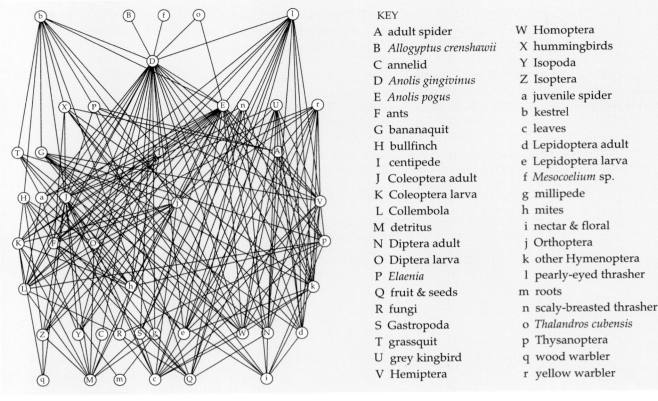

KEY

A	adult spider	W	Homoptera
B	*Allogyptus crenshawii*	X	hummingbirds
C	annelid	Y	Isopoda
D	*Anolis gingivinus*	Z	Isoptera
E	*Anolis pogus*	a	juvenile spider
F	ants	b	kestrel
G	bananaquit	c	leaves
H	bullfinch	d	Lepidoptera adult
I	centipede	e	Lepidoptera larva
J	Coleoptera adult	f	*Mesocoelium* sp.
K	Coleoptera larva	g	millipede
L	Collembola	h	mites
M	detritus	i	nectar & floral
N	Diptera adult	j	Orthoptera
O	Diptera larva	k	other Hymenoptera
P	*Elaenia*	l	pearly-eyed thrasher
Q	fruit & seeds	m	roots
R	fungi	n	scaly-breasted thrasher
S	Gastropoda	o	*Thalandros cubensis*
T	grassquit	p	Thysanoptera
U	grey kingbird	q	wood warbler
V	Hemiptera	r	yellow warbler

(b) St. Martin food web constructed around *Anolis* lizard species (*Anolis gingivinus* D and *Anolis pogus* E).

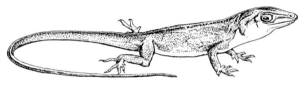

Anolis lizard

❑   How can ecologists determine the presence of *feeding* interactions between species *other* than by direct observation of one individual eating another?

■   There are several possible methods. One is to examine the gut or faecal contents of species. For example, the proportion of six insect orders in the diet of two species of spider is shown in Figure 2.4 (Wise, 1993). A second possibility is to radioactively label a prey item, e.g. a plant, and then record the species in which this radioactive label is found. An example of this method is shown in Figure 2.5.

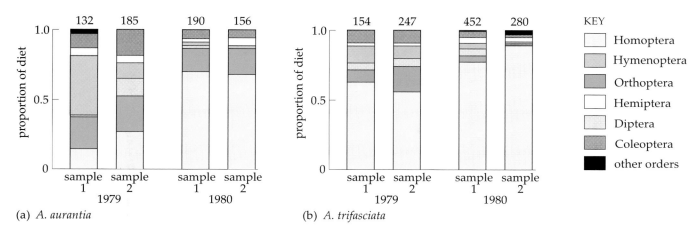

Figure 2.4   The proportion of insect orders found in the guts of two species of spider *(Argiope aurantia* and *A. trifasciata).* Numbers above each column are the total number of prey classified to order.

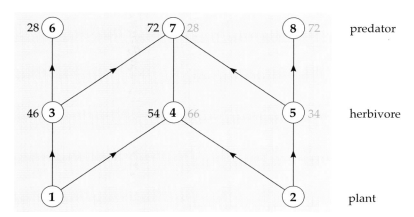

Figure 2.5   The pattern of flow of a ^{32}P radioactive isotope from two plant species in a grassland. The plant species are **1** *Ambrosia* sp. and **2** *Raphanus* sp. The numbers outside the circle show the percentage of label following a particular route (black numbers relate to plant species of 1 and green numbers to plant species of 2), e.g. 46% from plant species **1** to herbivore **3** and 54% to herbivore **4**.

The next problem is to determine the non-feeding interactions between species.

❑ Give examples of some *non-feeding* interactions between species.

■ Competition, mutualism and commensalism (see Book 1, Section 1.4).

❑ How can ecologists determine the presence of *non-feeding* interactions between species?

■ The only satisfactory way is to undertake experiments in the laboratory or field (preferably the latter). For example, recall the experiment on gerbils carried out by Abramsky *et al.* (Book 2, Section 3.5.1) and the experiment on the rocky shore carried out by Connell (Book 1, Section 3.2.3).

Throughout this Chapter, we will wrestle with the problem of community complexity and consider ways of dealing with it. Indeed, complexity is not just a problem but an issue in community ecology. For example, the question of whether complex communities are more stable than simple ones is a fundamental one. In the next Section, we consider a biome where terrestrial species richness reaches its heights and use the example to tease out some more of the principles of community ecology.

Summary of Section 2.2

Ecological communities are defined as either all species in a given area or all interacting species. Ecological interactions are categorized by the $0/+/-$ system. These interactions can be determined by direct observation, experiment, dissection and radioactive labelling. The strength of interaction is an important consideration in delimiting communities.

Question 2.1   *(Objectives 2.1 & 2.2)*

In Book 1, Section 1.8, we were introduced to the apparently mutualistic interaction between ants and acacias. The effect of ant removal on acacia survival and growth is shown in Table 2.1. Does this provide evidence of a mutualistic interaction? What further work would be required to support or refute this conclusion?

Table 2.1   The effect of ant removal on acacia survival and growth (from Krebs 1994, based on a study by Janzen, 1966).

	Acacias (ants removed)	Acacias (ants present)
survival rate over 10 months (%)	43	72
growth increment (cm):		
May 25–June 16	6.2	31.0
June 16–August 3	10.2	72.9

2.3   An excursion into the tropical forest

The communities in a tropical forest are considered to be amongst the most complex and species-rich in the world. If we can begin to make sense of the community structure and dynamics in tropical forests then perhaps we have some hope of understanding other communities! As noted in Chapter 1, many naturalists and ecologists have gloried in the complexity and richness of the tropical forests, as witnessed by the following quotation from Philip Gosse's *The Romance of Natural History*, published in 1860:

> '…the gorgeous gloom of a Brazilian forest, where the wiry-haired sloth hangs from the branches, the toothless ant-eater breaks up with its hoofs the great earthy nests of the termites, and the armadillo burrows in the soil; where the capybara and the tapir rush to the water; where painted toucans cry to each

other, golden-plumaged trogons sit on the top-most boughs, and sparkling hummingbirds flit over the flowers; where beetles, like precious stones, crawl up the huge trunks, and butterflies of all brilliant hues fan the still and loaded air.'

In fact there are several types of tropical forest, determined by their seasonal patterns of rainfall and temperature (recall the categorization of biomes by rainfall and temperature in Book 1, Section 3.4.1). These forest types include tropical rainforest, tropical deciduous forest and tropical montane forest. The distribution of tropical rain and deciduous forest around the world is shown in Figure 3.15a in Book 1.

We know that tropical forests are faced with a variety of threats, including direct loss of habitat and fragmentation of the remainder (some background on these threats is given in TV programmes 'Managing for biodiversity: forest in Trinidad' and 'The big picture'). Whilst we do not cover these threats here, they provide an impetus for much of the ecological work in tropical forests today.

2.3.1   Guilds in the tropical forest

One way of simplifying the community complexity is to concentrate on *guilds* of species (Root, 1967) that exploit a common resource in similar ways (Book 1, Chapter 2; Book 2, Section 3.5; see also functional feeding groups, Book 1, Section 4.10.2). Root envisaged a guild cutting across taxonomic boundaries but many studies have been restricted to particular taxonomic groups. The resource is usually food, for example, a guild of insects feeding on a plant species (recall the insect herbivores of ragwort in Book 2, Section 4.2.3) or a guild of birds feeding on seeds of a certain size. There is much debate about precisely what constitutes a guild. For example, are all the insect herbivores of ragwort in the same guild, or just those that feed, for example, on leaves, or in the stems? Once the guild is identified, the community can then be defined just as the guild itself, or widened to be the guild plus the resource (or the species producing the resource) plus the natural enemies of the guild. The guild approach has several advantages including easier identification of the community components; species sharing a common resource are more likely to compete (although we need experimental evidence to be certain) and members of the guild may share natural enemies.

The members of a guild may be specialists (monophagous, oligophagous) or generalists (polyphagous), examples of which were described in Book 1, Section 2.2. Tropical forests are noted for their species richness and much of this is due to the evolution of specialist groups, a process that we will consider in some detail below. It is worth bearing in mind that specialists are believed to evolve when a resource such as a host plant or parasitoid host is 'abundant, accessible and predictable' (Crawley, 1983). Many plants form a temporally and spatially predictable resource.

❑   What types of plants are likely to be most predictable?

■   Long-lived and widely distributed species, e.g. large dominant tree species. We would therefore expect most specialization on these resources.

The role of predictability in specialization can be illustrated by the fact that many insect herbivore species specialize on pre-dispersed seed, that is, seed still on the plant, but not on post-dispersed seed which may be equally abundant but less predictable in space and time. Finally, you should remember that generalists, although able to feed on a wide range of species, are selective and may prefer particular species.

We will now consider two guilds of species feeding in the tropical forest: pollinators and **frugivores** (fruit-eaters). In fact we will consider a small sub-set of the pollinators and frugivores in the forest. Both of these guilds are important because they serve important roles for the plant providing the resource – frugivores aid seed dispersal and may be essential for germination whilst pollinators ensure transfer of male gametes. They are both vital in tropical forests because individuals of the same species of tree may be hundreds or thousands of metres apart (TV programme 'Tropical forest: the conundrum of coexistence' describes the wide distribution of many tree species in the tropical forest of Barro Colorado Island) and require mobile organisms to link them for pollination, whilst seed may need to be dispersed away from the parent plant to suitable establishment sites (according to the Janzen–Connell hypothesis, Book 2, Chapter 3).

2.3.2 Pollinators

Nectar in flowers attracts pollinators. The shapes, colours and odours of flowers of different species (Table 2.2) are believed to have co-evolved with the shape and behaviour of their pollinators so that as the latter feeds on the nectar, pollen is deposited on its body. Indeed, Darwin was able to predict from the unusual shape and size of a Madagascan orchid flower the existence of a pollinator with a proboscis of 30 cm. Forty years later his prediction was proved correct when the appropriate hawkmoth was discovered. When the pollinator visits a new plant with receptive female parts, the pollen is transferred. This is the ideal scenario from the plant's point of view. But some potential pollinators have cheated along the evolutionary path. For example, carpenter bees are able to rob flowers of their nectar by piercing the base of the flower and *Heliconius* butterflies (introduced in Book 1, Section 1.7.1) eat the pollen as well as the nectar (which has fascinating implications for their life history, as we shall see below).

In the tropical forest we find a wide variety of pollinators, many of which are specialized to feed on particular plants. In Book 1, Section 1.7.1, we saw how many tropical orchids in Central and South America depend upon male euglossine bees for pollination. Table 2.2 gives examples of the various groups of species that are known to be pollinators, many of which occur in tropical forests. Whilst we cannot cover all of these in detail we will explore the life histories, interactions and guild structure of an important neotropical component – the butterflies in the subfamily Heliconiinae.

Table 2.2 Examples of pollinators and associated plant characteristics. Data from Howe and Westley (1986).

Agent	Flowering time	Flower colour	Odour
Insects the primary agents of pollination			
beetles	day and night	usually dull	fruity or aminoid
carrion and dung flies	day and night	purple-brown or greenish	decaying protein
syrphid and bee flies	day and night	variable	variable
bees	day and night or diurnal	variable but not pure red	usually sweet
hawkmoths	crepuscular or nocturnal	white, pale or green	sweet
settling moths	day and night or diurnal	variable but not pure red	sweet
butterflies	day and night or diurnal	variable; pink very common	sweet
Vertebrates the primary agents of pollination			
bats	night	drab, pale often green	musty
birds	day	vivid, often red	none
Primarily abiotic pollination			
wind	day or night	drab, green	none
water	variable	variable	none

The Heliconiinae

In the tropical forests of Central and South America, members of the Heliconiinae are conspicuous elements of the butterfly fauna (Figure 2.6). They often fly within a few metres of the ground and a short walk along a wide forest trail in this region may reveal 10 or more species in this subfamily. The Heliconiinae subfamily of butterflies has two distinct groups of species (Figure 2.7). One is the 50 or so species in the genus *Heliconius*. These butterflies are unique because of their ability to consume pollen as well as nectar. The other seven genera (e.g. *Dryas*) in the subfamily are unable to consume pollen. Thus an event in the early evolution of this subfamily has led to the division of the two groups (Figure 2.7). The larvae of all of the species feed on one or more members of the plant family Passifloraceae (the passion flower family, Figure 2.6).

Figure 2.6 *Heliconius* individual on a Passiflora vine (× 0.6). In real life this butterfly is black with a red bar on its wing.

The feeding behaviour of the adults and larvae and other aspects of the life history of the butterflies is described below.

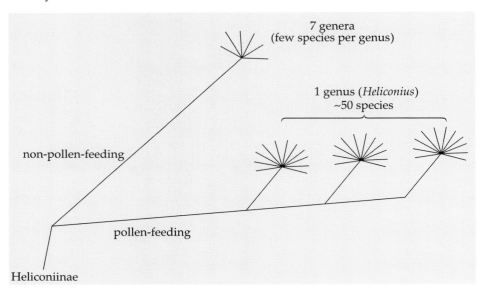

Figure 2.7   A simplified phylogeny of the Heliconiinae subfamily.

Adult *Heliconius* collect nectar and pollen, both of which they use as food. Pollen is collected from vines in the genera *Psiguria* and *Gurania* (Cucurbitaceae, cucumber family) in Central America and from other plants such as the common roadside weed *Lantana camara* (Verbenaceae). Vines of *Psiguria* and *Gurania* are widely scattered about the forest in gaps, along streams and on the sides of trails. The long-lasting inflorescences of *Psiguria* can produce a single new flower every one or two days for many months. Pollen transport is essential and *Heliconius* butterflies and hummingbirds are the main pollinators. Individual *Heliconius* butterflies appear to know where *Psiguria* plants are to be found and may visit them daily on a regular collecting tour within a home range (Figure 2.8). Identification of the flowers visited by the butterflies is made possible by placing dye in one plant and then tracking its transference to other plants (Murawski and Gilbert, 1986).

What are the ecological and evolutionary consequences of pollen consumption for *Heliconius* butterflies? We have already seen one consequence in Book 1, Section 1.7.1 – the longevity of adults, in particular females. What other consequences can we imagine? An obvious one is that if the females live longer they are more likely to be attacked by predators. To counteract this there has been evolution of chemical defences which make the adults unpalatable. Some of these chemicals are synthesized from the pollen that the adults feed on. The fact that the pollen-feeding *Heliconius* species are unpalatable in contrast to their non-pollen-feeding cousins has been confirmed by experimental predation tests with birds.

❑   By what other means might adults acquire toxic chemical defences?

■   Either from toxic chemicals in the larval host plant consumed by the larvae and modified in their bodies, or from toxins synthesized in the larvae.

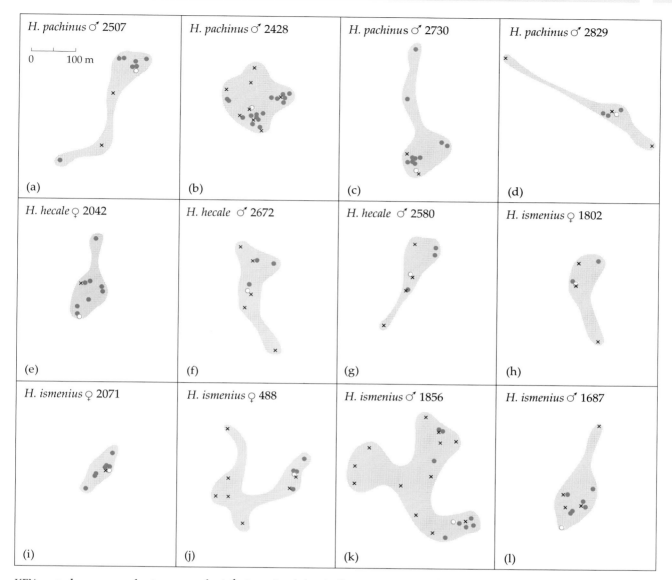

KEY   ○ dye-source plant   ● plant that received dye in flowers   × = butterfly location (1 or more captures)

Figure 2.8 Distribution of *Heliconius* pollen sources (*Psiguria*) and home range for 12 *Heliconius* individuals. The numbers represent the individual codes for each butterfly.

Associated with this chemical defence are two types of mimicry between the butterflies. Book 1, Section 1.7.1 introduced the idea of mimicry of insect bodies by flowers to attract pollinators. In **Mullerian mimicry** individuals of the butterfly (or other) species are all unpalatable and have similar markings to reflect this fact. Thus they share a common badge to reinforce the message of unpalatability to predators. In **Batesian mimicry** there are palatable and unpalatable forms which again share the same markings. This means that some species are cheating – they are pretending to be unpalatable by mimicking the coloration of the unpalatable species. Both forms of mimicry are found in *Heliconius* butterflies and their conmimics in other butterfly and day-flying moth families.

The fact that *Heliconius* females are long lived also allows them to be more precise about where they lay their eggs. For illustration, we can envisage two extremes of oviposition (egg laying). One female has 100 eggs and must lay them within a day. She cannot therefore afford to be choosy and may lay many of her eggs on the first *Passiflora* host plant she finds, even if it is poor quality, e.g. in terms of its chemical composition or position in the forest. A second female also has 100 eggs but has 100 days to lay them and so therefore has the time to seek out high-quality host plants and lay eggs individually in the right place. These extremes of oviposition strategy are reflected in the pollen and non-pollen-feeders in the Heliconiinae (Table 2.3). The pollen feeders (*Heliconius*) display the most careful oviposition strategy, placing solitary eggs on a meristem (growing point), in keeping with predictions for the longer life-span of females. The careful oviposition strategy is believed to be a more recent evolutionary event.

Table 2.3   Heliconiinae oviposition strategies (adapted from Benson *et al.*,1975). A, scattered eggs, usually under older leaves; B, very large raft of eggs on younger leaf; C, raft of eggs under an older leaf; D, cluster of eggs covering a plant meristem (growing point); E, loose groups of eggs, scattered about a meristem; F, solitary eggs on a meristem.

Butterfly genus	Oviposition strategy	No. of species in genus
Philaethria	A	1
Podotricha	A	1
Agraulis	A	1
Dryadula	A	1
Dryas	A	1
Dione	A–C	3
Euiedes	A–C	10
Heliconius	D–F	50

❑   What striking evolutionary feature appears to accompany careful oviposition in Table 2.3?

■   There are many more species per genus in the meristem oviposition strategists.

It seems that the *Passiflora* host plants have responded to the selective feeding of the Heliconiinae species. One fascinating response is the development of egg mimicry – some species of plant produce small egg-like structures on the leaves which deter the female butterflies from laying their eggs, presumably because they want their young to avoid competition with the offspring of other individuals.

Finally, an interesting feature of the guild structure of *Heliconius* is revealed by the relationship between the number of species in a local area compared with those in the wider region. Gilbert and Smiley (1978) reported that the maximum number of species was relatively constant in a locality, rarely exceeding 20 species. Although this seems to be independent of the number of species in the region (this requires more data for confirmation), it does depend on the number of *Passiflora* species in a locality (Figure 2.9).

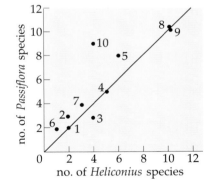

Figure 2.9   Relationship between number of *Passiflora* species and number of *Heliconius* species. The solid line is the line of unity where the number of *Passiflora* species equals the number of *Heliconius* species. Data are from Brazil (10), Costa Rica (1, 2, 5, 8, 9), Mexico (6, 7) and Trinidad (3, 4).

2.3.3 Frugivores

In contrast with pollinators, which may be vertebrate or invertebrate (see Table 2.2), frugivores are mainly vertebrates (mammals, birds, and even fish in the flooded Amazon forest). Many fruits are adapted for dispersal by animals, some even requiring passage through the gut for germination. The primate frugivores of Cocha Cashu in Peru have been studied in detail by Terborgh and colleagues (Terborgh, 1983). To understand the ecology of the primates, we need to know something of the seasonality (phenology) of the trees in the forest in Cocha Cashu.

The rainfall pattern at Cocha Cashu is seasonal with 87% of the rain falling between October and April (Figure 2.10). The pattern of fruit fall (Figure 2.11) was determined by collecting fruits which had fallen into traps.

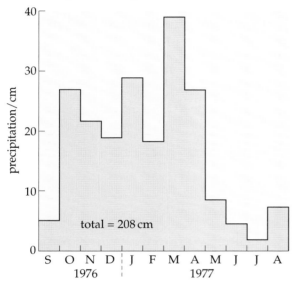

Figure 2.10 Monthly rainfall pattern at Cocha Cashu.

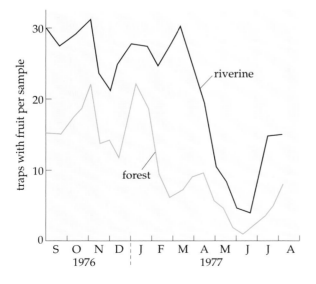

Figure 2.11 Pattern of fruit fall at Cocha Cashu, represented as number of traps out of 50 that contained fruit in riverine forest and forest away from the river.

❏ What is the pattern of fruit fall at Cocha Cashu and how does it correspond to the pattern of rainfall?

■ It is at its lowest in May and June (at the end of the rainy season) and reaches a peak from September to March throughout the rainy season.

For the period May to July, the number of fruits is greatly reduced and frugivores such as primates are dependent on a few key plant species (Table 2.4; Terborgh, 1983). Such species, which support a disproportionate number of other species, or have a disproportionate importance in the community, are called **keystone species**. As with guilds, studies of keystone species provide a means of unravelling the complexity of communities.

Table 2.4 The number of plant resources in the diet of four species of primate throughout the year. Each resource contributes less than 1% of the diet (Terborgh, 1983).

Species	Early rain (Oct–Dec)	Late rain (Jan–Apr)	Early dry (May–July)	Late dry (Aug–Sep)
Cebus apella	17	18	8	14
Cebus albifrons	14	17	3	8
Saimiri sciureus	9	14	6	11
Saguinus fuscicollis	4	3	4	11

The four primate species listed in Table 2.4 coexist together with at least seven other primate species at Cocha Cashu. Terborgh noted that this was the richest primate community known for the New World.

red-backed
squirrel monkey
(× 0.13)

emperor
tamarin
(× 0.18)

Figure 2.12 Two typical neotropical primate species.

The four primate species in Table 2.4 range from 3 kg or more in weight (adult male *Cebus apella*, brown capuchin; *Cebus albifrons*, the white-fronted capuchin is slightly smaller) through 1 kg (adult male *Saimiri sciureus*, squirrel monkey) to approximately 500 g (adult *Saguinus fuscicollis*, saddle-backed tamarin). All four species live in troops which vary in size from 2–10 individuals (*Saguinus*) to 30–40 individuals (*Saimiri*).

❑ Do all four species respond in the same way to the seasonal availability of fruit?

■ No. The two *Cebus* species, and to a lesser extent the *Saimiri* species, have a limited selection in the early dry season compared to other seasons, but *Saguinus fuscicollis* has a low choice from October to July.

Terborgh explored several lines of evidence to explain this pattern, including the importance of palms and figs in the diet of the primates.

Table 2.5   The seasonal importance of different food sources (palms, figs, other) for four primate species (dashes indicate unknown values).

Species	Early rain			Late rain			Early dry			Late dry		
	Palms	Figs	Other	Palms	Figs	Other	Palms	Figs	Other	Palms	Figs	Other
Cebus apella	1	17	82	4	6	90	64	9	27	14	49	37
Cebus albifrons	<1	17	82	4	19	77	56	41	3	10	73	17
Saimiri sciureus	0	59	41	0	7	93	15	77	8	0	56	44
Saguinus fuscicollis	0	14	86	<1	4	96	<1	0	>99	–	–	–

❑ Given the results in Table 2.5, what are the keystone species for the *Cebus* species and *Saimiri sciureus* in the early dry season?

■ Palms for *C. apella*, palms and figs for *C. albifrons* and figs for *S. sciureus*.

❑ Do the data in Table 2.5 explain why *Saguinus* does not show the same pattern in Table 2.4 as the other species?

■ Yes, because it does not take palm or fig in great quantities and uses 'other' species from October to July (early rain to early dry season inclusive). Its feeding preferences in the late dry season are not known.

Terborgh provides a useful summary table to show how the different primate species get through the early dry season (Table 2.6).

Table 2.6   Use of food resources by four primate species in Cocha Cashu during the early dry season (May–July).

Species	Early dry season feeding habits
Cebus apella	heavy use of *Scheelea* and *Astrocaryum* palm nuts, supplemented with pith, meristematic tissue of palms and figs when available
Cebus albifrons	figs when available, alternating with *Astrocaryum* nuts
Saimiri sciureus	figs when available, alternating with periods of total insectivory
Saguinus fuscicollis	exploitation of a sequence of resources that are too diffuse to be of significance to large monkeys

This detailed study of primates by Terborgh shows how apparently similar species can coexist during periods of low food abundance. The two most similar species (*Cebus*) show most divergence during the dry season, with

C. albifrons exploiting fig species more than *C. apella*. Furthermore, species such as *Saimiri sciureus* are able to take insects in addition to fruits. So, as with humans, omnivory is a key to survival success!

Summary of Section 2.3

This excursion into the tropical forest has illustrated some of the themes and complexities of community ecology. Communities can be studied by focusing on guilds, such as pollinators and **frugivores**. Butterflies and monkeys provide examples of these. Amongst the butterflies, we have seen the effect of the type of food resource (pollen versus nectar), the role of **Batesian** and **Mullerian mimicry** and the relationship between insect and plant species richness. The primate example has shown the importance of **keystone species** and seasonality.

Question 2.2   *(Objectives 2.1 & 2.2)*

Draw diagrams of the communities centred on (a) *Heliconius* butterflies and (b) *Cebus albifrons* in typical localities following the format of Figure 2.2. Identify in each case feeding and non-feeding interactions. How many species are found in each trophic level? (If unknown then state this or give an approximate number.) You will need to consider the diets of adults and juveniles.

Question 2.3   *(Objective 2.2)*

Figure 2.13 shows the variety of interactions that can lead to either a woodland or grassland community in the Serengeti–Mara region of East Africa. Describe the probable effects of the following changes:

(a)   increase in density of wildebeest;

(b)   reduction in density of elephants (a keystone species);

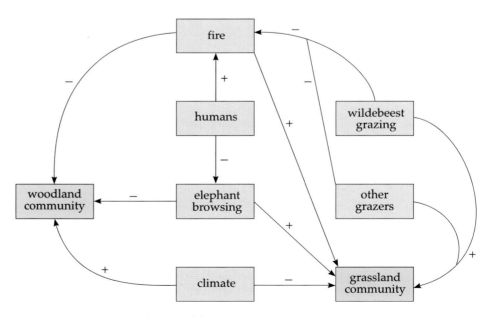

Figure 2.13 Factors affecting establishment of woodland or grassland communities in the Serengeti–Mara region of East Africa (Krebs, 1994 based on Dublin *et al.*, 1990).

(c)   increase in incidence of fires.

2.4 Themes of community composition, structure and function

Assuming we can define an ecological community, what properties of communities are of interest to ecologists? We have already met one – the relationship between stability and complexity. We saw in Chapter 2, Book 2, how stability could be defined with respect to perturbation. We could define **community stability** in the same way, seeing how a community responds to perturbation.

❏   What would be a perturbation of a community?

■   The loss or gain of species is an obvious example. Another would be the change in the abundance (without losing any species) of one or more species.

If we can measure stability, then it is possible to consider the relationship between complexity and stability.

❏   How could **community complexity** be quantified?

■   The simplest method is to assess the number of species in a community: a more complex community has more species. This could be modified by taking into account the relative abundance of the species. Another method would be the number of interactions per species. This leads to a distinction between the complexity of *composition* (e.g. number of species) and complexity of *structure* (e.g. the number of interactions per species) of a community.

The assessment of complexity will be explored in Section 2.5. We will consider the relationship between stability and complexity in Section 2.6.

Several other themes pervade the study of ecological communities and have been illustrated by the examples in the preceding Section. First, the importance of dominance of certain species, for example the idea of keystone species considered for frugivores above, the identification of which relies on measures of relative abundance at different times of year. Second, the issue postponed from Book 2, Chapter 4, of why the world is green – in other words, the regulation of communities. For example, what controls the abundance of *Heliconius* species – is it interactions with plants, with natural enemies or some other factor(s)? Such questions are considered in Section 2.8. Third, the problem of coexistence as considered in TV programme 'The conundrum of coexistence' – how can so many species coexist together? This theme overlaps with the ideas of dominance and the regulation of communities and is also considered in Section 2.8. Finally, the problem of spatial scale, illustrated by the relationship between local abundance and regional abundance of *Passiflora* and *Heliconius* species. We will consider this and other aspects of spatial scale in Section 2.7.

2.5 Measurement of community complexity

2.5.1 Defining and sampling species richness

One of the most important quantifiable characteristics of a community, however it is defined, is its **species richness**. Species richness, considered in this Section, is simply the number of species in the community and is one of two components of species diversity. Section 2.5.2 addresses estimates of species diversity. Assessing species richness may be relatively easy to achieve for large or sedentary animals and for certain plant species in small areas, but it is not usually possible to count the number of small and/or mobile species (e.g. many insects) accurately on an area basis, and specialized sampling techniques may be required (see the *Project Guide* and below). Indeed, even the largest animals on land (African elephants) may need to be sampled rather than counted directly, for example by counts of elephant dung for forest-dwelling elephants. Sampling will only capture some of the individuals in a community and therefore statistical techniques are required for extrapolation to estimates of maximum species richness. Two examples of this method are considered below.

Plant species richness in a temperate woodland

Figure 2.14 shows the cumulative numbers of plant species recorded in the 49 hectares of Hayley Wood in Cambridgeshire between 1860 and 1975.

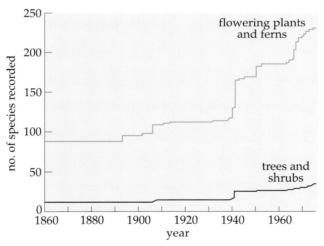

Figure 2.14 Cumulative numbers of species of flowering plants and ferns, and of trees and shrubs, recorded in Hayley Wood between 1860 and 1975.

❑ What evidence is there that by 1975 there was an accurate estimate of the number of flowering plants and ferns?

■ The large jumps in species numbers were due to records of new species, made at irregular intervals. New records during the last decade of sampling occurred at more regular intervals and appear as small steps in the curves – these were rare plants found only as a result of frequent visits to the wood. It appears that records are now very nearly complete and the curve levels off in the last five years of sampling. Before 1960, trees and shrubs, being large plants, were better known than the rest of the flora. But as late as 1972, a new species, the wild pear, was found there. It was probably present all the time but a long succession of botanists visiting the wood took over 100 years to find and record it!

Butterfly species richness in a tropical forest

A similar technique of recording the cumulative number of species with increasing sampling effort has been used for butterflies in tropical forests in south-east Trinidad and elsewhere (various forest types have been sampled in Trinidad and some of the work there is described in TV programme 'Managing for biodiversity: forests in Trinidad'). In this case, two methods have been used. These are **walk-and-count transects**, and **fruit traps**. (The latter are traps which catch butterflies as opposed to traps which catch fruit!)

The walk-and-count transect method originates from methods used for the Butterfly Monitoring Scheme (Pollard, 1977) which has been employed across Britain since 1976. The *transects* take about 30 minutes to walk. The sampling was carried out twice a day in forest in south-east Trinidad for four weeks, unless it was raining or it had been raining up to 1 hour previously (butterflies do not fly in the rain). All the butterflies seen 10 m either side of the transect route were recorded. An individual was chased and caught wherever possible, for positive identification. This was sometimes not possible and, because there are some very similiar species, which look identical in flight, this method can be inaccurate. Even in Britain there are species such as the Essex skipper and small skipper which look almost identical.

The basic design of the *fruit trap sampling* comes from work carried out in Costa Rica (DeVries, 1988; Figure 2.15). In each forest studied in Trinidad there was a series of locations where both a canopy and an understorey trap were placed. The traps in each forest were baited with mango or banana which attracted certain species of butterfly and were then rebaited for five or more consecutive days. The traps were inspected in late afternoon and early morning every day during the trapping period. Traps were located on walk-and-count transect routes. The advantage of the fruit trapping method is that species can be identified and the individuals marked with a permanent unique number and then released so that their movement between traps and longevity are recorded (this method is shown in TV programme 'Managing for biodiversity: forests in Trinidad'). This is a **mark–release–recapture** method which can also be used to estimate population size (*Project Guide*).

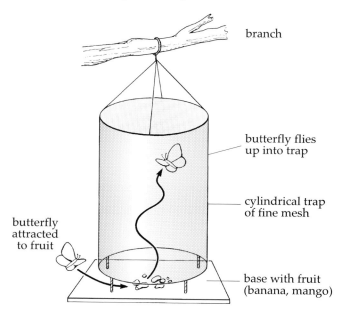

branch

butterfly flies up into trap

cylindrical trap of fine mesh

butterfly attracted to fruit

base with fruit (banana, mango)

Figure 2.15 Design of the fruit trap.

Plots of species accumulated against sampling time are given for both the
walk-and-count and fruit trap data (Figure 2.16). Clench (1979) has
proposed the use of a particular equation to describe the shape of the
cumulative species collected against sampling effort curve. This allows an
estimate of the total species richness of a habitat. Such analysis of species
accumulation curves gives a quantitative basis to the relationship between
collecting time and number of new species accumulated. This is
particularly useful in species-rich habitats such as tropical forests, allowing
more rigorous and quantitative comparisons between habitats.

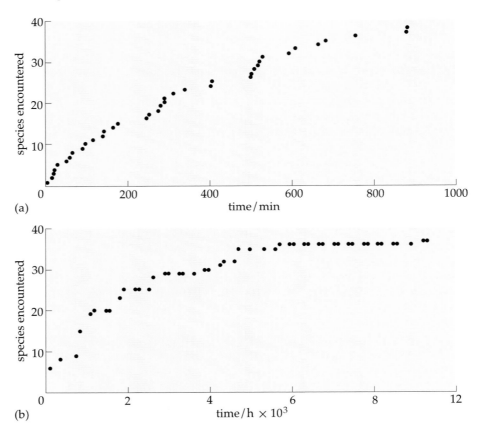

Figure 2.16 Cumulative number
of species encountered with
increasing sampling of butterflies
in tropical forest: (a) minutes of
walk-and-count transect method
and (b) hours of fruit trap
method (Wood, 1996).

Insects in the tropical forest canopy

Both of the above examples involve sampling the species richness of
manageable numbers of species. However, if one is interested in, for
example, the total number of insect species in a given area, the maximum
species richness is somewhat higher! Consider as an example the work of
Stork (1991) on ten trees in tropical forest in Brunei, Borneo. Insects were
knocked down from the trees using a canopy fogging technique in which
the trees are immersed in a cloud of synthetic pyrethroid insecticide. The
insecticide is non-residual, breaking down in minutes in direct sunlight
and is non-toxic to vertebrates. 200 m² of plastic was placed below the ten
fogged trees, that is, 20 m² per tree. It was thought that a few insects were
left on the tree after fogging (a fact confirmed by refogging). A staggering
23 482 individuals comprising more than 3000 species were collected from
the 200 m² of plastic, that is, an average of about 15 species and 117

individuals per m^2. These insects included 945 species of Hymenoptera (primarily parasitic wasps) and 860 species of Coleoptera (beetles, comprising 4043 individuals in 60 families).

To put these numbers into context, there is a total of about 4000 species in 95 families of beetle in the whole of Britain. Stork noted that the 1455 specimens of a particular group of parasitic wasps (Chalcidoidea) represented 739 species (i.e. each species was represented by an average of just two individuals), and that probably less than 100 species of these wasps had previously been recorded from the whole of Borneo.

2.5.2 The measurement of species diversity

Species richness is only one component of the ecological measure of diversity. The second is the **relative abundanc**e of the different species or the **evenness** (**equitability**) of a community. Since many species in a sample are likely to be rare (Section 2.7), we should not ignore this fact when measuring diversity. For example, compare two imaginary samples of 100 individuals, each with two species in them. In sample I there are 99 individuals of species A and only one individual of species B, but in sample II there are 50A and 50B. Is the diversity of these two samples really the same? Of course, if we choose to measure diversity as the number of species present in each sample (i.e. just species richness) then the answer is yes, but most ecologists would intuitively consider the community with 50A and 50B to be more diverse than the one with 99A and 1B. Since diversity is merely a concept with which we choose to describe the properties of a community, we can easily devise a different measure (or index) of diversity which will be sensitive to the relative abundance of species in a sample as well as to the number of species in it. There are many **diversity indices** to choose from, one of the simplest being the Simpson index (see below).

You will probably be aware of the phrase **biological diversity** (or **biodiversity**) which has come into prominence since the Earth Summit at Rio de Janeiro in 1992. Although politicians may have recently discovered diversity, ecologists have understood and measured diversity for many years! Biodiversity is a concept that includes the whole array of life-forms and their components, from genes through species to habitats and ecosystems. Thus it goes far beyond what we are concerned with in this Chapter.

The Simpson diversity index

The **Simpson diversity index** has the attractive property that the maximum theoretical value (highest diversity) is very close to one (although it can never equal one) and the minimum theoretical value is zero. To calculate the Simpson diversity index for any community we need to know the number (or biomass) of individuals of each species in that community. We could also measure the diversity of other taxonomic units, e.g. families. We then calculate the proportion of the total number of individuals contributed by each species. For example, if there are 30 individuals in an area and 10 of these are species A, then the proportion of species A individuals is 10/30 or 1/3. The proportion for each species is then squared, the squared values are summed and the total subtracted from 1 to give the Simpson index value. The following examples should make these calculations more clear and illustrate what determines whether a community has a high or low diversity according to this index.

Let us begin by considering a hypothetical community made up of four species, each with ten individuals, as shown in Table 2.7:

Table 2.7   Calculation of Simpson diversity index for a hypothetical community with four species.

Species	No. of individuals	Proportion	(Proportion)^2
A	10	1/4	1/16
B	10	1/4	1/16
C	10	1/4	1/16
D	10	1/4	1/16
total	40	1	1/4
1-total			3/4 = 0.75

So this community of four species has a Simpson diversity index of 0.75. Now compare this result with that obtained by keeping the same total number of individuals still in equal proportions but doubling the number of species, as shown in Table 2.8.

Table 2.8   Calculation of Simpson diversity index for a hypothetical community with eight species.

Species	No. of individuals	Proportion	(Proportion)^2
A	5	1/8	1/64
B	5	1/8	1/64
C	5	1/8	1/64
D	5	1/8	1/64
E	5	1/8	1/64
F	5	1/8	1/64
G	5	1/8	1/64
H	5	1/8	1/64
total	40	1	8/64 = 1/8
1-total			7/8 = 0.875

❑   What has been the effect of doubling the number of species?

■   The Simpson diversity index value has *increased* from 0.75 to 0.875.

Finally, let us return to a four-species community with 40 individuals, except that this time the distribution of individuals is different between species (Table 2.9). In this case, species A is *dominant.*

Table 2.9   Calculation of Simpson diversity index for a hypothetical community with one species dominant.

Species	No. of individuals	Proportion	(Proportion)^2
A	28	0.7	0.49
B	4	0.1	0.01
C	4	0.1	0.01
D	4	0.1	0.01
total	40	1	0.52
1-total			0.48

❑ What has been the effect of altering the proportions away from equal values for the hypothetical community of four species?

■ It has *reduced* the Simpson diversity index from 0.75 to 0.48.

❑ What is the relationship between dominance and diversity revealed by comparing the examples of Tables 2.7 and 2.9?

■ Dominance is *inversely* related to diversity.

These examples show that high Simpson diversity index values are produced by an increased range of species and/or a more even spread of individuals between species.

Another important and related index is the **Shannon–Wiener index**. This uses a similar method of calculation except that the proportion of a given species (p) is not squared but multiplied by its natural log, that is, $p \times \ln(p)$. These values of $p\ln(p)$ are then summed for all species and multiplied by -1 to make the index value positive. For example, the Shannon–Wiener index value for the community in Table 2.7 is $-1 \times 4 \times 1/4 \times \ln(1/4) = -1 \times \ln(1/4) = 1.386$. The effect of the natural log is to reduce the importance of the dominant values (those with a high proportion). The Shannon–Wiener index ranges from zero to numbers well in excess of 1 and it is therefore not bounded in the same neat way as the Simpson index.

2.5.3 Alpha, beta and gamma diversity

Different types of diversity have been categorized according to the scale of the study. If diversity is measured in small areas, within a habitat, it is known as **alpha diversity**. This is the diversity assumed in previous Sections. In contrast, **beta diversity** measures the diversity between habitats/plots (Whittaker, 1960). Beta diversity is also known as species turnover. Beta diversity and alpha diversity combine to give **gamma** (or regional) **diversity** (Whittaker, 1960). Harrison *et al.* (1992) studied the beta diversity of 15 taxa (including plants, vertebrates and invertebrates) in Britain by drawing out two transects of 50 km grid squares across Britain (Figure 2.17), one running north to south and one running east to west. They noted that beta diversity has two components – the variety of habitats within a region and the species replacement between separate units of the same habitat. They found that beta diversity was low in all groups. Total species richness only increased by 3–13% per 50 × 50 km square. They concluded that beta diversity, at least in Britain, is a minor component of gamma diversity.

Figure 2.17 The north–south and west–east transect of 50 km × 50 km grid squares across Britain used by Harrison *et al.* (1992).

2.5.4 Food web structure and the community matrix

The above measures of complexity are all based on the composition of the community, i.e. the number and relative abundance of species. These measures do not tell us very much about the functioning of communities. To quantify functional aspects of the community we need to know something about the links between species. Analysis of the feeding interactions is a move in that direction (Pimm, 1982).

We have already met two food webs in Figure 2.3. Their complexity was apparent in terms of the number of links. Attempts to describe this complexity has lead to a definition of **connectance** which is the actual number of interactions divided by the total possible number of interactions. We know it is difficult to determine the actual number of links. It is also difficult to determine the total possible number of links because this depends on the existence of clear trophic levels. Unfortunately, trophic levels, as described in Book 1, are not straightforward. Barnes and Hughes (1988) noted that the concept of the trophic level arose in terrestrial ecology and, whilst it is now of 'dubious validity' in terrestrial systems, in marine systems it is 'an abstraction bearing little relation to anything existing in the real world'. We are aware of this from our own feeding habits – some of us are vegetarians (herbivores) and some of us are omnivores. In the herring example of Figure 2.3, the adult fish eats *Ammodytes* and *Temora*, but *Ammodytes* also eats *Temora*. Thus we do not know how many potential interactions occur in a community because we cannot be sure which species will potentially eat which other species. If, instead of connectance, we use the average number of links per species, known as **linkage density**, then we avoid the problem of the potential number of interactions (see Question 2.5).

We have considered how to quantify the presence and absence of links in the food web. To determine the strength of the interactions we can use a value similar to the competition coefficients described in Book 2, Section 3.4. To understand community structure and stability we need to combine all of the interactions together in a single model. One way of achieving this is to produce a matrix of **interaction coefficients** (matrices were introduced in Book 2, Section 2.5.2, Box 2.4), for example a hypothetical four species community could be represented as shown in Table 2.10.

Table 2.10 A matrix of interaction coefficients for a four species community.

		on species			
		A	B	C	D
	A	−1.0	−0.5	0	+1.0
Effect of species	B	+0.5	-1.0	+0.5	0
	C	0	+0.5	−1.0	+0.8
	D	+1.0	0	−0.8	−1.0

This representation can include both feeding and non-feeding interactions, as discussed for Figure 2.1. For example, the effect of species A on species B is negative with a strength of 0.5. The intraspecific interactions (e.g. A on A) are all negative.

❑   A negative interaction can mean either predation or competition. For example, species A has a negative effect on species B because A is a predator of B. What does a positive interaction indicate?

■   It indicates a beneficial interaction. For example, the effect of species C on D is positive, so C may be the prey of D.

Some of the interactions are symmetric. For example, the mutualistic interactions are (+,+) therefore the effect of A on D is positive *and* the effect of D on A is positive. Other interactions are not symmetric, thus the effect of B on A is positive whilst the effect of A on B is negative.

❑   What does the magnitude of each matrix element represent?

■   It represents the strength of the interaction between species.

❑   How can values of the matrix elements represent linkage between species?

■   A value of 0 means no link between the species and so a non-zero value (positive or negative) indicates linkage.

Levins (1968) first devised a matrix of competition coefficients to describe community structure and predict community stability. This was a multispecies model of the two-species competition model presented in Book 2, Section 3.4. The theory was developed by May (1972, 1973) giving a general version of the matrix called the **community matrix** (sometimes referred to as the stability matrix) which expressed the effect of species j on species i *near equilibrium*. This included the whole suite of possible interactions described in Figure 2.1. The community matrix makes particular assumptions about the dynamics of its constituent species, some of which were described in Book 2, Chapters 3 and 4. In particular, it is assumed that prey and competitors will be regulated so that, in the absence of any interspecies interactions, they will return to equilibrium. It is also assumed that predators decline exponentially in the absence of prey.

The stability of the community can be derived by considering the community matrix model at equilibrium. We will not attempt the maths here but the important result on stability has parallels with the age- or stage-structured population model in Chapter 2 of Book 2. In that case, the behaviour of the matrix was represented by a single value called the finite rate of increase. This is a general property of such matrices, the single values being referred to as eigenvalues. The community matrix can also be replaced by eigenvalues; the number of possible eigenvalues is equal to the number of rows or columns of the matrix (the number of species). It is the largest or dominant eigenvalue which is most important (a positive value is larger than a negative value). Because the community matrix predicts behaviour near equilibrium (effectively in response to perturbation), if the largest eigenvalue is positive then the community is predicted to continue to move away from equilibrium following perturbation. In other words it is unstable. If the largest eigenvalue is negative then the community is predicted to return to equilibrium after perturbation, that is, it is stable. We will use this result in Section 2.6.

Summary of Section 2.5

Community complexity can be quantified in terms of the composition and structure of the community. Composition can be divided into components of **species richness** and **equitability** (i.e. **evenness** or **relative abundance**) which together constitute species diversity. High species diversity is defined as occurring when evenness is high and species richness is high. Total species richness in a habitat can be assessed from cumulative species richness–sampling effort relationships. Examples of these are given for plants and butterflies – the latter using **walk-and-count transects** and **fruit traps** (individuals captured in these can be used in **mark-release-recapture** programmes.) Species diversity can be measured using diversity indices such as the **Simpson diversity index** and the **Shannon–Wiener diversity index**. The diversity of other taxonomic levels such as families or the diversity of ecosystems or genes can also be assessed, leading to the concept of **biodiversity**. Species diversity can be categorized as **alpha** (within habitat), **beta** (between plots or habitats) and **gamma** (regional, alpha + beta) diversity. Community structure is described with reference to **food webs**. These can be quantified by **connectance** which is the actual number of feeding interactions divided by the theoretical number, or **linkage density** which is the mean number of interactions per species. The presence or absence of feeding interactions can be combined with non-feeding interactions and the strength of interaction which has a set of **interaction coefficients** in the **community matrix**.

Question 2.4   (Objectives 2.1 & 2.3)

(a) Calculate the Shannon–Wiener index values of the two hypothetical communities in Tables 2.8 and 2.9.

(b) In a study of unlogged and selectively logged forest on the island of Buru in Indonesia, Hill *et al.* (1995) found that the diversity of butterflies, sampled by walk-and-count, was higher in unlogged forest. This was true whatever measure of diversity they used. There were 37 species and 828 individuals in the unlogged forest and 29 species and 458 individuals in the logged forest.

Are the data on species and individuals consistent with the finding of increased diversity in the unlogged forest? What extra information do the diversity measures give above that of the species and individual data?

Question 2.5   (Objectives 2.1 & 2.4)

Consider the two food webs centred on two species of predatory starfish *Pisaster ochraceous* and *Heliaster kubiniji* (both keystone species) in Western North America (Figure 2.18, after Paine, 1966, in Pimm, 1982).

(a) What is the linkage density of the two communities in Figure 2.18?

(b) What characteristics of a predator species such as *Pisaster* or *Heliaster* and its prey will limit the food web linkage of the predator?

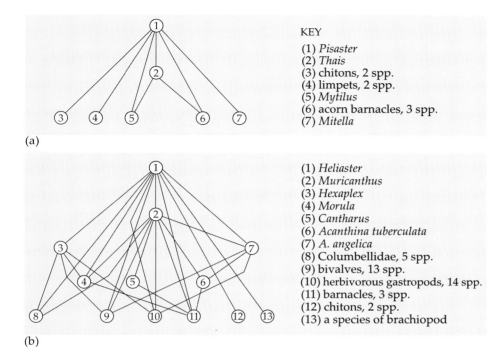

(a)

KEY

(1) *Pisaster*
(2) *Thais*
(3) chitons, 2 spp.
(4) limpets, 2 spp.
(5) *Mytilus*
(6) acorn barnacles, 3 spp.
(7) *Mitella*

(b)

(1) *Heliaster*
(2) *Muricanthus*
(3) *Hexaplex*
(4) *Morula*
(5) *Cantharus*
(6) *Acanthina tuberculata*
(7) *A. angelica*
(8) Columbellidae, 5 spp.
(9) bivalves, 13 spp.
(10) herbivorous gastropods, 14 spp.
(11) barnacles, 3 spp.
(12) chitons, 2 spp.
(13) a species of brachiopod

Figure 2.18 Two intertidal food webs based around the predatory starfish, *Pisaster ochraceous* and *Heliaster kubiniji*. In the *Pisaster* food web, species 2 and 7 are gastropods and *Mytilus* is a mussel (bivalve). In the *Heliaster* food web, species 2–7 are gastropods.

2.6   Are complex communities more stable than simple ones?

In the opening Section, it was noted that community complexity is more than just a problem frustrating the efforts of ecologists. It is an important issue, for example, in terms of its relationship with community stability. In this Section, we address that relationship.

2.6.1   Charles Elton and Robert May

The history of this debate is an interesting one because it pitches traditional field-based ecology against a revolution in theoretical models, typified by the community matrix. The traditional position was held by Charles Elton who claimed that complex communities are more stable than simple ones. His conclusions were partly based on detailed case studies of invasions by 'pests' such as the giant snail *Achatina fulica* into Hawaii (and the attempted control of it by the introduction of a carnivorous snail) and the red deer *Cervus elaphus* into New Zealand, which contributed to dramatic declines in the endemic species of those islands. An important corollary of complexity producing stability is that tropical communities should be more stable than temperate ones. The limited evidence available cannot support or refute this, although it is true that population outbreaks, which are perhaps diagnostic of community instability, have been recorded most frequently in northern and temperate regions (recall the larch bud moth and the lynx in Book 2, Chapter 4). However, these regions also contain the greatest concentration of ecologists.

During his work at Princeton University in the late 1960s and early 1970s, Robert May's perspective in this debate was based on analyses of community matrix models. His results conflicted with the ideas of Elton, suggesting that complexity was linked to *instability* rather than stability. The results of this work are given below.

2.6.2 Predictions from the community matrix

Several important results have emerged out of studies of the community matrix or similar models. Gardner and Ashby (1970) asked whether large systems (biological or otherwise) which were assembled at random would be stable. In their words, they were concerned with 'an airport with 100 planes, slum areas with 10^4 persons or the human brain with 10^{10} neurons … [where] stability is of central importance.' They showed for small numbers of species, aeroplanes or neurons (n) that stability declines with connectance between components. As the number of components increases, the system moves rapidly to a breakpoint situation when a small change in connectance will result in a switch from stability to complete instability (Figure 2.19).

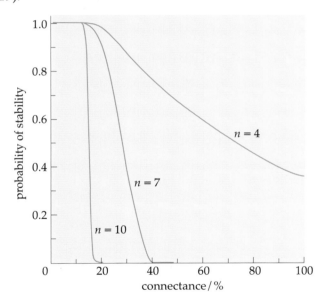

Figure 2.19 The relationship between stability and connectance (complexity) for a community matrix type system. A breakpoint or threshold of stability is observed at higher numbers of components (n). Data from Gardner and Ashby (1970).

May (1972) discussed and generalized the results of Gardner and Ashby and concluded that increased numbers of species do not automatically imply community stability and, in fact, may produce just the opposite effect. May also demonstrated that a species that interacts widely with many other species (high connectance) does so weakly (small interaction coefficient) and conversely, those that interact strongly with others do so with a smaller number of species. He predicted that communities which are compartmentalized into blocks (effectively communities within communities, e.g. guilds) may be stable whilst the whole may not be.

Tregonning and Roberts (1979) explored these ideas further by examining the stability of a randomly constructed model community in which the interaction coefficients were non-zero and the values chosen randomly. They began by running the model with 50 species, and used two methods of species elimination: a species was either chosen at random or the species with the most negative equilibrium value selected. Therefore, in the latter case they removed the most ecologically unrealistic species, as all species needed to have a positive equilibrium value. This process was continued until all species had a positive equilibrium value. This was defined by Tregonning and Roberts as the **homeostatic system** – one that was ecologically feasible and at equilibrium. Under *selective* removal the mean number of species comprising a homeostatic system was 25 and the largest 29. However, if elimination was *random* then the largest homeostatic system was 4 and the mean 3.3.

❑ What do the results of Tregonning and Roberts suggest about the existence of large complex communities?

■ They suggest that for a complex community to exist it needs to have been produced by selective elimination from a large species pool.

❑ What might produce selective elimination in real communities?

■ It could be produced by natural selection operating on individuals over long time-scales, and populations becoming extinct as a result.

Whilst there is no doubt that these predictions for community structure and stability are very exciting, it is easy to get carried away on the crest of a theoretical wave. In reality, there have been few studies of these ideas in the field. The next Section highlights a few examples where theory and fieldwork have been combined.

2.6.3 Analysis of community stability in the field

Seifert and Seifert (1976) have provided one of the few field tests of the community matrix using insects in neotropical *Heliconia* flowers (do not confuse with *Heliconius* butterflies!). The insects inhabit the water-filled bracts of two *Heliconia* species (*H. wagneriana* and *H. imbricata*) in rainforests in Costa Rica (bracts are leaf-like structures around or at the base of flowers, see Figure 2.20). The insect species include the larvae of leaf beetles and hoverflies, all of which are potential competitors.

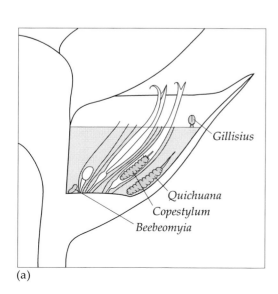

Figure **2.20** (a) Stylized view of *Heliconia wagneriana* showing dissected bract with common insect species. Data from Seifert and Seifert (1976). (b) Example of a *Heliconia* species.

(a)   (b)

Seifert and Seifert combined experimental manipulations with a statistical method which allowed them to estimate the magnitude (strength) and signs of the interaction coefficients in a community matrix model. The experiment involved emergent buds of *Heliconia* being enclosed in plastic bags to restrict immigration and oviposition. After a certain amount of growth, water was added and varying numbers of four species of insect introduced. Following this, the change in the numbers of individuals of the four species with time was determined, calculated as the change from initial density divided by the number of days over which the change took place. The rate of change of one species was regressed against the initial densities of each species to give values of r (intrinsic rate of change) and the interaction coefficient. (It is not important to know the details of the statistical method; note that the rates of change were not estimated near equilibrium as assumed by the community matrix.) A negative interaction value indicated competition whilst a positive value indicated mutualism (the possibility of predation was ignored given the choice of insects). Table 2.11 sets out the possible interactions between the four species of insect following the format of Table 2.10 (Section 2.5.4). For example, the effect of *Quichuana* on *Copestylum* is negative with a strength of 0.018. We can see that nine of the interspecific interactions for the *H. wagneriana* species were not significant (and therefore set to 0). Of the significant interactions *between* species, two were negative (competitors) and one positive (mutualism).

Table 2.11 Interaction matrix for four coexisting species in *Heliconia wagneriana* (see Figure 2.20 for details of species). Non-significant interactions are set to zero (data from Seifert and Seifert, 1976).

	Quichuana	Gillisius	Copestylum	Beebeomyia
Quichuana	0.001	0	-0.018	0.027
Gillisius	0	-0.003	0	0
Copestylum	0	0	-0.005	0
Beebeomyia	0	-0.005	0	-0.033

The equilibrium densities estimated from the model are shown in Table 2.12 and compared with those observed in the field. The fact that there are two negative (unrealistic) densities for insect species in *H. wagneriana* suggests one or more possibilities: (i) that the observed mean densities are not equilibrium densities; and/or (ii) they are results of processes not dependent on species interactions; and/or (iii) that the model and assumptions are inappropriate.

Table 2.12 Mean densities observed in the field and equilibrium densities predicted from the community matrix model (data from Seifert and Seifert, 1976).

	Mean densities in field (unmanipulated)	Species equilibrium estimated from model
Quichuana	51.00	−112.00
Gillisius	7.56	−23.20
Copestylum	8.78	4.09
Beebeomyia	6.67	10.62

Seifert and Seifert were also able to determine the eigenvalues of the community matrix and therefore examine the stability of the community. The four eigenvalues were:

−0.221, 0.052, −0.042 and −0.239.

❑   What do the eigenvalues tell us about the stability of this community?

■   The one positive eigenvalue indicates an *unstable* community which would move away from equilibrium if perturbed (see p.135).

Therefore, *H. wagneriana* insect communities were judged by Seifert and Seifert not to be stable. Instead, they concluded that migration and local extinction processes may be important in structuring these communities. In other words, it is probably not correct to model these communities as regulated entities in isolation around an equilibrium.

Although community matrices have been used infrequently, they have covered a wide range of taxa. Wilson and Roxburgh (1992) provided examples of the application of the community matrix to plant species mixtures. They predicted that initially unstable six-species mixtures will, by selective deletion (following Tregonning and Roberts, 1979), drop down to stable four-species mixtures. A study of the persistence of chironomid fly communities in the River Danube demonstrated differences in behaviour of communities following perturbation at different sites (Schmid, 1992).

The examples in this Section show that it is possible to determine the values of the elements in the community matrix using field data and make testable predictions about stability after perturbation. However, we need to be cautious as analysis of the community matrix assumes species are in the neighbourhood of equilibrium and that they have particular types of dynamics. For many applications we are likely to be interested in communities away from equilibrium (assuming they have one) or where non-equilibrium processes such as physical disturbance or pollution events may be important. Such non-equilibrium processes are considered in Section 2.8. Another problem highlighted by the analysis of Seifert and Seifert is that their 'community' may just be one part of a larger community. This echoes the discussion about community boundaries (see Section 2.2). In the next Section we shall look at how patterns of species richness (the composition of the community) change with area.

Summary of Section 2.6

The argument that complex communities are more stable than simple ones was based on field evidence. The opposite view is dependent on findings from community matrix models. The stability of the models depend on the type of 'experiment', for example the selective versus random removal of species to give a **homeostatic system.** Tests of the community matrix in the field are rare.

Question 2.6   (*Objectives 2.1, 2.4 & 2.5*)

Another approach to the complexity–stability debate has been the examination of connectance and linkage density in food webs. There are two opposing schools of thought. According to Cohen *et al.* (1990), linkage density remains constant regardless of the number of species in the food web. The other view is that proposed by Martinez (1992) that the total number of links increases in proportion to the square of the number of species in the web.

(a) Draw a graph of linkage density against number of species in the food web, with lines or curves showing the proposed relationships of Cohen *et al.* (1990) and Martinez (1992).

(b) Which relationship do the data from Question 2.5(a) support?

(c) Describe two alternative methods of producing more points for this graph of linkage density versus species number.

2.7 Local and regional patterns of species richness

The largest spatial and temporal (time) scales were dealt with in Chapter 1 and covered patterns across the whole globe over millions of years. In this Section, we shall concern ourselves with smaller-scale patterns and begin to ask what ecological processes may produce these patterns.

2.7.1 The species–area curve

Generally, the larger the area sampled, the more species are found in it. This is because we encounter new habitats (and therefore sample beta diversity) and encounter rare and/or clumped species within them. Although it is hardly surprising that larger woodlands, for example, generally contain more species of animals and plants than smaller ones, it is of interest to know how many more new species are encountered as a sampling area is increased. The relationship is described by a **species–area curve**.

❑ Examine Figure 2.21. How would you describe the relationship between plant species richness (*S*) and area in this graph?

■ There is a decelerating rate of increase in species numbers as area increases. Small increments in sampling area add many more species to the sample when the area sampled is small than when it is large.

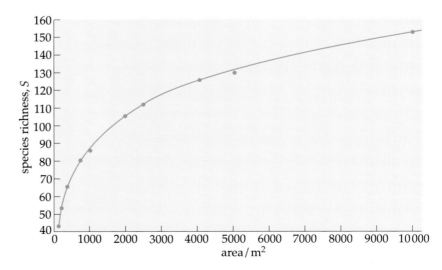

Figure 2.21 Species richness(S)–area curve for numbers of plant species in Purwell Meadow, Hertfordshire.

The relationship shown in Figure 2.21 is a common one for samples taken within a relatively homogeneous habitat such as a meadow. The slope of the curve declines as area is increased because the number of possible species in the habitat is limited. Note, however, that a few new species were still being found, even when the sampling area had reached 1 ha (10 000 m²).

❑ How does the species–area relationship contrast with the species–sampling effort relationship in Figures 2.14 and 2.16?

■ The latter represents an accumulation within a fixed area. The number of species increases due to the difficulty of locating new species (e.g. because they are small, mobile, rare or clumped) and also because of immigration into the sampling area. The species–area curve encapsulates both of these factors and the third factor of increasing species due to new habitats or microhabitats being sampled.

The first ecologists to study tropical forests, where over 200 tree species per hectare can be found, overlooked the importance of distribution pattern and clumping in making their estimates of the abundance of tree species, and came to the conclusion that rare tree species occur only as scattered individuals. One reason for this conclusion is that plots of 1 ha (the size often used) are far too small to sample the vegetation properly. Much larger areas of tropical forest (e.g. 50 ha) have now been mapped tree by tree in areas in central America and Asia. A description of the mapping of trees and records over 10 years (three censuses) is given for Barro Colorado Island in TV programme 'The conundrum of coexistence' (Hubbell, 1979; Hubbell and Foster, 1983; Condit et al., 1996). Amongst other things, Hubbell and co-workers have found that many of the tree species tended to be clumped and that this tendency was greater for the least abundant species. This is probably also true of tropical forests elsewhere. The species–area curves for Barro Colorado Island are shown in Figure 2.22.

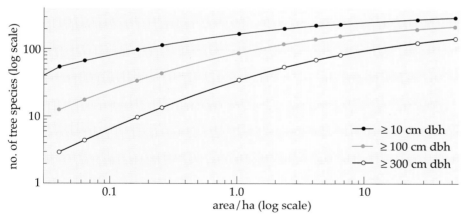

Figure 2.22 Three tree species–area relationships in 50 ha Barro Colorado Island plot from Condit et al. (1996). The three lines represent data for different sizes of tree (dbh is diameter at breast height).

In lakes, the number of fish species found increases with area. In a mixed sample from 70 lakes in Europe, America, Africa and Asia, Barbour and Brown (1974) found that surface area was by far the strongest variable correlating with the number of fish species in a lake, accounting for 30.5% of the differences in numbers of fish species between these lakes.

Species–area relationships can be described by equations of the form $S = cA^z$, where S is the species richness in area A, and z and c are parameters, that is, values held constant in a particular application of the equation. The values of z and c are estimated by taking logs (Book 2, Chapter 1, Box 1) to give the linear equation:

$$\log_{10}S = \log_{10}c + z \log_{10}A$$

Plotting $\log_{10} S$ against $\log_{10} A$ as in Figure 2.22 then gives the value of $\log_{10}c$ (the intercept) and z the gradient representing the rate at which species accumulate with area. Comparison of the slopes of the species–area curves has produced some useful insights into community structure and provided a basis for estimating species extinction (see Question 2.7). It is clear from Figure 2.22 that plotting log S against log A does not always produce a neat straight line, although the linear regression fit is usually quite good.

Several ecologists have examined the range of z values in the species–area relationship. These are listed in Table 2.13. Some of the values are derived from sampling continuous habitat or habitat islands whilst others are derived from real islands of different areas.

Table 2.13 z values for a range of habitats.

z values	Habitat type	Author
0.15–0.4	tropical forest (range of species)	Connor and McCoy (1979)
0.15–0.24	continental islands	Preston (1962)
0.34	beetles on West Indies	Darlington in Diamond and May (1981)
0.30	reptiles and amphibians on West Indies	Darlington (*as above*)

Values of z tend to be taxon and habitat specific so that the species–area relationship is a reasonably good predictor of potential extinction of particular taxa occurring through loss of habitat.

2.7.2 Rarity and abundance

As we have seen, the shape of the species-area curve is partly due to the spatial distribution and rarity of certain species. In this Section we describe the patterns of rarity and abundance.

The question 'What proportion of all species are rare?' turns out to have a surprisingly general answer. Where samples are taken from large areas over a long period of time so that accurate estimates of the number of species and of their abundances are obtained, we usually find that most species in an area are rare and that only a few species are very common. In fact, for samples of many types of organisms in many types of communities – insects, trees, grassland herbs, birds and many others – a particular pattern emerges. When species are divided into abundance classes of 1, 2–3, 4–7, 8–15. . . individuals per species in the sample (i.e. abundance size classes increase geometrically 1, 2, 4, 8....), and the number of species falling into each abundance class is plotted as in Figure 2.23 for the Barro Colorado trees, a normal distribution curve is often found. The scale on the x axis of Figure 2.23 is logarithmic (to base 2), and so this type of curve is described as **log-normal**.

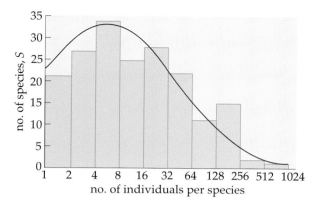

Figure 2.23 A log-normal curve fitted to the species abundance distribution of trees in the 50 ha Barro Colorado plot of tropical forest in Panama.

❑ The data plotted in Figure 2.23 were obtained in the tropical forest of Barro Colorado Island in Panama. Would you necessarily expect the species which are rare in that sample to be rare elsewhere?

■ No. Two different sites may both have log-normal species–abundance curves, but a species which is rare at one site may be common at the other.

Much theoretical analysis has been carried out in an attempt to find ecological reasons to explain why so many species–abundance distributions are log-normal. These include the *niche pre-emption* hypothesis in which it is envisaged that the dominant species takes (pre-empts) a fraction *k* of resources, the next most dominant species takes *k* of the remaining resources, and so on. Whilst this produces the required pattern, there is little evidence that such mechanisms operate in the field. In the next Section we discuss the implications of rarity and abundance for other species in the community.

2.7.3 Species richness of insects on trees

What are the consequences of rare or abundant species for those species with which they interact in the ecological community? The relationship between plant abundance and insect species richness has been extensively studied and provides an answer to this question. There are good records of the geographical distribution of plants in the British Isles (e.g. Perring and Walters, 1962, and the many atlases of county floras) which can be used to estimate the abundance of different species on a nationwide scale (e.g. number of 10×10 km squares occupied). It turns out that the most important factor determining the richness of insects feeding on a particular plant species in Britain is the distribution and abundance of the plant species.

In a study of insects associated with trees (Figure 2.24 overleaf), Kennedy and Southwood (1984) found that they could account for as much as 82% of the variation in insect species richness between the communities on different species of tree by relating this richness with the following variables: tree abundance, the time the tree species had been continuously present in Britain since the last glaciation, whether the tree was evergreen, taxonomic relatedness (number of other British species in the same order of plants), usual tree height and leaf length. The most important of these factors was tree abundance (accounting for 59% of variation in insect richness), followed by time present in Britain (accounting for another 8%) and evergreen status (another 7%).

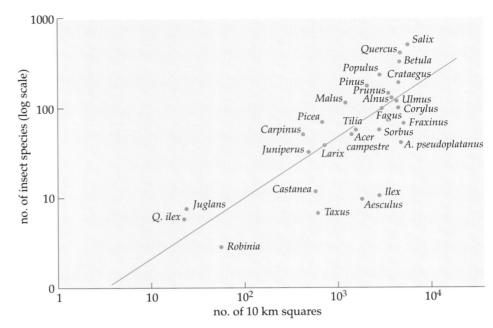

Figure 2.24 The richness of insect species on British trees. The horizontal axis shows the number of 10 × 10 km squares in which the plant species has been recorded, and the vertical axis is the total number of insect species recorded on that plant species.

Kennedy and Southwood used records of all known insect species on tree species. Another means of obtaining these data is to sample the insects on individual trees. One method is to use a beating tray of fixed area (e.g. 1m²) which is held under a branch. The branch is then rapidly beaten with a stick and the insects collected from the beating tray. To standardize the sampling, the number of beats per branch is fixed, with a given number of branches beaten on any one tree. The results of such an exercise completed on one day for two trees per species are shown in Figure 2.25.

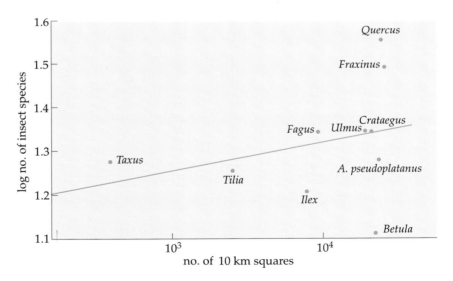

Figure 2.25 The richness of insect species sampled from ten tree species on one day at Juniper Hall, near Dorking Surrey. The horizontal axis is the same as that for Figure 2.24.

❏ Why do the results from sampling the insect faunas of individual trees give a much weaker relationship than Kennedy and Southwood's work ?

■ Because the samples are only taken from four branches of two trees per species, in one location on one day. The sampling therefore misses a substantial fraction of the potential insect fauna of each tree species.

The effect of plant abundance on the richness of their associated herbivorous insects is so strong that it is even possible to predict, within broad limits, how many species of insect pest will be found on an introduced crop species from the size of the area which is under cultivation with that plant. Relationships of the kind shown for cacao (the common name for *Theobroma cacao* which produces cocoa beans) and its pests in Figure 2.26 have also been found for tea and sugar cane and their respective pests. These pests tend to be different in each geographical area and are recruited to the introduced species from the local insect fauna.

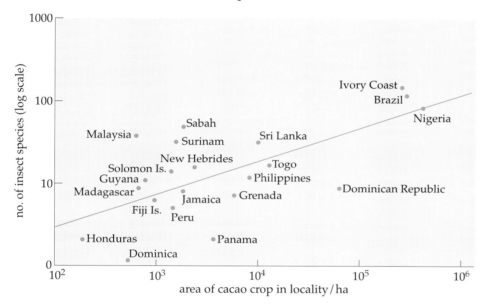

Figure 2.26 The relationship between the number of insect pest species found in cacao crops and the area of cacao grown in different localities.

Different herbivorous insects feed in different plant structures, and the larger a plant the more **structural diversity** it exhibits. Thus, a large plant has more types of microhabitat for insect species or epiphytic plant species. Indeed, when plant species of similar abundance are compared, larger plants such as trees, which are structurally complex, have over twice as many herbivores as shrubs, and shrubs have about twice as many herbivores as herbs. Similar effects on species richness due to structural diversity are found in grazed and ungrazed grassland.

❑ Figure 2.27 shows the relationship between species richness and vegetation height in calcareous grassland. What effect would you expect grazing by sheep to have upon insect herbivore species richness in such a grassland?

■ Insect richness should fall. In fact, this is the case: the more intense the grazing, the shorter the turf and the fewer the insect species (see Figure 2.27 overleaf).

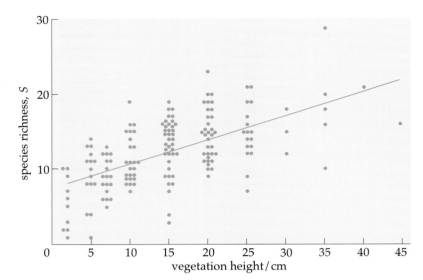

Figure 2.27 Species richness of plant-sucking bugs on vegetation of various heights in calcareous grassland.

Relationships between structural diversity and animal species richness are extremely common and there are many good examples for birds as well as insects. For example, Karr and Roth (1971) found that the structural diversity of plants explained much of the difference between the number of bird species at different latitudes.

Summary of Section 2.7

The increase in species with sampling area is described by the **species–area curve**. This is habitat- and taxon-specific and can be used to predict extinction rates. The abundance of species is characterized by the **log-normal curve**. Plant species that are rare over space and in time generally have fewer insect species associated with them. The number of insect species associated with the plant species is also determined by the **structural diversity** of the individual plants.

Question 2.7   (*Objectives 2.1 & 2.6*)

An example of a species–area relationship was found when plant species richness was recorded from different sizes of nature reserve in Yorkshire. By plotting species richness against reserve area, it was possible to construct the curve shown in Figure 2.28 (Usher, 1973).

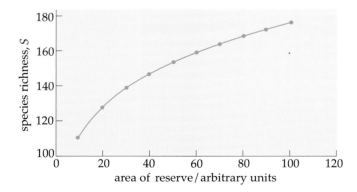

Figure 2.28 A species–area curve showing the relationship between plant species richness in some Yorkshire nature reserves and the area of the reserves.

We can use the graph in Figure 2.28 to illustrate the effect of decreasing the area by a fixed amount. With reference to Figure 2.28:

(a) (i) What is the effect on plant species richness of reducing the area by 20 units from 100 to 80 and from 40 to 20 units?

   (ii) How could the estimation of reduction be made more accurate?

(b) Given the results of (a), what do you conclude are the effects of habitat reduction based on considerations of species–area curves?

Question 2.8   (Objectives 2.1 & 2.7)

Below are the number of individuals of 37 butterfly species found in the forest in south-east Trinidad from the fruit trapping exercise in Figure 2.16 (data from Wood, 1996). Using the axes provided in Figure 2.29, draw a histogram of the number of species with 1, 2–3, 4–7, etc., individuals per species. Are the species abundance data distributed log-normally? How could the analysis be improved?

Species (no. of individuals)	Species (no. of individuals)
Archaeoprepona amphimachus (3)	Colobura dirce (54)
A. demophon (15)	Consul fabius (1)
A. demophoon (2)	Eryphanis automedon (4)
Cissia arnaea (8)	Memphis eribotes (5)
C. brixiola (1)	M. morvus (1)
C. cephus (1)	Mesosemia sp. (2)
C. hermes (39)	Morpho peleides (59)
C. hesione (14)	Opsiphanes cassiae (8)
C. junia (1)	O. cassina (23)
C. libye (1)	Pierella hyailinus (12)
C. myncea (10)	Prepona omphale (2)
C. penelope (237)	Pyrrohygyra tipha (1)
C. renata (2)	Taygetis andromeda (11)
C. terrestris (3)	T. echo (1)
Caligo eurilochus (18)	T. penelea (6)
C. teucer (25)	T. virgilia (7)
C. illioneus (2)	Temenis laothoe (2)
Catagramma astarte (1)	Zaretis itys (1)
Catoblepia berecynthia (9)	

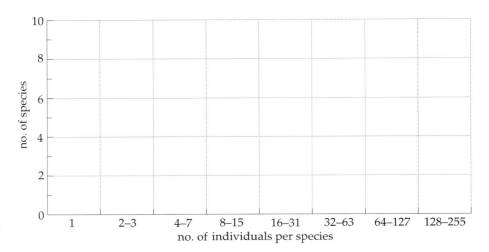

Figure 2.29 Axes for plotting histogram of number of species against number of individuals per species (log scale) for 37 species of butterfly found in the south-east Trinidad fruit trapping exercise.

2.8 Regulation of communities

2.8.1 Top-down and bottom-up

In this Section we consider how communities are regulated. By this we mean how the number and abundance of species are maintained in a community. The possible mechanisms fall into two groups – equilibrium and non-equilibrium. Equilibrium mechanisms include predation and competition whilst non-equilibrium processes include physical disturbance and climate (see Section 2.8.2 below). In Book 2, Chapters 2–4, models were used which explicitly assumed an equilibrium. The general assumption is that prey, in the absence of predators or competitors, will regulate their own density by intraspecific competition. In the presence of predators or interspecific competitors, these equilibria will change in size or become unstable, causing cycles or possibly extinction. The community matrix (Section 2.6) makes similar assumptions.

❑ What did the discussion of the community matrix indicate about the relative importance of equilibrium and non-equilibrium processes?

■ The community matrix is based on a particular type of equilibrium process. When applied to the *Heliconia* insect communities, it failed to provide an adequate explanation of their structure. However, it may be that a combination of equilibrium and non-equilibrium processes are more appropriate for such communities.

An important distinction in regulation is between the *top-down* and *bottom-up* processes introduced in Book 1, Section 4.8.2. In the former, predators control the abundance of prey. In the latter, the growth rate of predators is regulated only by prey abundance. This is referred to as **donor control**. In the equilibrium models mentioned above, both top-down and bottom-up processes can occur together.

❑ How do the ideas of Hairston, Smith and Slobodkin (1960; Book 2, Chapter 4) relate to top-down and bottom-up control?

■ The authors believed that the type of control was related to the trophic level of the organism (notwithstanding the difficulty of identifying trophic levels!).

Hairston *et al.* thought that herbivores were controlled by their natural enemies, that is, top-down regulation, whereas plants, and natural enemies of herbivores were regulated by competition for their prey (in the case of plants, competition for space, nutrients, etc.; see Book 2, Chapter 3) that is, bottom-up regulation.

In Book 2, Chapter 4, we considered the evidence for the ideas of Hairston *et al.* from the six case studies and noted that there was little support for them. What about a community level analysis of the ideas of Hairston *et al.* and top-down and bottom-up processes?

One line of investigation is to examine the response of communities to removal of predators. In a review of 19 predator-removal studies, Pimm (1982) noted that in 17 of the studies, additional species were lost. In other words, there was strong evidence for 'top-down' control of communities. For example, Paine (1966) showed that removal of the predatory starfish *Pisaster* (Figure 2.18a) resulted in dominance by *Mytilus* (mussel) which crowded out other species. These predator removals may be due to planned experiments or to unplanned circumstances such as a pollution event. Such experiments are the converse of the introduction events considered by Elton (Section 2.6.1), but both address the same problem – what is the effect on community structure, composition or function, of altering one species in the community? This echoes the discussion of community complexity and stability in Section 2.6. Indeed, if regulation occurs due to equilibrium processes, then the arguments from the community matrix may apply.

A further consideration is that the argument of Hairston *et al.* that 'the world is green so all herbivores are limited by their natural enemies' is spurious because *all that is green is not edible*. In other words, plant defence may be important in affecting herbivore abundance. The previous two Books have given a number of examples of the biochemical and physical defence of plants (see Book 1, Section 2.3 and the example of alkaloids in ragwort, Book 2, Chapter 4). What evidence do we have that plant defences regulate the number and abundance of herbivore species? We need to be cautious about whether we are considering specialists or generalists. Specialists such as the cinnabar moth are able to utilize the defences of the ragwort and are certainly not limited by them. On the other hand, in a world full of ragwort, vertebrate herbivores such as horses would be limited by their inability to feed on the plant. So, perhaps we should ask, is there any evidence that generalist herbivores are limited by their food? The answer is likely to be no because an effective generalist will be able to switch between a wide variety of plant species. Thus, specialists can overcome plant defences whilst generalists can avoid them, which suggests that defence is likely to be unimportant in controlling herbivore numbers.

2.8.2 Non-equilibrium processes

In Book 2, Chapter 2, it was hinted that not all ecologists are happy with the idea of equilibrium processes regulating populations or communities. Can communities be regulated by non-equilibrium processes? Perhaps regulation is the wrong word. Let's consider this in the light of an example. It has been argued that the coexistence of tree species in a tropical forest can be determined by physical disturbance due to tree fall. When a tree falls, a gap is opened. Species arrive (or are already in that gap) and they then grow. The key feature promoting coexistence is that the species that succeeds in any one gap is produced by the *chance* arrival of the species. Thus the competitive superiority of a species is of little importance. This is known as the **lottery model** (Sale, 1982) and was originally used to explain the coexistence of coral reef fish.

❑   In the light of this example, is regulation the appropriate word?

■   As the events are due to chance, it is strictly inappropriate to use the word regulation. However, even if regulation is not exactly right, certainly species richness (coexistence), and therefore community structure and composition, is being maintained by chance.

As mentioned above, lottery models require disturbance to create gaps in non-recruitment habitat into which recruitment occurs. The appealing feature of this model is that it can be applied to a variety of habitats. In Table 2.14 the disturbance, size of gaps, cause of gaps and patterns of recruitment are described for different habitats. Chesson (1986) has described the conditions under which lottery models can persist.

Table 2.14   Recruitment conditions for a variety of habitats.

Habitat	Examples of recruits	Recruitment phase	Examples of cause of gap	Typical gap size
tropical forest	tree species	fruit/seed	tree fall	tens of m^2
rocky shore	barnacles, mussels	plankton	wave action	tens of cm^2
grassland	annual plants	seed bank	earthworms, moles	less than ten cm^2
coral reef	fish	plankton	loss of territory	tens of m^2

Connell (1978), who has worked mainly on plants and sessile animals, gave the name **intermediate disturbance hypothesis** to the idea that certain minimum levels of disturbance are necessary to prevent a habitat being dominated by one or a few long-lived species and to permit high species richness to occur. He argued that very frequent disturbance creates low species richness because few species can tolerate such conditions.

The intermediate disturbance hypothesis is difficult to test because the frequency and intensity of disturbance in a habitat have to be assessed, and this is seldom easy to do. Kimmerer and Allen (1982) attempted to relate the diversity of bryophytes growing at different heights above water level on the banks of a stream to the intensity of disturbance at each height.

❑   How would you expect height above water level to be related (if at all) to disturbance of the bryophyte community?

■   At low height, small changes in stream flow would frequently flood the bryophytes and perhaps sweep some away. At greater heights, flooding would happen less often.

Kimmerer and Allen did find that there was a gradient of flooding frequency (which they interpreted as disturbance frequency) from near water level, where it was high, to 75 cm above water level where it was low.

❑ The abundance of the three main species of bryophyte at four different levels is given in Table 2.15. Do the Simpson diversity values shown suggest that this study supports the intermediate disturbance hypothesis?

■ Yes. Values for the Simpson diversity index are highest at 55 cm.

Table 2.15 The relative proportion of cover of three species of bryophytes and the corresponding Simpson diversity values at four heights above water on a stream side in south western Wisconsin, USA (Kimmerer and Allen, 1982).

| | Proportion cover | | | |
Height above water/cm	*Fissidens obtusifolius*	*Conocephalum conicum*	*Gymnostomum aeruginosum*	Simpson diversity index
15	0.90	0.10	0.00	0.180
35	1.00	0.00	0.00	0.000
55	0.20	0.65	0.15	0.515
75	0.00	0.95	0.05	0.095

Note, however, that the data in Table 2.15 can also be interpreted in other ways. In addition to a gradient in disturbance from water level to the top of the stream bank, there will be a gradient in moisture, perhaps in soil type and pH, and possibly in the activities of animals.

Additional support for the intermediate disturbance hypothesis comes from the pattern of bryophyte colonization that Kimmerer and Allen found in patches of denuded stream-bank at higher levels (Figure 2.30).

❑ How does Figure 2.30 support the intermediate disturbance hypothesis?

■ It shows that bare patches were initially colonized by several species, but that after two years, the abundance of three species was low whilst *Conocephalum conicum* became dominant. If there was no further disturbance, the diversity of the bryophyte community would remain low. Thus, consistent with the initial hypothesis, disturbance is necessary to maintain diversity.

Summary of Section 2.8

The regulation of communities can be produced by equilibrium or non-equilibrium processes. The former include predation and competition and are themselves divided into top-down and bottom-up (**donor**) control. Hairston *et al.* have argued that these control types are characteristic of trophic levels. Experimental manipulations of communities have supported the top-down mechanism. Non-equilibrium processes are illustrated by the **lottery model** that involves the chance recruitment of individuals into gaps. The level of disturbance may be important in determining species coexistence, predicted by the **intermediate disturbance hypothesis**.

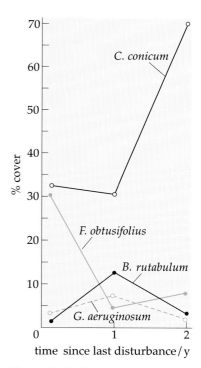

Figure 2.30 Change in bryophyte density (four species) with time in disturbed patches on the bank of a stream.

Question 2.9   *(Objectives 2.1 & 2.8)*

Consider the following:

(i)   the Janzen–Connell hypothesis;

(ii) high species richness of grazed grasslands;

(iii) lottery models.

Do they support top-down or bottom-up control, or neither?

Question 2.10   *(Objectives 2.1 & 2.8)*

Seashore and subtidal ('littoral') communities of animals and plants are often subject to the physical disturbance of wave action and grazing by molluscs, sea-urchins and fish. Ayling (1981) found that grazing by a fish *Parika scaber* and a sea-urchin *Evechinus chloroticus* cleared over 80% of the rock surface at some sites in New Zealand. Areas cleared by grazers were recolonized by the prey species; the animals in this encrusting community included sponges, ascidians and small sea-anemones.

(a) What effect does the disturbance caused by grazing have on species richness, according to Figure 2.31? (*Stylopus* is an encrusting sponge, *Cnemidocarpa* is an ascidian, and *Cliona* is a sponge which bores into and lives in the rock.)

(b) Do the data in Figure 2.31 support the intermediate disturbance hypothesis?

Figure 2.31 The number of animal species and the percentage cover of the three most important encrusting species in relation to the level of disturbance for species found on rocks at four sites in New Zealand.

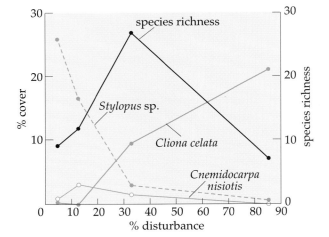

2.9 The relationship between species richness and latitude

We have already seen in Chapter 1 that the greatest richness of species for most taxa of animals and plants occurs in the tropics. With a few exceptions, this appears to be true.

2.9.1 Hypotheses

A variety of hypotheses have been suggested to account for these latitudinal gradients in species richness (Krebs, 1994). The hypotheses fall into two linked types: (i) those which explain the difference between tropical and temperate zone richness on the grounds of historical events, and (ii) those which explain the difference on the grounds of differences in the abiotic and biotic environment. In the light of knowledge from Chapters 1 and 2, we can now review the evidence for all these hypotheses.

Historical hypotheses

(a)   Richness is low in temperate zone habitats because these were disrupted by the Pleistocene glaciations and there has been insufficient time for species to recolonize.

(b)   Richness is low in temperate zone habitats because there has been insufficient time for new species to evolve since the Pleistocene. It is assumed that the tropics have been climatically stable for much longer than the temperate zone and that this has favoured the evolution and accumulation of new species.

❑   From Chapter 1, what is the evidence for these hypotheses?

◼   There have certainly been marked changes in the distribution of plant and animal species in temperate regions during the Pleistocene (Section 1.4, Chapter 1). However, there were also fluctuations in the tropical region, with species retreating into refugia. Thus, it is not clear that richness has been disrupted more in temperate zones, nor that tropical regions have been climatically stable (Section 4.8, Chapter 1).

Barbour and Brown (1974) suggested that lake history has an important effect on species richness, and that the northernmost lakes in their North American sample were the most recent to be colonized after the retreat of the ice-sheet, as well as the furthest from a source of fish colonists (the nearest were in the Mississippi Basin and on the Atlantic coast). These northern lakes are also more seasonal and less productive than lakes at lower latitudes.

Abiotic and biotic environment hypotheses

(c)   There is greater spatial heterogeneity in tropical terrestrial ecosystems; the geometric complexity of plant structures allows a greater number of niches to be present than in the similar communities at higher latitudes.

We have seen from Section 2.7.3 how important structural diversity is. Whilst there is some evidence to suggest that in comparisons of temperate forest and tropical forest, the latter has a more complex structure, it is difficult to conceive of this accounting for the much higher number of species.

(d)   There is less abiotic environmental variation in the tropics; this allows organisms to have niches which are narrower and more specialized. Hence there are more niches and more species in the tropics than there are in temperate and polar areas – the environment becomes progressively more variable at higher latitudes and niches are, of necessity, wider.

This argument has an intuitive appeal; however, we need to look carefully at our evidence. Certainly there are clear patterns of abiotic environmental variation at higher latitudes, but these are also present in the tropics (e.g. Figure 2.10). It may be that variation in temperature is important – more species have evolved to cope with prolonged dry periods than prolonged cold periods. Surviving the dry season in the tropics may depend on the availability of keystone species. To understand why less variation might lead to higher number of species, we need to consider equilibrium mechanisms of coexistence, one of which is outlined in the next hypothesis (e).

(e)   The composition of communities in the tropics is largely determined by biotic interactions: competition for limited resources results in species occupying narrower niches, with the result that more niches are present than at higher latitudes where the species composition is determined by the different tolerances of organisms, e.g. polar bears or penguins, for various physical and chemical factors.

The key here may be to understand how high species richness of plants is maintained. If we can do this then the increased species richness of insect herbivores and other herbivores may follow (see Section 2.3 – increased *Heliconius* with increased *Passiflora* ; Section 2.7.3 and Question 2.11 below). The species richness of natural enemies, e.g. parasitoids, would also be expected to increase with increasing herbivore species richness.

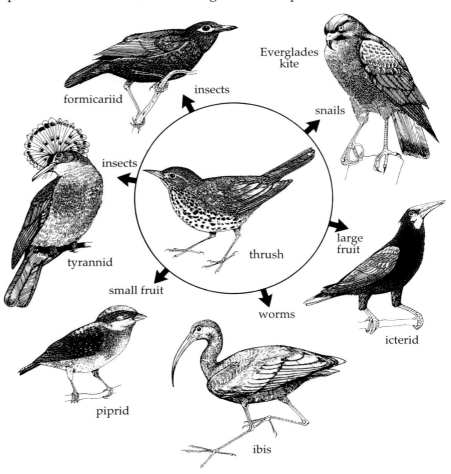

Figure 2.32 The niche of the thrush compared to those of tropical birds.

The greater variety and availability of fruit and insects in tropical forests (which would follow from increased plant species richness) during the year is probably also responsible for the greater richness of bird species in these forests. No bird can restrict its diet to one or other of these foods in temperate forests (see Figure 2.32) as Cain (1969) noted:

'It occurred to me while studying birds in British Guiana (now Guyana) that in the course of the year, the common thrush in England passes through ecological niches appropriate to many different families of South American birds. When it is pulling up worms it is an ibis, when it is eating snails it is an Everglades kite, when it is boring into large fruit it is, I suppose, an icterid, when it is gulping down small fruit it is a cotingid or manikin (piprid), when it is taking caterpillars off leaves it is probably some form of tyrannid or formicariid. Now all these activities can be staple modes of life throughout the year in the non-seasonal wet tropics. In England a bird that tried to live by any one of them alone would be extinct in a year.'

(f)   There are more predators, both as individuals and as species, in the tropics than at higher latitudes; predation regulates prey populations at low numbers, so there is little competition between herbivore species in the tropics and great richness is possible. Predation pressure is less at high latitudes, so there is greater competition between species of herbivores and hence fewer of these are present.

Hypotheses (e) and (f) lead to the same outcome via different mechanisms. Thus in hypothesis (e) the high species richness is a product of intense competition whilst in (f) competition occurs rarely due to high predation. Many ecologists have argued that insect herbivores rarely compete in part due to the high predation pressure by parasitoid and other species. This agrees with the theory of Hairston *et al.* (1960) that herbivores are controlled by their natural enemies. Yet as we have seen in this Chapter and in Book 2, Chapter 4, these arguments do not hold across taxa. Whether the generalizations are more robust in tropical versus temperate habitats is uncertain. The main problem with all of these hypotheses is lack of data, particularly in the tropical regions. Until we have more data, these hypotheses will remain the source of speculation.

Summary of Section 2.9

Two types of hypothesis have been advanced to account for latitudinal gradients of species richness:

(i)   Historical hypotheses:

*   Glaciation has recently disrupted temperate biotas.
*   Climatic instability in the temperate zone has slowed or interrupted the evolution of new species.

(ii)   Abiotic and biotic environment hypotheses:

*   There is greater spatial heterogeneity, and so more niches, in the tropics.
*   There is less abiotic variation, and so narrower niches, in the tropics.
*   There is greater competition, leading to narrower niches, in the tropics.
*   There are more predators, leading to less competition and so higher richness among prey species, in the tropics.

The validity and relative importance of these hypotheses cannot be determined until more dates are available, particularly from tropical habitats.

Question 2.11   *(Objective 2.9)*

In Table 2.16 the species richness of tropical Trinidad and temperate Britain are compared for six taxa. Do these data support the theory that tropical species richness among animals can be largely explained by increases in plant species richness? Explain your answer.

Table 2.16   Number of species in different taxa in Trinidad and Great Britain (Britain is approximately 47 times larger than Trinidad).

Taxa	No. of species	
	Trinidad	Great Britain
plants	2160	1400
mammals	100	47
reptiles	55	6
amphibians	25	6
breeding birds	400	240
butterflies	630	59

Objectives for Chapter 2

After completing Chapter 2, you should be able to:

2.1   Recall and use in their correct context the terms shown in **bold** in the text. (*Questions 2.1, 2.2, 2.4–2.10*)

2.2   Describe how communities are constructed based on interactions between species. (*Questions 2.1, 2.2, 2.3 & 2.5*)

2.3   Calculate and understand the diversity values of a community using the Shannon–Wiener or Simpson index. (*Question 2.4*)

2.4   Quantify food web structure using linkage density. (*Questions 2.5 & 2.6*)

2.5   Describe, with examples, the relationship between community stability and community complexity. (*Question 2.6*)

2.6   Describe and explain the relationship between species richness and area of sample or habitat. (*Question 2.7*)

2.7   Examine community data for evidence of the log-normal species distribution. (*Question 2.8*)

2.8   Provide examples of the intermediate disturbance hypothesis and discuss the evidence for top-down or bottom-up control. (*Questions 2.9 & 2.10*)

2.9   Give reasons, with examples, for the gradient in latitudinal species richness. (*Question 2.11*)

References for Chapter 2

Barbour, C. D. and Brown, J. H. (1974) Fish species diversity in lakes, *American Naturalist*, **108**, 473–89.

Barnes R. S. K. and Hughes R. N. (1988) *An Introduction to Marine Ecology*, 2nd edn, Blackwell Scientific Publications.

Benson, W. W., Brown, K. S. and Gilbert, L. E. (1975) Coevolution of plants and herbivores: passion flower butterflies, *Evolution*, **29**, 659–80.

Chesson, P. L. (1986) Environmental variation and the coexistence of species, in J. Diamond and T. J. Cale (eds), *Community Ecology*, pp. 240–56, Harper and Row, N.Y.

Clench, H. (1979) How to make regional lists of butterflies: some thoughts, *Journal of the Lepidopterists' Society*, **33**, 216–31.

Cohen, J. E., Briand, F. and Newman, C. M. (1990) *Community food webs: data and theory*, Springer-Verlag, N.Y.

Condit, R., Hubbell, S. P., Lafrankie, J. V., Sukumar, R., Manokaran, N., Foster, R. B. and Ashton, P. S. (1996) Species–area and species–individual relationships for tropical trees: a comparison of three 50 ha plots, *Journal of Ecology*, in press.

Connell, J. (1978) Diversity in tropical rainforests and coral reefs, *Science*, **199**, 1302–10.

Connor, E. F. and McCoy, E. D. (1979) The statistics and biology of the species–area relationships, *American Naturalist*, **113**, 791–833.

Crawley, M. J. (1983) *Herbivory: The dynamics of animal : plant interactions*, Blackwell Scientific Publications, Oxford.

DeVries, P. J. (1988) Stratification of fruit feeding nymphalid butterflies in a Costa Rican rainforest, *Journal of Research Lepidoptery*, **26**, 98–108.

Diamond, J. M. and May, R. M. (1981) Island biogeography and the design of nature reserves, in May, R. M. (ed.) *Theoretical Ecology*, 2nd edn. Blackwell.

Dublin, H. T. Sinclair, A. R. E. and McGlade, J. M. (1990) Elephants and fire as causes of multiple stable states in the Serengeti-Mara woodlands, *Journal of Animal Ecology*, **59**, 1147–64.

Gardner, M. R. and Ashby, W. R. (1970) Connectance of large dynamic (cybernetic) systems: critical values for stability, *Nature*, **228**, 784.

Gilbert, L.F. and Smiley, J. T. (1978) Determinants of local diversity in phytophagous insects: host specialists in tropical environments, *Symposium of The Royal Entomological Society*, **9**, 89–104.

Goldwasser, L. and Roughgarden, J. (1993) Construction and analysis of a large Caribbean food web, *Ecology*, **74**, 1216–33.

Hairston, N. G., Smith, F. F. and Slobodkin, L. B. (1960) Community structure, population control and competition, *American Naturalist*, **44**, 421–5.

Harrison, S., Ross, S. J. and Lawton, J. H. (1992) Beta diversity on geographic gradients in Britain, *Journal of Animal Ecology*, **61**, 151–8.

Hill, J K., Homer, K. C., Lace, L. A. and Banham, W. M. S. (1995) Effects of selective logging on tropical forest butterflies on Buru, Indonesia, *Journal of Applied Ecology*, **32**, 754–760.

Howe, H. F. and Westley, L. C. (1986) Ecology of pollination and seed dispersal, in M. J. Crawley (ed.) *Plant Ecology*, Blackwell Scientific Publications, Oxford.

Hubbell, S. P. (1979) Tree dispersion, abundance and diversity in a tropical dry forest, *Science*, **203**, 1299–309.

Hubbell, S.P. and Foster, R. B. (1983) Diversity of canopy trees in a neotropical forest and implications for conservation, in Sutton, S. L., Whitmore, T. C. and Chadwick, A. C. (eds), *Tropical Rain Forest: Biology and Management*, pp. 25–41, British Ecological Society Special Publication No. 2, Blackwell Scientific Publications, Oxford.

Janzen, D. H. (1970) Coevolution of mutualism between ants and acacia in Central America, *Evolution*, **20**, 249–75.

Kennedy, C. E. J. and Southwood, T. R. E (1984) The number of species of insects associated with British trees: a re-analysis, *Journal of Animal Ecology*, **53**, 455–78.

Kimmerer, R. W. and Allen, T. F. H. (1982) The role of disturbance in the pattern of a riparian bryophyte community, *American Midland Naturalist*, **107**, 370–83.

Krebs, C. J. (1994) *Ecology*, Harper Collins.

Levins, R. (1968) *Evolution in changing environments*, Princeton University Press, Princeton, N.J.

Martinez, N. D. (1992) Constant connectance in community food webs, *American Naturalist*, **139**, 1208–18.

May, R. M. (1972) Will a large complex system be stable? *Nature*, **238**, 413–14.

May, R. M. (1973) *Stability and Complexity in Model Ecosystems*, Princeton University Press, Princeton, N.J.

Murawski, D. A. and Gilbert, L. E. (1986) Pollen flow in *Psiguria Warscewiczii*: a comparison of *Heliconius* butterfies and hummingbirds, *Oecologia*, **68**, 161–7.

Paine, R. T. (1966) Food web complexities and species diversity, *American Naturalist*, **100**, 65–75.

Perring, F. and Walters, S. M. (eds) (1962) *Atlas of the British Flora*, Botanical Society of the British Isles, Nelson.

Pimm, S. L. (1982) *Food Webs*, Chapman and Hall, London.

Pollard, E. (1977) A method for assessing changes in the abundance of butterflies, *Biological Conservation*, **12**, 116–34.

Preston, F. W. (1962) The canonical distribution of commonness and rarity, *Ecology*, **43**, 185–215.

Root, R.B. (1967) The niche exploitation of the blue-grey gnatcatcher, *Ecological Monographs*, **37**, 317–50.

Sale, P. F. (1982) Stock–recruit relationships and regional coexistence in a lottery competitive system: a simulation study, *American Naturalist*, **120**, 139–159.

Schmid, P. E. (1992) Community structure of larval Chironomidae (Diptera) in a back water area of the River Danube, *Freshwater Ecology*, **27**, 151–67.

Seifert, R. P. and Seifert, F. H. (1976) A community matrix analysis of *Heliconia* insect communities, *American Naturalist*, **110**, 461–83.

Stork, N. S. (1991) The composition of the anthropod fauna of Bornean lowland rain forest trees, *Journal of Tropical Ecology*, **7**, 161–80.

Terborgh, J. (1983) *Five New World Primates*, Princeton University Press, Princeton, N.J.

Tregonning, K. and Roberts, A. (1979) Complex systems which evolve towards homeostasis, *Nature*, **281**, 563–4.

Usher, M. B. (1973) *Biological Management and Conservation*, Chapman and Hall. London.

Whittaker, R. M. (1960) Vegetation of the Siskiyou Mountain, Oregon and California. *Ecological Monographs*, **30**, 279–338.

Wilson, J. B and Roxburgh, S. H. (1992) Application of community matrix theory to plant competition data, *Oikos*, **65**, 343–8.

Wise, D. H. (1993) *Spiders in ecological webs*, Cambridge University Press.

Wood, B. C. (1996) *The effects of disturbance on forest butterfly communities in Trinidad*, unpublished PhD thesis, Open University.

ECOLOGICAL SUCCESSION   CHAPTER 3

Prepared for the Course Team by Mike Gillman

3.1 Introduction

When volcanic eruptions produce new islands in the middle of an ocean, the bare rock slowly becomes colonized by plants and animals and, eventually, species-rich communities, such as those on the islands of Hawaii or Krakatau may develop. If shrubs or trees are cleared and the land is perhaps ploughed or cultivated in some way and then left alone, a progression of community change ensues, often beginning with annual plants, followed by perennial plants and shrubs and finally by large trees. The process by which these transformations occur is called **succession**.

The essence of succession is that communities (and ecosystems – see Book 4, Chapter 3) change through time in a directional way with species being replaced over time. In the simplest scenario communities develop through a number of **seral** (intermediate) stages or **seres** until a **climax** stage is reached which is regarded as the end-point of succession. When the starting point is a bare and more-or-less lifeless area, such as volcanic islands, sand dunes and abandoned quarries, the succession is described as **primary**. When existing vegetation is removed, e.g. through fire or tree-felling, and the seeds and rootstocks of previous plants may be present along with some of the soil, the succession is described as **secondary**. Succession is not restricted to terrestrial regions and may occur in intertidal systems and water bodies (Book 1, Chapter 4).

The idea of *directional* change is an important one and it is necessary to distinguish clearly between directional (successional) change and non-directional fluctuations in composition, including possible cyclic change. Cyclic change (discussed in Section 3.6) does not lead to a stable state and it may occur either because of regular (e.g. seasonal) changes of climate or because of the life cycle and pattern of regeneration of the dominant species.

In Section 3.2 we describe examples of primary and secondary succession and then, in Section 3.3, we discuss how community composition and species, life histories change during succession. In Section 3.4 the concept of climax communities is examined. In Section 3.5, we discuss various mechanisms of succession and generalizations about *why* succession occurs.

3.2 Three examples of successional change

The following examples will illustrate the main changes in plant and animal communities during succession.

3.2.1 Old-field

An **old-field succession** is a secondary succession which occurs following the abandonment of cultivation. The details of this process are known from a number of studies. Studies of succession rely on two methods of determining the successional sequence (Figure 3.1). In the first the sequence is simply followed in the same site over as many years as possible. In the second method different areas (usually adjacent), have different successional ages, and are pieced together to form one successional sequence.

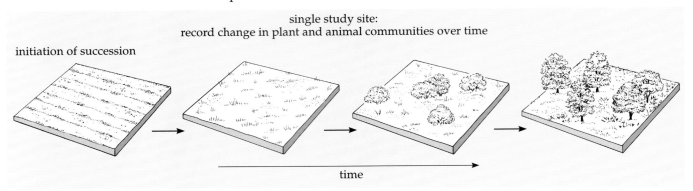

(a)

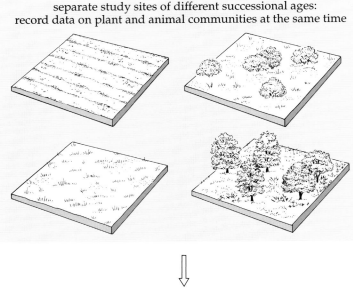

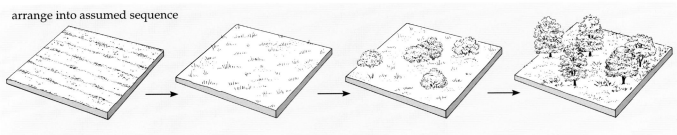

(b)

Figure 3.1   Two approaches to the study of succession. (a) Study undertaken in a single site over time. (b) Study undertaken in different sites at the same time.

❑   What is the disadvantage of using the second method?

■   Different sites may have different characteristics, e.g. a different seed bank at the time of clearing or a different soil type which may influence the course of succession.

One study of old-field succession which has used the first method is described in Pickett (1982) for a field in Somerset County in New Jersey, USA. The study began in 1960 and lasted for 20 years. The soil is derived from clay and the forest in the region is dominated by oak (*Quercus* spp.). The field was being used for soybeans and sorghum prior to ploughing. After ploughing, 48 permanent plots of 2.0 m × 0.5 m were established in a grid. The cover of each plant species and the number of stems of tree species were then recorded in each grid over 20 years. (See *Project Guide* for methods of assessment of plant cover.) The changes in annuals, biennials, herbaceous perennials and woody perennials are shown for the first 17 years in Figure 3.2.

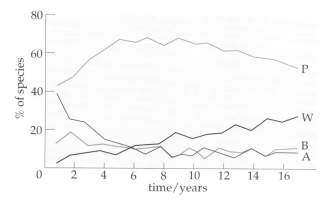

Figure 3.2   Changes in annuals (A), biennials (B), herbaceous perennials (P) and woody perennials (W) over 17 years after ploughing.

❑   Describe the patterns of change shown in Figure 3.2.

■   At the beginning of the study, plant cover was dominated by a mixture of annuals and herbaceous perennials. Over time the abundance of annuals rapidly declined to about 10% whilst the perennials increased to a peak between 6 and 8 years and then declined slowly. Woody perennials increased more or less linearly to about 25% after 17 years, whilst the biennials changed little over the period.

Extrapolation over time from Figure 3.2 suggests that the cover will eventually be dominated by woody perennials, i.e. shrubs and trees. The identities of the species in any one secondary succession may vary from site to site. Pickett divided the first 20 years into three phases: years 1–4, 5–15 and 16–20, which were characterized by different dominant species. The dominant species were those which attained 5% or more of cover in any one year. Many of the genera and some of the species will be familiar to those with a knowledge of the British flora. The dominant species are listed in Table 3.1 (overleaf) and some examples of species also found in Britain are shown in Figure 3.3.

Table 3.1 Dominant species and year of peak cover during 20 years of vegetation change (data from Pickett, 1982).

Phase	Species	Year
I	*Ambrosia artemisiifolia*	1
	Mollugo verticillata	1
	Digitaria sanguinalis	1
	Barbarea vulgaris	2
	Erigeron canadensis	2
	E. annuus	3
	Plantago lanceolata	3
	P. rugellii	2–3
	Oxalis stricta	3
II	*Rumex acetosella*	5
	Daucus carota	5
	Aster spp.	7
	Chrysanthemum leucanthemum	8
	Hieracium pratense	10
	Hieracium florentinum	12
	Lepidium campestre	10
	Trifolium pratense	11
	Convolvulus sepium	13
	Poa pratensis	15
	Agrostis alba	12
III	*Rhus glabra*	19–20
	Lonicera japonica	17
	Juniperus virginiana	19
	Acer rubrum	20
	Poa compressa	17
	Acer negundo	18
	Solidago graminifolia	19
	Rhus radicans	20
	Rosa multiflora	20
	Solidago juncea	19

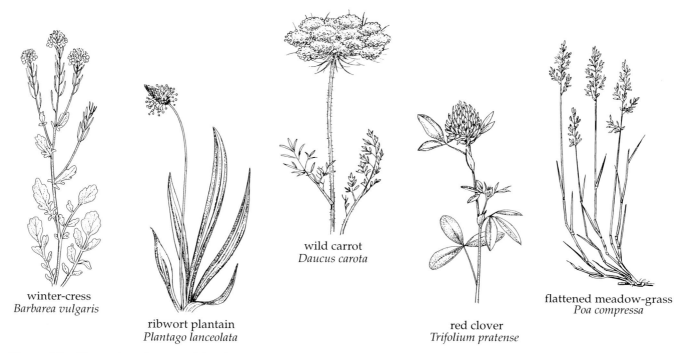

Figure 3.3   Examples of some of the dominants from Table 3.1. Phase I, *Barbarea vulgaris* (× 0.25), *Plantago lanceolata* (× 0.3); phase II, *Daucus carota* (× 0.5), *Trifolium pratense* (× 0.4); phase III, *Poa compressa* (× 0.3) (this species is not native to North America).

3.2.2 The hydrosere

The term **hydrosere** refers to all the successional stages that occur when aquatic habitats, such as lakes or ponds, become infilled with sediment and develop into terrestrial habitats. A hydrosere typical of many shallow lakes was described by Godwin (1956) for the fens and broads of East Anglia and elsewhere and his description of the stages involved is summarized below.

1   Silt is brought in by streams and rivers and the remains of phytoplankton and larger free-floating plants accumulate to form clay-textured muds and so raise the bottom level.

2   Rooted, floating-leaved plants become established, e.g. water-lilies, (*Nymphaea, Nuphar*) or pondweeds (*Potamogeton*) and their remains lead to the formation of organic-rich detritus, which further raises the bottom level.

3   A series of reed-swamp communities now develop, each further raising the level and each characteristic of shallower water than its predecessor: for example, bulrush (*Schoenoplectus lacustris*) is followed by reedmace (*Typha latifolia*), then reed (*Phragmites australis*) and finally saw sedge (*Cladium mariscus*). Reed-swamp peat is formed from their remains.

4   This succession leads to 'sedge fen' communities just at or above water level and sedge peat often forms. Shrubs and trees – willows (*Salix* spp.), birch (*Betula pubescens*) and alder (*Alnus glutinosa*) – invade the drier areas.

5   Eventually a shrub community, known as **fen carr**, develops and this may gradually be succeeded by climax woodland, often dominated by oak (*Quercus robur*).

If the original lake was basin-shaped, the hydrosere develops inwards from the shore and its progress is visible as belts of different vegetation round the edge (Figure 3.4). Figure 3.5 shows this kind of hydrosere viewed in vertical section.

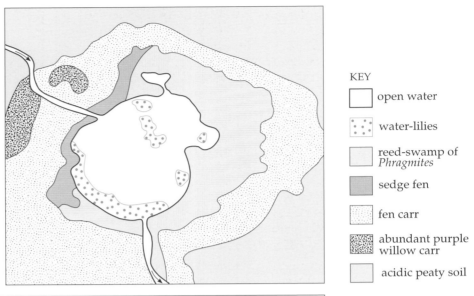

Figure 3.4
Representation of hydrosere zonation at Outdubs Tarn, English Lake District.

KEY

☐ open water

⣿ water-lilies

☐ reed-swamp of *Phragmites*

▨ sedge fen

⣿ fen carr

▨ abundant purple willow carr

☐ acidic peaty soil

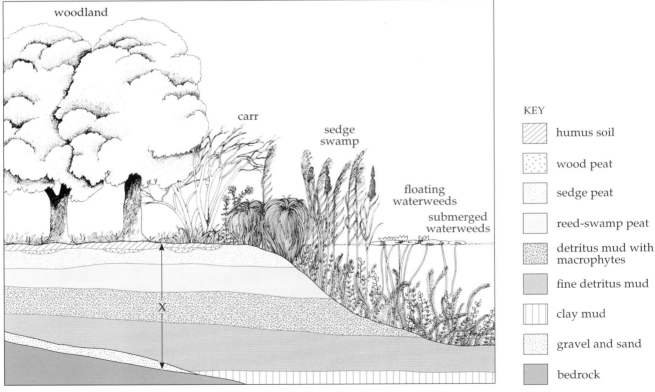

KEY

▨ humus soil

⣿ wood peat

⣿ sedge peat

☐ reed-swamp peat

⣿ detritus mud with macrophytes

▨ fine detritus mud

▥ clay mud

⣿ gravel and sand

▨ bedrock

Figure 3.5 Interrelationship of hydrosere vegetation and sedimentation at the margin of an idealized, moderately eutrophic lake. The width of the vegetation zones is greatly condensed. The line X represents a vertical section through the different layers of sediment.

❑   Is the hydrosere an example of a primary or secondary succession?

■   It is a primary succession as it begins on silt which does not contain propagules and does not involve clearing of previous vegetation.

❏ What two approaches could be used to identify and describe the stages in a hydrosere?

■ If all stages from open water to fen carr were present as marginal belts (as in Figure 3.4) then the stages could be studied directly. But if the early stages were missing and all open water had disappeared, for example, then an alternative approach would be to take a vertical core through the sediments and identify the stages from the different layers of sediment (see X in Figure 3.5). This can be done by pollen analysis, as described in Chapter 1.

Several other kinds of hydrosere may develop, depending mainly on the nutrient levels and pH in the original lake and rainfall. In acid, nutrient-poor conditions, for example, *Sphagnum* mosses may invade at the reed-swamp or sedge-fen stage (stages 3 and 4 above), forming dense floating mats that may subsequently be colonized by acid-loving bog plants and even trees. This forms the kind of land that quakes if jumped on vigorously! *Sphagnum* may also invade at the fen carr stage and, if rainfall is high and the surface of the fen peat becomes leached and acid, the *Sphagnum* forms a dense layer that prevents further growth of trees.

Sphagnum has the remarkable property of absorbing water like a sponge and as hummocks grow upwards they catch and retain their own water supply so that **raised bog** may form, underlain by *Sphagnum* peat and, below that, peat derived from other fen species and lake sediments. Raised bogs are usually dome-shaped and, because their water supply derives directly from rainfall and not from groundwater, they occur only in wet areas such as the north and west of Britain. If they become sufficiently dry, moorland communities and eventually oak–birch or birch–pine woodland may develop on raised bog sites.

a sphagnum moss
Sphagnum palustre (× 0.25)

3.2.3 Volcanic islands

Between 20 May and 27 August 1883 a series of increasingly violent eruptions resulted in the clearing of vegetation on the existing Krakatau islands between Java and Sumatra. The largest island, Rakata, is the remnant of the active volcano (Figure 3.6a, overleaf) which existed with Sertung and Rakata Kecil prior to 1883. Anak Krakatau is a new volcano which has become established since 1930. The primary succession of vegetation on the islands has been described in detail by Whittaker *et al.* (1989).

Virtually none of the soil or vegetation remained on the existing islands after the eruption. Very little is known of the vegetation prior to 1883. In October 1883 and May 1884 explorations of Rakata revealed no plant life. By September 1884 a few grasses were found and by 1886 pioneer vegetation could be seen across the whole island. Most of these were blue-green algae (Cyanophyceae) and ferns (Figure 3.6b, overleaf). It has been suggested that the blue-green algae were important in providing establishment conditions for the ferns.

❏ Why should ferns be early colonists?

■ Their light wind-dispersed spores would reach the island rapidly.

❏ What conditions would the blue-green algae create for fern colonization?

■ They would provide a moist surface allowing the spores to adhere and germinate.

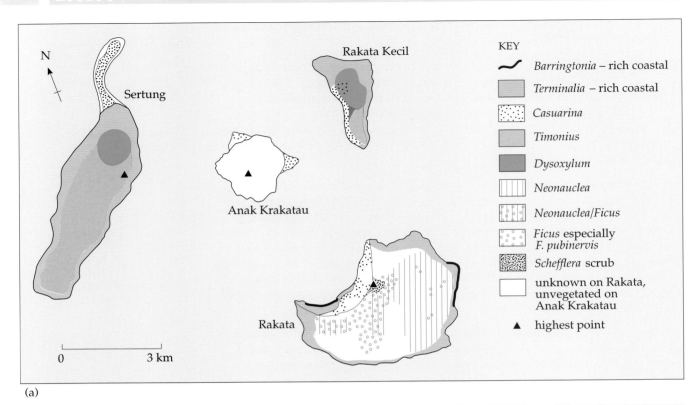

(a)

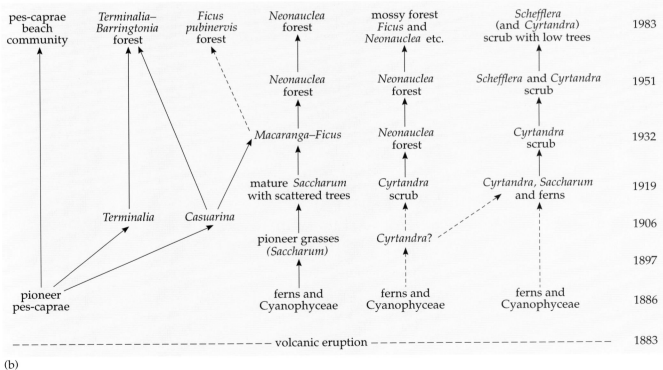

(b)

Figure 3.6 (a) Principal vegetation types of the Krakatau islands in the early 1980s. The names *Barringtonia*, *Terminalia*, etc. refer to the genera of the dominant plant species (mainly trees). (b) Principal successional pathways on Rakata. Dates indicate the time at which vegetation types were first recorded. Dashed lines indicate uncertain transitions. Pes-caprae is a plant community typical of tropical beaches, named after the creeper *Ipomoea pes-caprae*.

In the early years there were a few angiosperms which were restricted to the beach. By 1897 the interior of Rakata was covered in a savannah-like grassland dominated by species such as *Saccharum spontaneum* (Figure 3.6b; sugarcane is in the genus *Saccharum*) with small clusters of trees. Already the balance had shifted towards the flowering plants, with ferns now only dominating the higher regions. On different parts of the island different successions proceeded (Figures 3.6a and b). In all parts this was characterized by an increase in the dominance of woody species such as *Ficus* (fig) and *Macaranga*, which are typical disturbed forest species on the mainland. Between 1919 and 1932 the savannah grassland was replaced by mixed species forest (Figure 3.6b).

❏ How do you imagine most of these plant species arrived on the islands?

■ Either by water or air (particularly the first colonists, such as the ferns) and then later by birds and bats.

Until the late 1920s the succession on the cleared islands was very similar. After that point they began to diverge. This is believed to be partly due to chance arrivals of different birds on the islands bringing different seeds with them. There are now four species of frugivorous bat and eleven species of frugivorous bird on the islands. By the early 1980s, when the vegetation maps shown in Figure 3.6a were produced, over 400 species of fern and flowering plant had established on Rakata, with no obvious reduction in the rate of colonization. It is therefore likely that the plant and animal species composition is still in a state of flux, over 100 years after the initial eruption.

Summary of Sections 3.1 and 3.2

Three examples of **succession** are given here. Two **primary successions** are discussed, one due to sedimentation (**hydrosere**) leading to **fen carr** or **raised bog** and one due to volcanic activity. The example of **secondary succession** is **old-field succession,** occurring after the cessation of cultivation. The successions pass through a series of **seral** stages, leading to a **climax** state.

Question 3.1   *(Objectives 3.1 & 3.2)*

From the examples given in Section 3.2, list the characteristics of communities that change as primary or secondary succession occurs.

Question 3.2   *(Objectives 3.1 & 3.2)*

Would the following events lead to primary or secondary succession?

(a) Light burning of a small area (about 500 m²) of hill grassland in northern England.

(b) A severe fire over hundreds of square kilometres of northern conifer forest, with the peaty soil burnt to an average depth of 10 cm.

(c) A drainage scheme that lowered the water table by 50 cm around a small lake fringed by a hydrosere.

(d) Clear-cutting of several square kilometres of tropical forest.

(e) The removal of mussels and barnacles from a rock due to wave action.

3.3 Patterns of community change during succession

Is each succession unique or are there patterns of community change common to different successional sequences? It is important to look for these patterns because this might give some clues as to *why* succession happens, although, as we shall see in Section 3.5, experimentation rather than detailed observation *per se* is likely to provide better insights into mechanisms. In this Section we cover three complementary patterns of community change during succession. (We are not concerned here with changes in the soil and nutrients – these will be covered in Book 4, Chapter 3.)

3.3.1 Plant biomass and species richness

The thumbnail sketches of succession in Section 3.2 suggest that a major change over successional time is plant biomass, with early stages dominated by small, low-growing plants and later stages dominated by large, tall plants. Studies of later stages in succession are hampered by the time-scales involved. The culmination of secondary succession as forest may take hundreds of years, so there are no complete studies of the process. In their study of the Hubbard Brook Forest (see the TV programme 'Hubbard Brook: the chemistry of a forest'), Bormann and Likens (1981) used a computer model to predict long-term trends in succession. The model simulated the growth and death of individual trees. By combining real measurements of biomass change after complete deforestation (clear-cutting) with long-term computer predictions, the model shown in Figure 3.7 was developed for secondary succession at Hubbard Brook. For some older hardwood forests outside the Hubbard Brook area, the model predicted biomass values that were close to actual values.

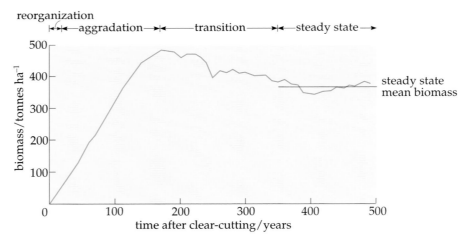

Figure 3.7   Changes in biomass during secondary succession after clear-cutting at Hubbard Brook, based on computer simulations.

Bormann and Likens, like Pickett, identified phases during forest succession. During the **reorganization** phase, lasting 10–20 years, biomass increased as plants regenerated from roots, buried seeds or seeds carried in from outside. The early colonists in either a secondary or primary succession are described as **pioneer species**. By the end of this phase, herbaceous pioneer species had largely disappeared and the dominant plants were rapidly growing, shade-intolerant trees (such as the pin cherry *Prunus pensylvanica;* for a description of shade tolerance see Book 1, Section 3.8.2). In many British woodlands, birch (*Betula* spp.) behaves in a similar way to the pin cherry.

During the **aggradation** phase, lasting for about 100 years, biomass increased rapidly (Figure 3.7) and slower-growing, more shade-tolerant trees gradually overtook the early species, preventing their regeneration from seed because of the shade cast. At Hubbard Brook these second-phase dominant trees included various species of maple (*Acer* spp.) and the ash *Fraxinus americanus* and, towards the end of the phase, sugar maple (*Acer saccharum*) and a beech species (*Fagus grandifolia*) were becoming dominant. In Britain, where there is a lower richness of tree species, birch may be overtaken by the beech *Fagus sylvatica*, ash *Fraxinus excelsior* and/or oak (*Quercus* spp.), depending on soil and local climate.

At this point, trees are more-or-less even-aged, having started to grow when the forest was felled. During the **transition** phase, many of these trees reach the end of their normal lifespan and die – hence the predicted fall in biomass. They are replaced either by shade-intolerant pioneer trees that grow in the gaps created or by shade-tolerant species that were growing slowly in the shade of the dominant trees. Thus, from being even-aged, the forest is predicted to shift towards a mixture of species for all ages and, eventually, in the steady state, it comprises a mosaic of species of various ages. Bormann and Likens use the term **shifting mosaic steady state** to describe this climax forest but the original idea goes back to the work of a British ecologist, A. S. Watt (1947). During this phase, tree fall and local regrowth will result in areas where there is net loss of biomass and other areas where there is a net gain (Figure 3.8). But for the forest as a whole when considered over a sufficiently long time interval, there is no net accumulation of biomass. These ideas are also relevant to tropical forests, as we will see below.

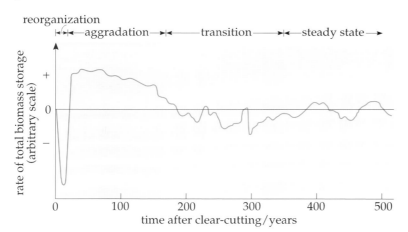

Figure 3.8 Changes in rate of biomass storage for the Hubbard Brook Forest after clear-cutting (year 0). + = Accumulating biomass; − = losing biomass.

Because this was a theoretical exercise, aimed at simulating the changing biomass, the focus was on the identity of the dominant plant species rather than change in plant species richness, although Bormann and Likens did estimate that plant species richness was high during the reorganization phase, lowest during the mid-aggradation phase and probably high in the

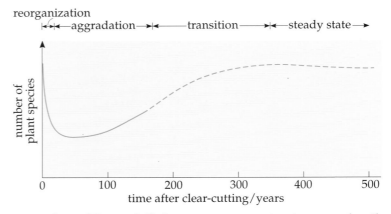

Figure 3.9   Observed (solid line) and predicted (dashed line) changes in the number of plant species during secondary forest succession at Hubbard Brook.

steady-state phase (Figure 3.9). Let us now examine in more detail some successions where the precise changes in plant species richness are known.

Some of the earliest studies of succession were on sand dunes on Lake Michigan (Cowles, 1899). These events occurred over long periods of time following the last glaciation. As the glaciers retreated so a series of raised beaches was formed, each with its own dune system (Figure 3.10). As with dune systems in other parts of the world, stabilization of the dune depends on the growth of vegetation. Once stabilized, succession can proceed. The most important species in this process in both North America and Europe is marram grass (*Ammophila arenaria*, see Book 1, Section 3.5.2). This has a complex rhizome structure which can stabilize the dune within a few years, but it does not grow well in more mature dunes. The change in plant species richness over time on sand dunes in Britain is shown in Table 3.2.

Table 3.2   Numbers of plant species occurring at different stages in sand dune succession in Britain.

		Embryo dunes	Young dunes	Medium-aged fixed dunes	Late fixed dunes	Dune scrub
herbaceous	annuals	9	44	60	17	-
	biennials	2	5	18	4	-
	perennials	7	24	65	124	68
	sub-total	18	73	143	145	68
woody	shrubs	-	-	2	14	29
	trees	-	-	-	2	8
	sub-total	-	-	2	16	37
total		18	73	145	161	105

❑   When is total plant species richness at its highest?

■   It is highest on late fixed dunes and declines as dune scrub develops.

❑   Does the change in the components of species richness: annual, biennial, etc., agree with the total?

■   Only for the herbaceous perennials. Annuals and biennials peak earlier on medium-aged fixed dunes whilst woody perennials peak later on dune scrub.

An important result of the studies of sand dunes on Lake Michigan and in Europe has been to show that there are alternative dune successions. Olson (1958) was able to show this for the dunes on Lake Michigan, which could be aged by radiocarbon dating or tree ring counts. A profile through the dunes is shown in Figure 3.10 and the possible successional pathways in Figure 3.11. Olson demonstrated that, for example, black oak was not a seral stage leading to beech–maple (which Cowles had believed) but a climax dominant in its own right.

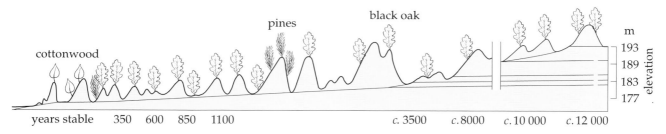

Figure 3.10 A profile through the sand dunes at the southern end of Lake Michigan.

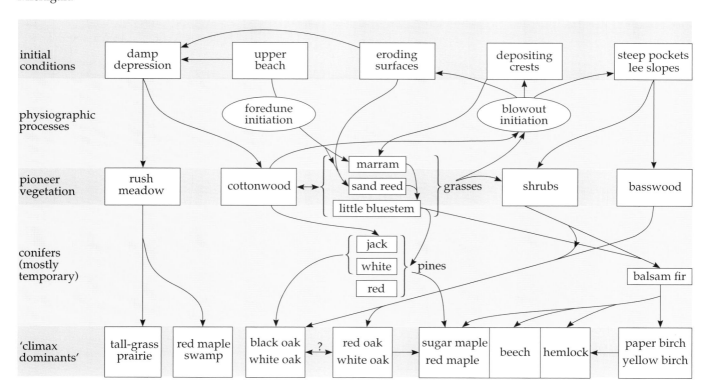

Figure 3.11 Alternative successional pathways of sand dune systems at Lake Michigan.

A similar web of successional trends has been found in the dunes of The Netherlands (Figure 3.12, overleaf). The reasons for any one pathway being followed may be due to chance fluctuations in, for example, climate or frequency of disturbance. The main point is that **multiple successional pathways** are likely to be the norm rather than the exception and the likelihood of any particular pathway over another may be unpredictable (Miles, 1987). This reinforces the point made earlier that successions need to be studied in one place as piecing together spatially separate communities into a single successional sequence may be very misleading.

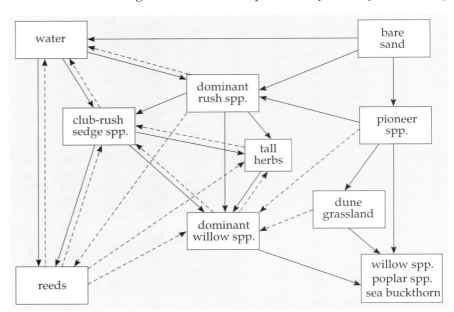

Figure 3.12 Alternative successional pathways on the dunes near Haarlem in The Netherlands.

A second detailed study of change in plant species richness was the old-field study of Pickett (1982) described in Section 3.2.1. Over the first 17 years of the study, plant species richness increased gradually, fluctuating at around 60 species in the last five years (Figure 3.13a). Species diversity, measured by the Shannon–Wiener index (Section 2.5.2), levelled off after four years, at about 1.2 (Figure 3.13b). The species richness will depend on the sampling scale, according to the species-area relationships in Section 2.7.1.

Patterns in the species richness of tropical forests during succession have also been recorded in some detail. For example, Swaine and Hall (1983) examined the early stages of succession in clear-cut forest in the Atewa Forest Reserve in Ghana, West Africa. A 10 m × 80 m transect was marked out and divided into sixteen 5 m × 10 m quadrats. The changes in plant species richness were followed in each of these quadrats over five years. Two sets of their results are shown in Figures 3.14 and 3.15. In both cases species are divided into pioneer species which required light for germination, that is they were shade-intolerant (as described for the succession of temperate forest at Hubbard Brook above), and shade-tolerant species which could establish under at least limited shade.

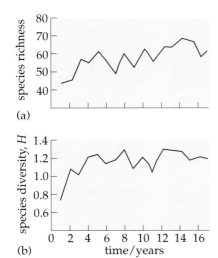

Figure 3.13 (a) Change in plant species richness with time in an old-field succession. (b) Change in plant species diversity (measured by Shannon–Wiener index).

❑ Are the pioneer and shade-tolerant species present together from the onset of succession?

■ Yes, although there are more pioneer species than shade-tolerant species earlier than later. By the end of the five-year period the number of shade-tolerant species equalled or exceeded the number of pioneer species.

❑ Where do the species come from at the beginning of the succession?

■ Either from the seed bank in the soil or from windfall or passing birds or bats.

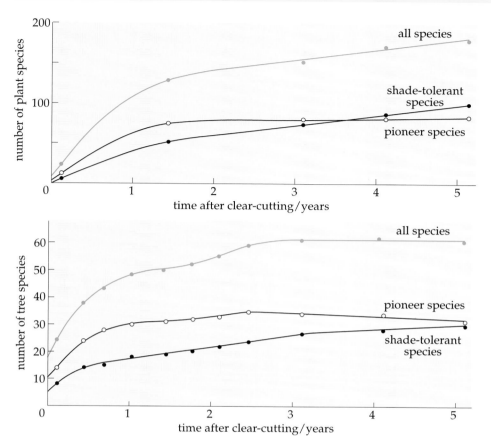

Figure 3.14 Change in the number of all plant species in the first five years of succession following clear-cutting of tropical forest.

Figure 3.15 Change in the number of tree species in the first five years of succession following clear-cutting of tropical forest.

The successional change in tropical forests over longer periods of time has been reviewed by Finegan (1996). He focused on neotropical (new world) forests in contrast to the old world study of Swaine and Hall (1983). The recovery of tropical forests through secondary succession is an important issue in conservation and forestry. Studies have either considered recovery following shifting cultivation where forests are cut, often burnt and then planted with a crop such as cassava, or following clear-cutting. Finegan noted that the secondary forests may become as species rich as mature forests, although the dominant species may be different. Species of the families characteristic of mature forests (e.g. Leguminosae, Moraceae, Lauraceae and Annonaceae) are relatively rare amongst the dominants in secondary forests. This is illustrated by the data in Table 3.3.

Table 3.3 The number of dominant species found in secondary forests of different age and the percentage of dominant species shared with undisturbed forests (modified from Finegan, 1996 based on the data of Saldarriaga *et al.*, 1988).

Forest age (years)	Number of dominant species	Percentage of dominants also found in undisturbed forests
9–14	5	0
20	13	0
30–40	8	13
60	10	30
80	15	20

From Table 3.3 we can see that the dominant species shared by both secondary and undisturbed forests is low and, even after 80 years, a secondary successional forest may only have 20% of the dominant species of a mature undisturbed forest. In addition, the species richness among the larger trees is relatively low. The apparent recovery in terms of overall species richness is therefore misleading.

As any succession proceeds the change in vegetation will be accompanied by change in animal species, which in turn will affect the vegetation. The changes in animal species are considered in the next Section.

3.3.2 Animals and fungi

So far we have considered cases where plants are the dominant species (in terms of biomass). However, there are ecological successions where plants are peripheral or even absent and animals (or at least non-plants) may be the dominant species, for example the succession of fungi feeding on leaf litter (Figure 3.16) or the succession of insects that feed in decomposing carcasses (the sequence of which, in humans, enables forensic scientists to determine the time since death). In Figure 3.16 species of fungi on the left of the diagram attack the living pine needles and needles in the litter layer (L). These species are then succeeded by genera characteristic of the upper fermentation (F_1) layer. Finally, species characteristic of the lower fermentation (F_2) layer continue the decomposition (discussed in Book 4, Chapter 2). Some genera are found throughout the three layers, for example *Trichoderma* and *Penicillium*.

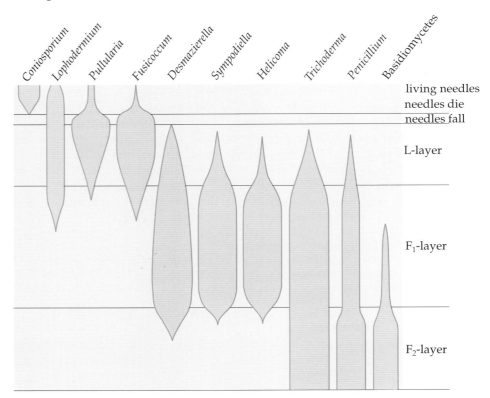

Figure 3.16 Successional sequence of fungi attacking pine needle litter. The L, F_1 and F_2 layers are described in the text.

The strong dependence of animal species richness on plant structural diversity in many terrestrial communities (Section 2.7.3) suggests that animal species may respond to changes in plant communities through succession. Structurally simple plant communities such as grassland, left ungrazed and without some exogenous disturbance such as burning, quite rapidly become structurally more complex through succession. For example, in Figure 3.17 we see the change in some bird species with secondary succession. Bird species will respond to the structural complexity of the habitat, e.g. in looking for nest sites, as well as to the plant species richness and identity of particular species, e.g. in searching for food sources. Many animal species will be characteristic of particular successional stages, although some generalist feeders, e.g. the slug species *Deroceras reticulatum*, may occur throughout all stages of a secondary succession in lowland Britain, from arable fields through to mature woodland.

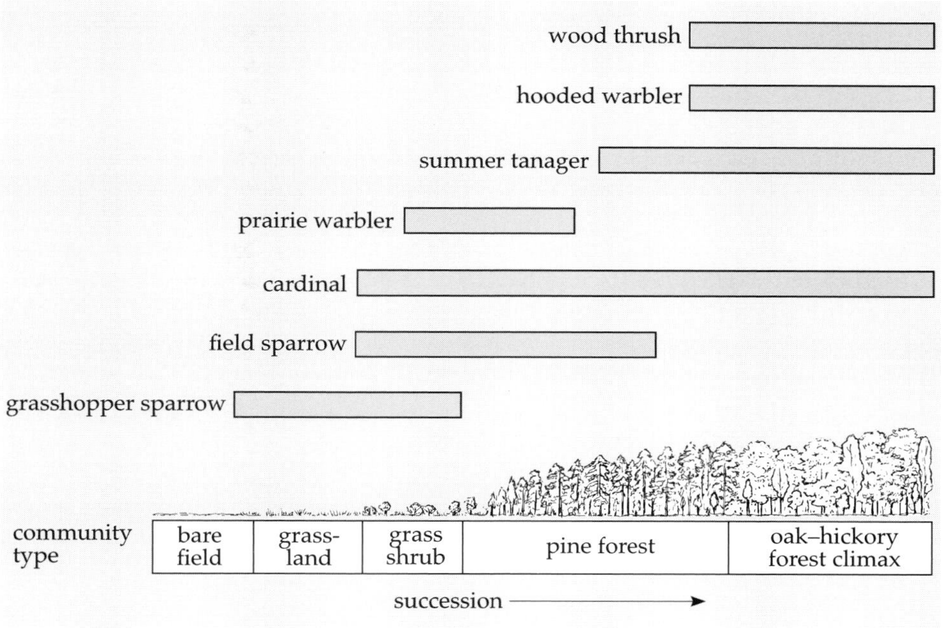

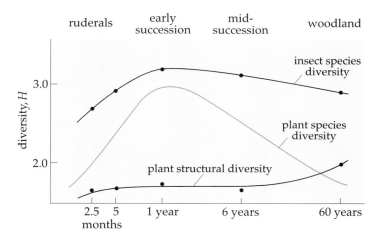

Figure 3.17 Change in bird species with secondary succession in the Piedmont region of Georgia, USA.

Southwood *et al.* (1979) compared the diversities (measured by the Shannon–Wiener index) of insect species, plant species and plant structure of a 60-year-old birch woodland in Berkshire with those of a six-year-old ungrazed field, a one-year-old field, and a newly abandoned field nearby (at 2.5 and 5 months after it was abandoned) where succession had just begun (Figure 3.18). Note that this study used the problematic method of piecing together spatially separate sites into one successional sequence.

Figure 3.18 Diversity (measured as Shannon–Wiener index) for insect species, plant species and plant structure in habitats of different successional age.

❑   How do the three types of diversity change during succession in Figure 3.18?

■   Insect and plant species diversities both rise initially, but thereafter plant species diversity falls while insect diversity remains high. Plant structural diversity rises slowly throughout the succession.

All three of these diversity trends have been observed in other successions (e.g. the Hubbard Brook Forest) but much more study is required before we will know how general they are.

It is not true that animals will only follow plant successional change. There will be a continual cycle of interaction, for example, some of the birds in Figure 3.17 may bring in seeds of new species which then germinate and contribute to succession. This can be inferred from the fruit types of tree species in the study of Swaine and Hall (above). After five years there were 41 species with fleshy fruits (bird- or bat-dispersed) and 46 species had plumed or winged seeds (wind-dispersed). Swaine and Hall also showed that the latter were not abundant in the seed bank under established forest, whereas the former were. Therefore fruit-dispersed seeds could either have germinated from the seed bank or been brought in by birds/bats whilst the arrival of wind-dispersed seeds had to occur from outside the cleared area. This would depend on whether mature trees were growing nearby, which again introduces a chance element into the successional sequence, as discussed for the multiple successional pathways in the previous section.

The syndromes of propagule dispersal (reviewed in Book 2, Section 1.6.1) have also been characterized for old-field succession. In Figure 3.19 we see how wind-dispersed plants (anemochores) are dominant in the early stages, peaking about 5 years after abandonment. Seeds attached to the outside of animals (epizoochores) also peak after 5 years, while barochores (seeds dispersed ballistically) and endozoochores (seeds that pass through the guts of animals) increase as anemochores decline.

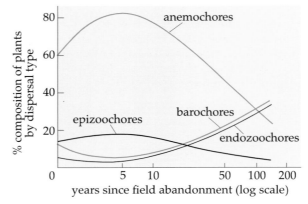

Figure 3.19 Relative frequency of four methods of propagule dispersal at different points in an old-field succession.

The study of dispersal mechanisms during succession is relevant to conservation. For example, Mclannahan and Wolfe (1993) looked at primary succession after mining for phosphate in Florida. They found that seed deposition abundance and species richness were enhanced by bird-attracting structures (perches) which simulated the appearance of pioneer trees: seed fall beneath perches had a higher richness of seed genera and seed numbers were 150 times greater (340 seeds m^{-2} year^{-1}) than in sites without perches.

3.3.3 Life histories

We have already seen that annual species are characteristic of the early stages of many terrestrial successions whilst long-lived woody perennials are characteristic of later stages. Similarly shade-tolerance is necessarily a feature of many late successional plant species. Annual, biennial and perennial are all composites of many life-history traits such as time to first reproduction and longevity (Book 2, Sections 5.5 and 5.6) which in turn confer particular population dynamics on those species, such as high rates of population increase (quantified by λ or r; Book 2, Sections 1.1, 2.2.1 and 2.3.2).

In this Section we examine some of these life-history traits for a number of taxa and ask if they show directional changes during succession. Brown and Southwood (1987) provide a useful overview of several life-history traits, two of which are shown in Figure 3.20 – generation time and reproductive allocation or effort (Book 2, Section 5.2). For the species groups studied generation time increases and reproductive allocation decreases through succession. The difference in reproductive allocation, measured as the ratio of dry weight of reproductive structures to dry weight of non-reproductive structures, is striking (Table 3.4).

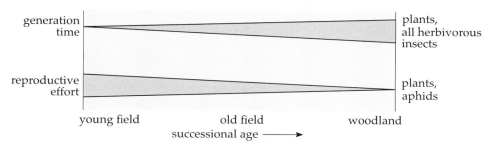

Figure 3.20 Change in generation time and reproductive effort (allocation) during secondary succession. The patterns have been observed for the taxa on the right of the Figure.

Table 3.4 Ratio of dry weights of reproductive to non-reproductive structures for herb and grass species during secondary succession (data from Brown and Southwood, 1987).

Successional age	Herb	Grass (*Holcus*)
0–2 yr	0.76	0.146
6–8 yr	0.082	0.112
60 yr	0.001	0.017

The reduction in reproductive allocation with successional time may also be accompanied by changes in mean seed size. For example, four out of five species of *Solidago* in prairie grassland had increased mean seed weight in later successional stages (Table 3.5, overleaf; Werner and Platt, 1976). This increase in seed weight *within* species mirrors the tendency for later successional species to have larger seeds than early successional species (Fenner, 1987). The reasons why later successional species have larger seeds is explored in Question 3.4.

Table 3.5 Mean weights of seeds (achenes) of five species of goldenrod (*Solidago*) which have populations in early and late successional stages of prairie (data from Werner and Platt, 1976).

Species	Mean weight in early succession/g	Mean weight in late succession/g
S. nemoralis	26.7	104
S. missouriensis	17.6	39.3
S. speciosa	19.5	146.3
S. canadensis	27.3	58.3
S. graminiolia	24.5	10.6

The shorter generation times characteristic of early successional species are often combined with other traits which contribute to overall higher rates of natural increase (Brown, 1985). The pooling of life-history traits into strategies is controversial and discussed in Book 2, Section 5.6.

Summary of Section 3.3

Changes in plant biomass and species richness are illustrated by examples from temperate and tropical forest, sand dunes and abandoned fields. The stages in temperate forest succession have been categorized into four phases (**reorganization, aggradation, transition** and **shifting mosaic steady state**). Sand dune succession (and probably other successions) are characterized by **multiple successional pathways**. Animal species and fungi change throughout succession, often accompanying changes in plant species and structural diversity. Life histories change predictably through succession, beginning with **pioneer species** such as annual plants.

Question 3.3   *(Objectives 3.1 & 3.3)*

Using the information in this and the previous Section, describe the characteristics of pioneer species.

Question 3.4   *(Objective 3.3)*

Give two hypotheses aimed at explaining why plant species tend to have larger seeds later in succession. How would you test these hypotheses?

3.4 The climax state

At the beginning of this chapter the climax was described as an 'end-state' – a stable state towards which communities develop, given enough time and freedom from disturbance. We now discuss more critically what this means because ideas about the climax have changed considerably during this century and the usefulness of the concept has been questioned.

Until the 1930s, thinking about the climax was dominated by the ideas of an American ecologist, F. E. Clements, who believed that climax communities were dependent on only one factor – the climate. Over large areas, therefore, there would be only one end-point of succession, the **climatic climax** or **monoclimax**, which was determined by the regional climate and had a characteristic species composition (Clements, 1916). Cowles also believed in this for his sand dune work, describing the beech–maple community as the climatic climax.

❑   Based on the reassessment of the Lake Michigan sand dunes by Olson (Section 3.3.1), is there evidence of a climatic climax?

■   No, several climax communities are possible (although they may be influenced by prevailing climatic conditions).

❑   From examples in this chapter and from general knowledge, is there a climatic climax in Britain?

■   Certainly deciduous forest would be likely to cover most of the south and conifer forest (probably Scots pine, *Pinus sylvestris*) most of the north of Scotland. However, the species composition of the southern deciduous forest is difficult to predict because it will vary with factors such as soil type, site history and availability of seeds or vegetative structures underground.

It appears that many factors may modify or redirect succession so that the concept of a single climatic climax becomes meaningless.

❑   Recall from this chapter an example where succession to a deciduous forest climax was deflected.

■   The hydrosere (Section 3.2.2) when invasion by *Sphagnum* led to the development of a raised bog.

Raised bog may persist for thousands of years if the climate remains wet and might reasonably be regarded as a climax in its own right. But, on this sort of timescale, climate also may change so, if oak–birch woodland develops on a raised bog, is this because of a drier climate or 'self-directed' succession? And do oak and birch grow because they are uniquely adapted to the conditions or because, by chance, acorns and birch seeds reached the site before those of any other tree species? Ecologists now recognize that climax vegetation may be determined by a whole range of factors – climate, soil, chance, biotic factors such as level of grazing, and catastrophic factors such as repeated fires, hurricanes or flooding. Many of these will be unpredictable over particular time scales. We shall say more about this in Section 3.5 when discussing the mechanisms of succession.

This broader view of the climax means that within a zone of similar climate there can be many types of climax vegetation because of variation in the other determining factors. In practice, climate remains a major determinant of the most common *type* of climax vegetation as summarized in the biome classification in Book 1, Chapter 3 – e.g. tundra, forest or desert – but in no sense does it allow predictions to be made of the precise nature or species composition at a particular site. Consider the example of tropical grassland (**savannah**). This type of habitat, which ranges from near desert (drought-resistant grasses mixed with small thorny trees or shrubs) to relatively lush communities with many trees but a continuous cover of tall grasses, is prominent in Africa, Australia and South America. Repeated fires, grazing by large herbivores (Figure 3.21) and local soil conditions may all play a part in maintaining the savannah; in the past they were natural agents but now might be under human management. Communities which are maintained in an apparent climax state are known as **plagioclimaxes**. The term **fire climax** is used to describe ecosystems such as savannah, Mediterranean scrub (or chaparral) and some grasslands and forests where the characteristic vegetation is maintained chiefly by repeated lightning-induced fires (details are given in Book 1, Section 3.9).

Figure 3.21 African savannah scene.

Knowledge of the successional state of a community or of the factors maintaining an apparently stable climax can be important in management of ecosystems, either for agriculture or conservation. For example, a fire climax community cannot be conserved by protecting it from fire because many plant species may regenerate only after burning off the litter layer. It is also unwise to assume (although belief in a predetermined climatic climax encouraged such thinking) that areas altered by human activities will inevitably return to their 'original' climax state if left alone: soils in deforested areas, for example, may be so altered by leaching and erosion that they can no longer support the original forest. Even if they can, propagules of the original tree species may no longer be available for colonization.

Considerations of the biology and life cycles of dominant plants or animals, their dependence on other species and on particular features of the environment (e.g. soil type) is essential for understanding how climax communities are maintained. The theories of succession described in the next section have combined many of these factors.

Summary of Section 3.4

The end-point of succession was traditionally believed to represent a steady state characteristic of particular climatic conditions – the **climatic climax** or **monoclimax**. In fact there may be many end-points of a successional sequence, dependent on a range of biotic and abiotic factors. Some types of climax are maintained by periodic disturbance (e.g. **fire climax**) or held at a particular preclimax state (**plagioclimax**), for example by grazing.

Question 3.5   *(Objective 3.4)*

Using examples from this and previous Sections, briefly give evidence for and against the statement that 'habitat conservation is the management of succession'.

3.5 The mechanisms of succession

We begin this Section with some examples of how experiments can illuminate aspects of the mechanisms of succession. These focus on the role of animals, as they are often forgotten in traditional plant-dominated views of succession. The particular examples are followed by an overview of the different mechanisms.

3.5.1 Using experiments to investigate the role of animals

Understanding the mechanisms of succession, like any other ecological process, requires experimental manipulations. Consider the analogy of a watch or clock. To understand how the watch or clock works it is not sufficient to measure carefully how the hands go round or the digits change. Instead we need to take the back off and remove parts of the mechanism (this analogy works better with non-digital timepieces!) or tinker with it in some way. Similarly, with succession, it is not sufficient simply to record in great detail how succession proceeds. We need to undertake experiments in the field.

❑   What types of manipulations could be used to investigate the mechanisms of succession?

■   The removal or addition of biotic components or the alteration of abiotic conditions.

These experiments may or may not be planned. A familiar example of an unplanned experiment is the successional change that took place following the reduction of the rabbit population in Britain due to myxomatosis (Book 1, Section 1.2). In species-rich grasslands the first effects of removing grazers were observed even before tree invasion had begun. Plant species richness dropped steadily because the most vigorous grasses were no longer held in check by predation and low-growing, less competitive species were outcompeted by the other plants. Figure 3.22 shows the results of a planned experiment in which numbers of plant species decreased after rabbits were excluded from a Breckland grassland plot in Norfolk in 1936 (Watt, 1974). There were also large changes in the relative abundance of species: these would probably have been detectable within months of the exclusion of grazers. As was made clear in Book 1, Section 1.2, animal species also responded to the change in vegetation following the rabbit decline.

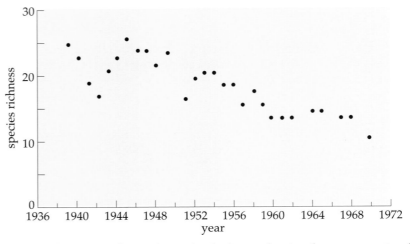

Figure 3.22 Change in plant species numbers with time after the exclusion of rabbits from a chalk grassland plot in Breckland, Norfolk.

Next we will focus on planned manipulations of animal components of communities leading into an overview of successional mechanisms.

Davidson (1993) reviewed 34 investigations of animals in succession, some of which were experiments. In 10 out of 34 cases, including five experiments, she noted that herbivores fed preferentially on early seral species and *hastened the course of succession*. However, in the other 24 out of 34 cases, including 20 experiments, herbivores *slowed down succession* by feeding preferentially on invading later successional species. Davidson also looked at granivory (seed feeders): in all four cases studied, differential predation of larger-seeded, later seral species retarded plant community succession.

We will look in detail at two examples cited by Davidson before trying to reconcile these apparently conflicting results.

Invertebrate herbivory

Brown, Gange and colleagues have explored the effects of invertebrate herbivory on the early stages of secondary succession. They used replicated plots in which insect herbivory was reduced by the application of a non-persistent insecticide in a relatively species-poor acid grassland (at Silwood Park, near Ascot; Brown and Gange, 1989).

Brown and Gange applied a soil insecticide and above-ground (foliar) insecticide in a factorial experiment (i.e. soil insecticide on its own, foliar insecticide on its own, both treatments together and a control of just water applied) at Silwood in the first and second season after clearing plots of existing vegetation. The insecticides were applied in five replicates of 3 m × 3 m plots. The effect of the insecticide treatments was dramatic with herbivore density reduced to a small fraction of its normal density.

The removal of the insects had significant effects on species richness (Figure 3.23) and abundance of the plant species (Figure 3.24).

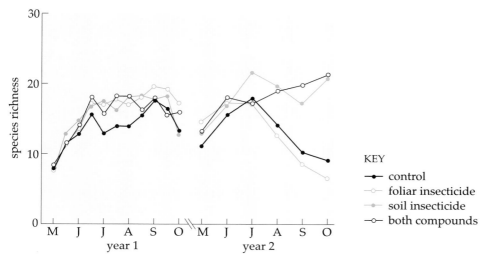

Figure 3.23 Change in mean plant species richness following application of three treatments of insecticides and a control treatment of water.

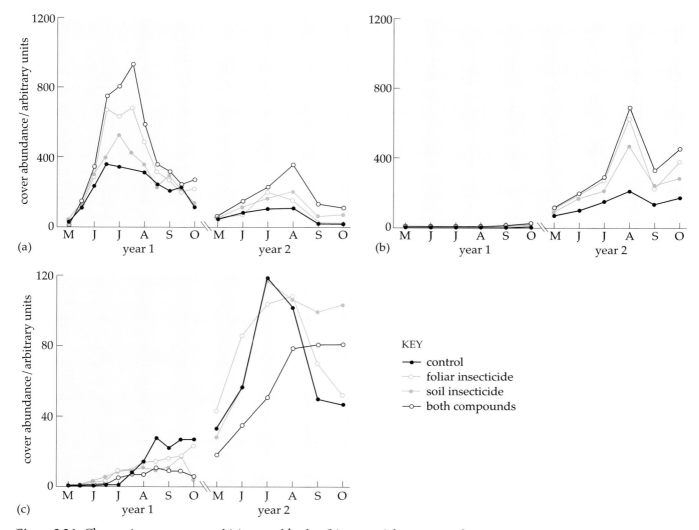

Figure 3.24 Change in mean cover of (a) annual herbs, (b) perennial grasses and (c) perennial herbs following application of three treatments of insecticides and a control treatment of water.

❑   Describe the effects of the foliar and soil insecticides on species
     richness.

■   By the end of the second year the soil insecticide and both insecticides
     had increased mean species richness by about 10 species. This suggests
     that the soil fauna is important in limiting species richness under
     natural conditions.

Brown and Gange provided further details on the fate of the components of
the flora, categorized by annual herbs, perennial herbs and perennial
grasses (Figure 3.24). The annual herbs differed from perennial grasses and
herbs in their responses to the insecticide treatments. Annual herb cover
was highest in the middle of both years in the insecticide treatments, with
foliar insecticide having a greater effect than soil insecticide in the first
year. In the second year perennial grass and perennial herb cover were also
higher in the insecticide treatments.

The overall effects of the insecticide experiment were summarized by
Brown and Gange as 'direction and rate of plant succession influenced by
natural levels of herbivory'. It is interesting to note that herbivory is
perceived here as a treatment *extrinsic* to the plant system rather than an
integral component of the community.

Vertebrate granivory

A long-term manipulation of rodent and other species in the Chihuahuan
desert in Arizona has been undertaken by Brown (a different one from
above!) and colleagues (see Figure 3.1 in Book 2 for a view of the desert).
The experiment, which has shed light on interspecific competition (Book 2,
Section 3.2.2), is also relevant to community dynamics. The experiment is
briefly described again here. In 1977 24 plots of 50 m × 50 m were fenced
with fine wire mesh and assigned at random to experimental manipulations in relatively homogeneous desert scrub (Book 2, Figure 3.4). The
various treatments included a control, all rodents removed, all rodents and
ants removed, kangaroo rats removed and the large dominant kangaroo rat
Dipodomys spectabilis removed. Populations of rodents, ants, birds and
plants were monitored in a grid of permanent sample sites within each
plot. Here we will focus on removal of the dominant species.

Long-term removal of *D. spectabilis* (analysed in 1989, after 12 years; Brown
and Heske, 1990) caused a marked change in habitat from desert shrubland
to grassland. Tall perennial and annual grasses colonized the open spaces
between the shrubs and increased approximately threefold in the absence
of *D. spectabilis*. Much of the change was due to two species: the perennial
grass *Eragrostris lehmanniana* which increased more than 20-fold and the
annual *Aristida adscensionis* which increased approximately threefold
(Figure 3.25a). None of the changes outside the experimental plots were
statistically significant. Other rodent species were also affected. A higher
species richness of other rodents was recorded on *D. spectabilis*-removal
plots. Granivorous species (competing with *D. spectabilis*) increased with
D. spectabilis removal whilst non-granivorous species feeding on foliage
and insects did not respond to *D. spectabilis* removal (Valone and Brown,
1995). Increase in grass cover due to long-term removal of *D. spectabilis*
resulted in significant increased colonization of one rodent species
characteristic of grassland.

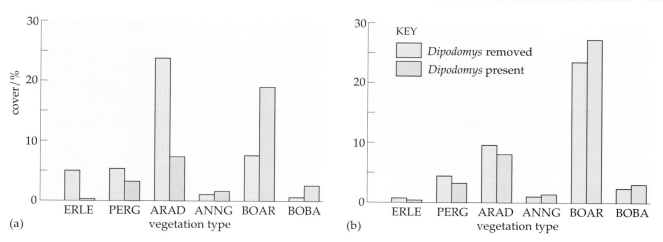

Figure 3.25 Changes in grass species following removal of kangaroo rats. The components of the vegetation are *Eragrostris lehmanniana* (ERLE), all other tall perennial grasses (PERG), *Aristida adscensionis* (ARAD), all other tall annual grasses (ANNG), *Bouteloua aristidoides* (BOAR) and *B. barbata* (BOBA). (a) Data from transects inside plots where kangaroo rates were removed or present. (b) Data from transects immediately outside these plots.

Overall the changes indicated the *keystone* effect of the rodent guild and an overall effect on community structure. For example, seed-eating birds decreased their foraging on plots with rodents removed, even though it is expected that the two groups would compete. The decrease was due to increase in grass and other herbaceous vegetation and decrease in bare ground, making conditions for seed harvesting more difficult. Although the experiments of Brown and colleagues have shown that the rodent guild determined various gross features of the habitat, is this is a change in succession or a flip in community state? In other words it may be that there are two 'stable states' in this habitat. In these cases it may be unreasonable to talk of a directional succession with a start and end-point(s).

Having described the two case studies, let us return to the conflicting results in Davidson (1993). How can we resolve this conflict? One key piece of evidence is that all plants in the first category, where the course of succession was accelerated, were trees. Thus the 'early' seral species referred to were relatively late in the overall succession. It may be that herbivores can both hasten and retard succession at different points in the *same* succession. The experiments of Brown and Gange show that different plant species groups may be affected in different ways within just two years of early secondary succession. At each point in the successional sequence we need to look at the relative herbivore loads on invading and invaded plant species. We also need to look at whether the herbivores are specialists or generalists and the defences of the dominant plant species (Davidson, 1993). Thus a high specialist herbivore load on an invading plant species may slow down (or even stop) its colonization rate, whereas it may not slow succession as a whole. In contrast a high generalist herbivore load (e.g. grazing sheep) may stop succession altogether. Similarly, a high specialist load on an invaded plant species may increase its rate of loss but not affect the overall rate of succession. What is now needed is some way of putting all these (and other) possibilities together in a cohesive system of successional mechanisms. This is the subject of the next section.

3.5.2 An overview of the mechanisms of succession

Debate about successional mechanisms hinges on if and how plant or animal species early in the succession may modify the environment creating conditions which are better or worse for potentially colonizing species and the importance of life-history characteristics of species – such as longevity. Connell and Slatyer (1977) described three mechanisms which draw on both of these phenomena. Below we review these mechanisms and evidence for their existence.

(a) The facilitation model

If you think back to the hydrosere described in Section 3.2.2 or the sand dune succession in Section 3.3.1, then it is reasonable to suggest that the growth of early species, for example by raising the bottom level or by stabilizing the sand dune, could make conditions less suitable for their own regeneration and more suitable for the establishment of new species. Marram grass, the major colonist of young dunes, grows vigorously only if shoots are repeatedly covered by blown sand, and yet the effect of its growth is to stabilize dunes and reduce the movement of sand. This is the essence of the **facilitation model** (Connell and Slatyer, 1977) or obligatory succession (Horn, 1976) which suggests that early species modify the environment in a way that inhibits their own regeneration and facilitates the entry of later species.

This is the classic mechanism of succession culminating in a climax state, which was based on the ideas of Clements (1916). For many years it was considered to be the only mechanism. Connell and Slatyer cited the **heterotrophic succession** of consumers such as fungi or insects feeding on carcasses, logs, dung or litter as classic examples of facilitation. In these cases the later successional species can *only* feed once the earlier successional species have broken down the substrate – for example, only certain kinds of fungi can break down cellulose. This process can be likened to the passage of food through a complex digestive system: later parts of the system require that the food has been broken down by earlier parts, indeed other organisms may be needed within the gut to break down cellulose (Book 1, Section 1.5.5). Other examples of facilitation include the attraction of frugivorous animals into an area by pioneer tree species. These frugivores (e.g. birds) then bring in new plant species by depositing seed. The early stages of primary succession may have many examples of facilitation. For example, nitrogen-fixing species may predominate in the early stages, creating suitable soil conditions for incoming species (Book 4, Chapter 3).

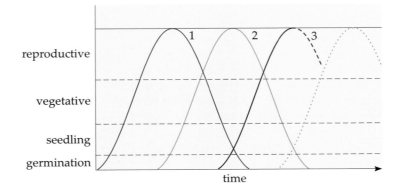

Figure 3.26 Representation of the facilitation model for succession. Species or species group 1 becomes established. Only once it is established can species (group) 2 become established, and so on.

Connell and Slatyer described two other mechanisms: tolerance and inhibition.

(b)   The tolerance model

In Figure 3.15 we saw how pioneer and shade-tolerant tropical tree species occur together in the first few years after clearance. In general fast-growing pioneer species cover the area whilst slower-growing shade-tolerant species follow. Therefore the sequence of succession depends primarily on species tolerating changing conditions (although slower-growing species may also *need* fast-growing ones, i.e. facilitation). This was characterized by Connell and Slatyer as the **tolerance model** - equivalent to another mechanism of Horn (1976) in which species arrive together in a forest gap, but only the long-lived persist into the community. A general model of tolerance is given in Figure 3.27.

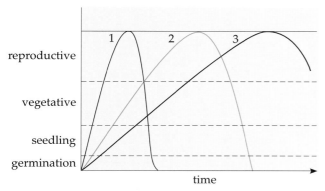

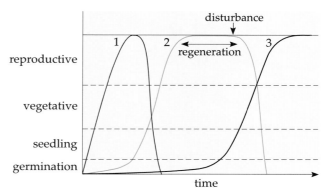

Figure 3.27 Representation of the tolerance model for succession. Species 1 to 3 become established at the start of succession and dominate the site in turn because of the different lengths of time they take to reach maturity. Species 2 tolerates conditions during dominance by 1 and species 3 during dominance of 1 and then 2.

Figure 3.28 Representation of the inhibition model for succession. Species 1 and 2 establish initially and 1 rapidly attains dominance and inhibits further development of 2. Species 1 does not regenerate and death of individuals leads to growth and dominance of 2 and invasion by species 3. Species 2 regenerates and inhibits species 3 until a disturbance kills or prevents its regeneration, allowing species 3 to develop.

(c)   The inhibition model

The difference between this and the facilitation model is that instead of early species creating conditions for the growth of later species, they would instead inhibit such growth. This is the **inhibition model** of Connell and Slatyer. Figure 3.28 illustrates this idea diagrammatically.

Sousa (1979) has provided experimental evidence for inhibition in intertidal successions. *Ulva* spp. are pioneer green algae species on rocky shores in California. They are followed by various red algae, including *Gigartina caniculata*. Sousa showed that colonization of the substrate by *Gigartina* could only occur once *Ulva* was removed (Figure 3.29, overleaf). This may occur due to natural disturbance processes during autumn and winter. This disturbance may be physical, or due to desiccation leading to mortality or due to the preferential feeding of a *Pachygrapsus* crab species. This example of succession emphasizes the continuing role of disturbance through succession – as discussed for communities in general in Section 2.8.2. Figure 3.30 summarizes the three models for succession using the original descriptions of Connell and Slatyer.

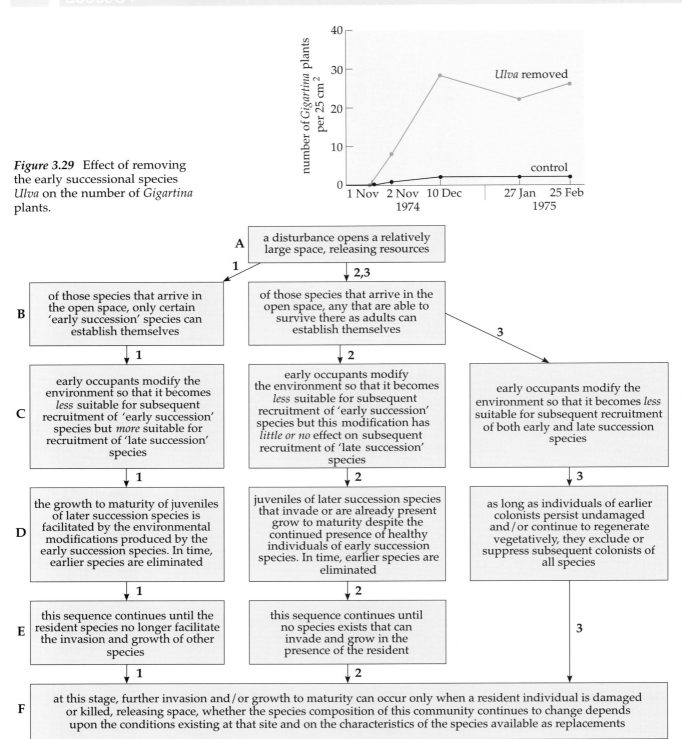

Figure 3.29 Effect of removing the early successional species *Ulva* on the number of *Gigartina* plants.

Figure 3.30 Three models of the mechanisms for succession. A–F represent stages in the successional sequence.
1 = Facilitation; 2 = tolerance; 3 = inhibition.

There is no evidence suggesting that any of these models operates as the sole mechanism for any complete succession. In a review of forest succession, Finegan (1984) suggested that a more realistic approach is to assume that different mechanisms operate for different individual species. Thus a late successional tree could be inhibited during an earlier stage of succession whereas a mid-successional species could show tolerance over the same period. This reflects the multiplicity of possibilities of effects of herbivores on plants during succession. If facilitation, tolerance and inhibition can all operate during succession, is there a comprehensive scheme which can tie all three together? One such scheme (Noble and Slatyer, 1980), classifies all important or potentially dominant plant species in successional communities in terms of certain features of their life histories, called **vital attributes**. Species can then be classified according to their array of vital attributes which would define the need for facilitation, tolerance of other species or susceptibility to inhibition. Predictions could then be made about the sequence of dominant species during succession and the effects of particular disturbances on succession.

The Noble and Slatyer scheme was developed primarily for communities that are subject to repeated disturbances, such as fire. It utilized three groups of vital attributes:

1   The method of arrival or persistence of a species during or after a disturbance. This might depend, for example, on whether a species had widely dispersed but short-lived seeds or a long-lived store of seeds in the soil.

2   The ability to establish and grow to maturity in the developing community, that is, tolerance of competition.

3   The duration of certain phases in the life cycle, for example time to reach reproductive maturity, longevity of the mature plant and longevity of seeds.

Thirty commonly occurring species types were identified based on the combination of the first two characteristics. When each species type was combined with life-cycle attributes from the third, Noble and Slatyer were able to predict correctly the course of succession for two forest communities where fire was the usual type of disturbance. One of these examples is described below.

Aspen–conifer succession, Montana, USA

In the forests of western Montana, aspen *Populus tremuloides* is usually a prominent tree in the community and four species of conifer – lodgepole pine *Pinus contorta*, larch *Larix occidentalis*, spruce *Picea* sp. and Douglas fir *Pseudotsuga menziesii* – are present in varying numbers. The vital attributes of these species are:

- aspen – a short-lived species that usually reproduces vegetatively by root sprouts after a disturbance. Seeds are short-lived and the species is intolerant of competition and cannot regenerate in a closed community (a characteristic abbreviated to I for intolerant).

- lodgepole pine – also an intolerant (I) species but longer-lived than aspen and reproduces by seeds. These are retained in resinous cones that may survive for several decades; fire releases seeds, which germinate immediately.

- larch – also intolerant and has widely dispersed, long-lived seeds. Plants live for about 300 years.

- spruce and Douglas fir – have the same vital attributes: they are long-lived, tolerant of competition (classified as T) and have widely dispersed but short-lived seeds.

Life-cycle characteristics for the species are shown in Figure 3.31a. The absence of a solid line for lodgepole pine during the first 20 years following a fire in Figure 3.31a means that the species is not present in a form capable of regeneration (i.e. as a viable seed or as a plant able to regenerate vegetatively). For lodgepole pine this occurs because all stored seeds die after a fire and, until the plants reach maturity (m), they would be unable to regenerate if another fire occurred or if trees were felled.

Figure 3.31b shows the successional sequence after fire in the Montana forest. Numbers above the solid arrows indicate years since the original fire.

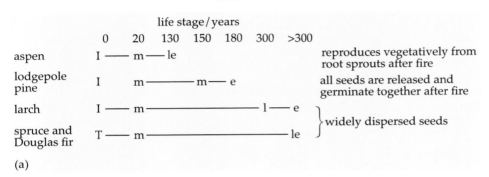

(a)

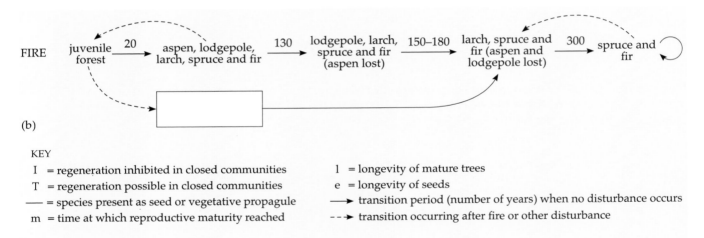

(b)

KEY

I = regeneration inhibited in closed communities
T = regeneration possible in closed communities
── = species present as seed or vegetative propagule
m = time at which reproductive maturity reached

l = longevity of mature trees
e = longevity of seeds
──▶ transition period (number of years) when no disturbance occurs
--▶ transition occurring after fire or other disturbance

Figure 3.31 (a) Life-cycle diagram and (b) composition of vegetation during secondary succession following fire in an aspen–conifer forest, western Montana, USA. (The box in (b) is for completion when answering Question 3.8.)

The vital attributes scheme predicts, therefore, that a juvenile forest (probably dominated by fast-growing aspen) will eventually change into a self-regenerating community dominated by spruce and fir if it remains undisturbed for more than about 400 years. The scheme indicates which species will be present at different stages during succession but it does not predict which species will be dominant in a mixed community; to do this it would be necessary to quantify attributes such as I and T and probably include attributes relating to growth rate.

Summary of Section 3.5

Three **models of succession** – **facilitation**, **tolerance** and **inhibition** – have been identified as determinants of successional change. Facilitation is frequently found in **heterotrophic succession**. All three mechanisms may operate in a particular replacement sequence and all depend on characteristics of the life cycle and growth pattern of the major plant species, the most important of which have been identified as **vital attributes**.

Question 3.6   *(Objective 3.5)*

(a) In the study of Brown and Gange we have assumed that large-scale insecticide application was equivalent to simply removing insect herbivores. Why may this not be the case?

(b) In the same study sucking Hemiptera were identified as primarily responsible for attacking perennial grasses and chewing Coleoptera (Table 3.6) were identified as primarily responsible for attacking perennial herbs.

Table 3.6 Abundance of herbivorous insects in untreated plots. Densities are m^{-2}.

Insect order	July 1985	July 1986
Hemiptera (true bugs)	108	90
Coleoptera (beetles)	69	15
Thysanoptera (thrips)	163	101

How might the data in Table 3.6 affect the interpretation of the effects of insects in early secondary succession?

Question 3.7   *(Objectives 3.1 & 3.6)*

Figure 3.32 shows the numbers of individuals of three species present in abandoned chalk quarries in south-east England. Histograms show the age structure of the populations excluding seedlings under five years old.

(a) Describe the succession in abandoned chalk quarries.

(b) Do the data for oak provide any support for the facilitation, tolerance or inhibition models of succession?

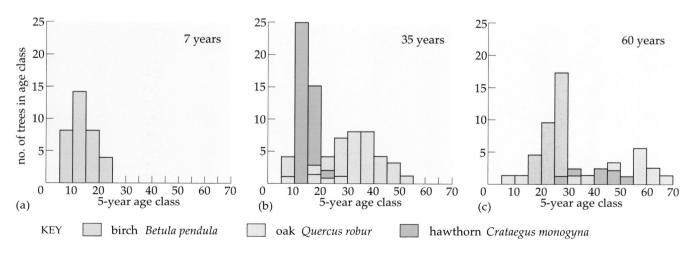

Figure 3.32 Succession in chalk quarries in south-east England 7, 35 and 60 years after abandonment. Note that birch colonized before abandonment.

Question 3.8 *(Objective 3.6)*

From Figure 3.31 and information in the text, answer questions (a)–(c).

(a) Why is aspen lost if more than 130 years elapse between one fire and the next?

(b) Why is lodgepole pine lost if the inter-fire period is more than about 180 years?

(c) Which species will be present if fire occurs again less than 20 years after the original fire (fill in the empty box after the dashed arrow from juvenile forest)?

3.6 Cyclic changes

Because organisms have a finite lifespan, there can never be uniformity in a community unless the dominant species are all of much the same age. This occurred during the development phase of secondary forest succession at Hubbard Brook (Section 3.3.1) but, in the steady state, a shifting mosaic of different species of different ages was present. Treefalls create gaps in the canopy that are colonized either by light-demanding species or by shade-tolerant species whose seedlings had been growing very slowly on the shaded forest floor. Eventually these colonists themselves die and may fall and create gaps similar to those into which they first colonized. Mosaics occur, therefore, because of **cyclic changes** which are out of phase in different parts of a community and reflect the life cycles of the dominant species. These were studied in detail by A. S. Watt and many of his ideas are summarized in Watt (1947). Two examples are described to illustrate such **regeneration cycles**.

(a) Heather (*Calluna vulgaris*)

Heather is often a dominant moorland plant and there are four stages in its growth (see Figure 3.33, and for a full account see Gimingham, 1972). Unless disturbed by burning, grazing or cutting, each heather plant ages over about 30 years and finally dies leaving a fragile mat of lichens, which erodes when not sheltered by heather. Heather may recolonize the gaps, starting the whole cycle again. If tree seedlings establish in the gaps, heather moor may be succeeded by woodland, because heather is not tolerant of shade.

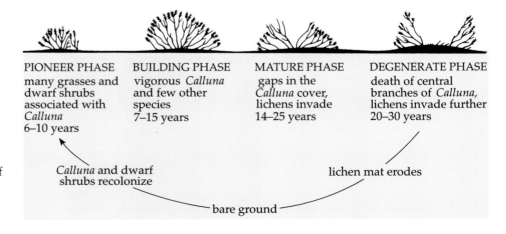

Figure 3.33 Phases in the cycle of heather *Calluna vulgaris* and associated cyclic changes in the community.

(b) Western hemlock (*Tsuga heterophylla*)

This conifer is a dominant species in the evergreen forests of north-west America and occurs along the Pacific coast from Alaska to northern California. Its seedlings are very shade tolerant but they cannot establish in the thick litter layer that covers the floor of old forests, and can only establish in partly decayed logs of grey Douglas fir *Pseudotsuga menziesii* (Christy and Mack, 1984). This leads to the cycle shown in Figure 3.34.

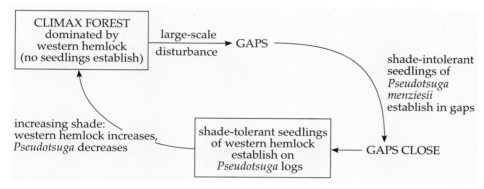

Figure 3.34 Cyclic changes in western hemlock forests.

☐ What two factors are necessary to sustain the regeneration cycle of western hemlock?

■ 1   Periodic disturbances (at least once every 500 years) that open up large gaps (fire or local felling are possible agents).

2   A seed source for grey Douglas fir so that this species may colonize the gaps.

Watt (1947) described several other examples of cyclic change, for example the cyclic formation of grassy hummocks and their decay to form hollows in grassland dominated by sheeps fescue (*Festuca ovina*), which resembles the *Calluna* cycle; and a beech–ash regeneration cycle with ash seedlings establishing among brambles (*Rubus fruticosus*) under beech, and beech seedlings establishing under ash in the absence of brambles. The essential points are that even apparently stable communities are in a state of constant, dynamic change because of the death and regeneration of dominant species.

Summary of Section 3.6

Both during succession and in the climax state, **cyclic changes** may occur because of the life-history characteristics of the dominant plant species, e.g. the cyclic changes on heather moors and the **regeneration cycles** when large trees die in mature forests.

western hemlock *Tsuga heterophylla* ($\times 1.25 \times 10^{-3}$)

Question 3.9   *(Objectives 3.1 & 3.2)*

The high altitude forests of the north-eastern USA are dominated by balsam fir (*Abies balsaminifera*). The forests are constantly disturbed by waves of total mortality that move at about 0.8–3.0 m yr^{-1}. At any given point it takes about 5 years for a wave to pass through, during which time the canopy dies and completely vigorous stands of balsam fir seedlings develop behind the waves. Waves are usually found moving into stands that are about 60 years old, which is close to the natural lifespan of balsam fir (waves of mortality in *Abies* were introduced in Book 1, Section 1.5).

(a) Which of items (i) to (iv) can be used to describe the changes occurring in this forest ?

(i) Primary succession; (ii) secondary succession; (iii) cyclic change; (iv) regeneration cycle.

(b) Compare and contrast the changes occurring in this forest with those predicted in mature forest at Hubbard Brook.

Objectives for Chapter 3

After completing Chapter 3, you should be able to:

3.1 Recall and use in their correct context the terms shown in **bold** in the text. (*Questions 3.1, 3.2, 3.3, 3.7 & 3.9*)

3.2 Describe examples of and distinguish between primary and secondary succession and cyclic change. (*Questions 3.1, 3.2 & 3.9*)

3.3 List and recognize examples of the main types of plant, animal and life-history change that occur during succession. (*Questions 3.3 & 3.4*)

3.4 Describe how a knowledge of succession can be applied to conservation. (*Question 3.5*)

3.5 Describe how succession may be studied by field experiments. (*Question 3.6*)

3.6 Distinguish between different mechanisms of succession and give examples of each. (*Questions 3.7 & 3.8*)

References for Chapter 3

Brown, J. H. and Heske, V. K. (1990) Control of a desert–grassland transition by a keystone rodent guild, *Science*, **250**, 1705–1707.

Brown, V. K. (1985) Insect herbivores and plant succession, *Oikos*, **44**, 17–22.

Brown, V. K. and Gange, A. C. (1989) Differential effects of above- and below-ground insect herbivory during early secondary plant succession. *Oikos*, **54**, 67–76.

Brown, V. K. and Southwood, T. R. E. (1987) Secondary succession: patterns and strategies, in *Colonization, Succession and Stability* (eds A. J. Gray, M. J. Crawley and P. J. Edwards), pp. 315–38, Blackwell.

Bormann, F. H. and Likens, G. E. (1981) *Pattern and Process in a Forested Ecosystem*, Springer-Verlag.

Christy, E. J. and Mack, R. N. (1984) Variation in demography of juvenile *Tsuga heterophylla* across the substratum mosaic, *Journal of Ecology*, **72**, 75–91.

Clements, F. E. (1916) *Plant succession: an analysis of the development of vegetation*. Carnegie Institute Publication No. 242, Washington D.C.

Connell, J. H. and Slatyer, R. O. (1977) Mechanisms of succession in natural communities and their role in community stability and organization, *American Naturalist*, **111**, 1119–44.

Cowles, H. C. (1899) The ecological relations of the vegetation on the sand dunes of Lake Michigan, *Botanical Gazette*, **27**, 95–117, 167–202, 281–308, 361–91.

Davidson, D. W. (1993) The effects of herbivory and granivory on terrestial plant succession, *Oikos*, **68**, 23–35.

Fenner, M. (1987) Seed characterisation in relation to succession, in *Colonization, Succession and Stability* (eds A. J. Gray, M. J. Crawley and P. J. Edwards), pp. 103–114, Blackwell.

Finegan, B. (1984) Forest succession, *Nature*, **312**, 109–114.

Finegan, B. (1996) Pattern and process in neotropical secondary rain forests: the first 100 years of succession, *Trends in Ecology and Evolution*, **11**, 119–24.

Gimingham, C. H. (1972) *Ecology of Heathlands*, Chapman and Hall.

Godwin, H. (1956) *The History of the British Flora*, Cambridge University Press.

Horn, H. S. (1976) Succession, in *Theoretical Ecology* (ed. R. M. May), pp. 187–204, Blackwell.

Mclannahan, T. R. and Wolfe, R. W. (1993) Accelerating forest succession in a fragmented landscape: the role of birds and perches, *Conservation Biology*, **7**, 279–88.

Miles, J. (1987) Vegetation succession, past and present perceptions, in *Colonization, Succession and Stability* (eds A. J. Gray, M. J. Crawley and P. J. Edwards), pp. 1–30, Blackwell.

Noble, I. R. and Slatyer, R. O. (1980) The use of vital attributes to predict successional changes in plant communities subject to recurrent disturbances, *Vegetatio*, **43**, 5–21.

Olson, J. S. (1958) Rates of succession and soil changes on southern Lake Michigan sand dunes, *Botanical Gazette*, **119**, 125–70.

Pickett, S. T. A. (1982) Population patterns through twenty years of old-field succession, *Vegetatio*, **49**, 45–59.

Saldarriaga, J. G., West, D. C., Thorp, M. L. and Uns, C. (1988) Long-term chronosequence of forest succession in the upper Rio Negro of Columbia and Venezuela, *Journal of Ecology*, **76**, 938–58.

Sousa, W. P. (1979) Experimental investigations of disturbance and ecological succession in a rocky intertidal algal community, *Ecological Monographs*, **49**, 227–54.

Southwood, T. R. E., Brown, V. K. and Reader, P. M. (1979) The relationships of plant and insect diversities in succession, *Biological Journal of the Linnean Society*, **12**, 327–48.

Swaine, M. D. and Hall, J. B. (1983) Early succession on cleared forest land in Ghana, *Journal of Ecology*, **71**, 601–27.

Watt, A. S. (1947) Pattern and process in the plant community, *Journal of Ecology*, **35**, 1–22.

Watt, A. S. (1974) Senescence and rejuvenation in ungrazed chalk grassland, *Journal of Applied Ecology*, **11**, 1164.

Werner, P. A. and Platt, W. J. (1976) Ecological relationships of co-occurring goldenrods (*Solidago:* Compositae), *American Naturalist*, **110**, 959–71.

Whittaker, R. J., Bush, M. B. and Richards, K. (1989) Plant recolonization and vegetation succession on the Krakatau islands, Indonesia, *Ecological Monographs*, **59**, 59–123.

Valone, T. J. and Brown, J. H. (1995) Effects of competition, colonization and extinction on rodent species diversity, *Science*, **267**, 880–883.

Answers to Questions

CHAPTER 1

Question 1.1
A The Oriental region has characteristics 4, 7 and 9.
B The Australian region has characteristics 2, 6 and 9.
C The Neotropical region has characteristics 8 and 9.
D The Nearctic region has characteristic 3.
E The Ethiopian region has characteristics 4, 5, 9 and 10.
F The Palaearctic region has characteristics 1 and 3.

Question 1.2
One the one hand, species may be young endemics such as Darwin's finches or members of the succulent plant genus *Aeonium* (Figure 1.14) which have diversified to occupy a range of available niches after dispersal of the parent species to the island. On the other hand, islands may also shelter taxa which have become extinct on continental mainland(s), as a result of competition or climatic change. These are relict endemics. Examples include, in New Zealand, the tuatara *Sphenodon punctatus*, a lizard-like reptile sometimes described as a living fossil, and a few surviving flightless birds which still occur on small offshore islands, having been exterminated by human-introduced rats, cats or dogs on the main islands. Similarly, the floras of the Azores and the Canary Islands contain several plant genera and even species that are now endemic there but occurred in southern Europe before the Quaternary Ice Age.

Question 1.3
Amongst your observations might be:

(i)   The various taxa probably evolved on a tectonic plate carrying a single, continuous land mass, even then isolated from the continental mainland, which subsequently split up.

(ii)   The present patterns of distribution result from a vicariance event rather than from dispersal, because several taxa show broadly similar present-day distributions.

(iii) Populations of these species became isolated between 12 Ma and 6.5 Ma ago but have either remained more or less unaltered or have only undergone small evolutionary changes since that time.

(iv)   The sea has been a major dispersal barrier, apparently preventing dispersal of populations to the continental mainland since the Late Tertiary, and indeed through the climatic and environmental changes of the Quaternary, which will be discussed in Section 1.4.

Question 1.4
Ginkgo is a deciduous gymnosperm and the period of its greatest abundance and widest distribution was the Jurassic, sometimes called the

Age of Gymnosperms. In the Cretaceous, flowering plants – angiosperms –
first appeared in the fossil record. The decline of *Ginkgo* at this time is
likely to be related in part to increased competition from the rapidly
diversifying angiosperm flora. During the Tertiary, this decline continued,
in part due to the same reasons. However, it was also a period of declining
global temperatures with deciduous forest belts gradually disappearing
from northern territories such as Greenland, Alaska and northern Europe
where *Ginkgo* thrived in the Early Tertiary. It is also clear that after India
collided with the Eurasian plate, the climate of Central Asia became much
drier and unsuitable for supporting deciduous forest. This must have
separated the European and East Asian populations of *Ginkgo*.

Question 1.5

The formation of ice-sheets abstracts large amounts of water from the
oceans, so that global sea-levels fell by well over 100 m at the height of the
last glacial stage. This would affect the relative height and land surface of
these islands. Ice-sheet and related pack-ice formation is accompanied by
changes in atmospheric and ocean circulation patterns, which are more
likely to affect the climate of oceanic islands rather than any direct global
temperature fall, which would be fairly minimal at sea-level, at least in the
tropics and subtropics. Migratory seabirds form an important element in
the fauna of oceanic islands. Their preferred seasonal fishing grounds will
certainly be affected by changes in the Atlantic and Southern Oceans, so
that this is likely to affect their abundance, breeding sites etc.

Question 1.6

Plants such as ferns and mosses can be widely dispersed as spores, usually
windborne, which germinate to produce haploid gametophyte plants;
pollen grains, although they may travel long distances, cannot extend the
range of a species – a female plant has to be there to receive the pollen.
They do however provide a means by which new genes may be carried
from one population to another. The seeds of many plants have many
adaptive features which aid dispersal, whether by air currents, water or by
ectozoic or endozoic transport by animals (see Book 2, Section 1.6.1).

Question 1.7

The sum of total land pollen from the sample at 45 cm depth amounts to
500 grains. The calculated percentages (which happen purely by chance to
be round numbers!) are: birch 2%, pine 1%, elm 13%, lime 9%, oak 26%,
alder 32%, hazel 14%, grasses 1%, other herbs 2%. The summary balance
between trees and herbs is 97%/3%. If there had been 10 fern or *Sphagnum*
moss spores, these would have been excluded from the sum on which the
percentage was based, but their values are still calculated on the basis of
the pollen sum (i.e. 10 grains would have been plotted on the diagram as
2%).

Question 1.8

The three most important factors are as follows:

(i)   Tree birches are important components of boreal forest or woodland,
so, therefore, the areas where they have been growing during the glacial
stages are likely to be much closer to Britain and other areas of north-west
Europe than the refugia for oaks (which will be discussed in Section 1.4.7).

(ii)   Birches have very light wind-dispersed fruits, which can be blown and dispersed long distances, whereas oaks have heavy acorns, which are mainly bird-dispersed, so that the rate of migration is at most a few kilometres or less a year.

(iii)   Birches are pioneer trees and thrive on raw soils, but oaks grow best in mature soils which have already incorporated humus and developed a soil microfauna and flora.

Question 1.9

Many of the species that are now almost confined to mountain areas in the British Isles have been shown from plant macrofossil remains to have been quite abundant in unglaciated lowland areas of Britain during the last glacial stage. There is therefore no need to invoke either refugia on nunataks or long-distance dispersal from arctic or alpine regions. As the mountainous areas of the north and west of the British Isles became free of ice, probably during the Late-glacial, there would have been colonization of such areas by these species, after relatively short-distance dispersal from lower altitudes. During the Flandrian, rapid forest growth would have exterminated these species not only in the lowlands, but from all but the most exposed areas, where trees could not grow. Even in high mountain areas, their distribution may have been still further reduced with the introduction of sheep and heavy grazing and trampling. The present localities for these species should be regarded as potential per-interglacial refugia.

Question 1.10

As climatic conditions deteriorated, the deciduous forests in northern Europe would initially be replaced by boreal forest, or in areas of high rainfall by bog and heathland. The decline of deciduous trees can be effected in various ways. We have already seen that lime can no longer reproduce regularly by seed in its northern localities in Britain, so that reproductive failure is one mechanism; another mechanism could be direct effects of climate, such as repeated frost damage; and a third could be competition from boreal trees as both growth and reproductive capacity weakened. The growth of bogs dominated by *Sphagnum* moss can also overwhelm trees by creating heavily waterlogged conditions. As the trees die (and there is, of course, no southward 'return migration' of such species), they are replaced by boreal species, which are able to migrate (if not already present, as is obviously birch). As conditions deteriorate still further, with low temperatures and permafrost conditions disrupting the growth of even boreal forest trees, open-ground steppe–tundra plants expand. Some of these will have dispersed from per-interglacial refugia, such as the Arctic, or from residual high mountain populations, but others will be species of such present-day open-ground habitats as river banks, coastal dunes, arable or forest clearings. These species may in fact be quite cold-tolerant (Section 1.4.5).

Question 1.11

The present montane forest in the uplands of New Guinea, Sumatra and Java shows complex altitudinal changes. Usually, gymnosperms, in fact conifers such as *Podocarpus*, today occur in the upper part of the lower montane forest. However, between about 15–10 000 BP, pollen evidence at sites 5 and 6 suggests that a complex and interrupted transition took place from subalpine grassland directly to montane forest with gymnosperms. Thus, at this particular time and at these particular areas and altitudes, gymnosperms seem to have extended through the montane forest right up to the forest limit.

Question 1.12

The main conclusion must be that lime originally colonized these areas, when climate was consistently rather warmer than at present. This probably takes us back to at least 5000 years BP, the end of the Flandrian thermal maximum, when we know from pollen evidence that limes were a much more important component of woodland/forest vegetation than they are today and that other thermophilous taxa extended their ranges farther north than today. This then raises the question of how populations of limes have managed to persist for several thousand years in these marginal areas. First, it is probable, that despite the present generally adverse climatic conditions, there are occasionally 'years of establishment' when some young seedlings are produced. Secondly, there is likely to be vegetative propagation through suckering. This will be stimulated if the parent trees are subject to severe browsing or storm damage, and will in fact lead to rejuvenation of the stock. In lowland woods, it is known that ancient lime stools can persist for very long periods indeed. However, if in fact most individuals in a colony have ultimately been derived vegetatively from a single parent, there may be a loss of fertility even when reproduction by seed becomes possible.

Question 1.13

During the glacial stages of the Quaternary, world sea-levels were lowered by about 100 m because of the storage of water as ice in the great ice-sheets, particularly those covering North America and northern Europe. The effect of this was that the southern North Sea and the Straits of Dover were dry land and Britain was linked to the Continent. The rise in sea-level between about 15 000 and 8000 years ago flooded these areas, and Britain became an island, as it probably was during the last (Ipswichian) interglacial stage and some earlier interglacial stages.

The Straits of Dover and the southern North Sea therefore provide a corridor for the immigration of plants and animals from the Continent to Britain (and *vice versa*) when sea-level is low, and provide a barrier to such movements when sea-level is as high, or higher, than at present. During the Flandrian, it is critical that the climate had already ameliorated dramatically *before* sea-level rose again (i.e. it took a long while for the ice-sheets to melt in some areas, even if no more ice was accumulating). The result was that quite a large number of temperate plants and animals were able to colonize Britain before the marine barrier was formed. After 8000 years ago, only species with sufficiently good natural dispersal mechanisms to cross over 30 km of seawater or those brought in by human agency have reached Britain. During the glacial stages, there were certainly species of animals – e.g. mammoth and woolly rhinoceros (both now extinct), musk-ox and lemming – which are unlikely to have survived interglacial conditions in Britain but would have been able to reach here after sea-levels fell at the end of the interglacial periods. The same was probably true for some plant species. The migration of many plant species into Britain during the past 15 000 years is recorded in pollen diagrams.

Question 1.14

The spread of pastoralism is indicated by increases of pollen of grasses and of perennial 'weeds' such as ribwort plantain and docks, as well, of course as a decrease in tree pollen. It should be remembered that there are other sources of grass pollen such as reeds and annual weed grasses. The best indicators of arable cultivation are pollen of crop plants such as cereals, and later hemp and flax, as well as of annual weeds such as poppies and cornflower. Nettles, which thrive on manured land, could occur under both pastoral and arable conditions.

Question 1.15

The pollen assemblage at 45 cm represents a heavily forested environment in which oak, elm, lime and alder are all abundant. That from 28 cm still shows a forested environment, but one in which a sharp decline in elm, and to some extent lime, has occurred. The fall in elm must be ascribed to the elm decline event at about 5000 BP, perhaps resulting from an epidemic of Dutch elm disease. Some forest clearance has begun, shown by a rise in grass pollen. However, you have no details as to which pollen types are included in the category 'other herbs' and thus whether or not indicators of pastoral or agricultural activity are present (though this is probable).

Question 1.16

In southern Britain, late-immigrating trees make their appearance and are seen to spread (e.g. the Diss Mere pollen diagram – Figure 1.46). There, beech *Fagus* arrives at about 5000 BP (zone DM5) and shows a small expansion, despite the very great decline of woodland at that time. Hornbeam *Carpinus* appears rather later at about 2500 BP (zone DM7a) and behaves in a similar way. Such trees are characteristic of the late-temperate substage. It would be harder to deduce this from pollen diagrams from northern England (Figures 1.38 and 1.43), because these species failed to spread naturally that far north, though they have been widely planted. Some people see the spread of blanket bog in mountain areas as an analogous vegetational development resulting from soil and climatic change, but this is difficult to separate from possible effects of human activities.

Question 1.17

(a) *Elminius* is now believed to have arrived on the hulls of flying boats (amphibious aircraft), during the Second World War, perhaps from Tasmania. This allowed larvae to be produced and dispersed at a time when convoys of ships were sheltering for long periods in British harbours and whose hulls could also be colonized. Chichester Harbour and the Thames Estuary, where this barnacle was first recorded, lie close to the major ports of Southampton, the Medway and the Port of London itself.

(b) Notice that the numbered areas are mainly ports; *Elminius* was probably dispersed to these areas as adults living on ships, and then produced larvae that were able to settle in new areas. After adults had established themselves on rocks near these ports, there could be local dispersal and increase of range once larvae were produced which could be carried by local coastal currents. There is evidence that larvae have not been dispersed over distances greater than 50 km from existing colonies, and that larvae cannot reach new areas against strong currents. Increase in range along the coast of North Wales was at a rate of about 32 km per annum, presumably by dispersal of planktonic larvae.

(c)   The North Cornwall coast is subject to violent wave action; even the harbours are exposed to rough seas. The shell plates of *Elminius* are not so strong as those of native barnacles, and probably not strong enough for *Elminius* to establish itself.

(d)   The Severn Estuary is less exposed to rough seas than the coast of Cornwall; under these conditions, *Elminius* competes successfully with the native barnacles. In fact, it tolerates estuarine conditions better and breeds and grows faster than the native barnacles in places where the water is not too turbulent for it to settle. *Elminius* is now a nuisance on oyster beds (usually found in estuaries), unlike native barnacles which usually do not survive under conditions where oysters flourish.

Question 1.18

Ancient woodlands relates to woodland on sites which appear to have been continuously wooded since before 1600 (probably much longer) *and* have a tree and shrub layer composed of species native to the site, derived from natural regeneration or coppice regrowth. Secondary woodland includes woodland which has recolonized arable land, grassland or moorland which had previously been effectively completely deforested. Plantations occur where native or introduced trees are planted on open sites or on ancient wooded sites which have been completely or partially cleared.

Question 1.19

In pollarding, the trees are cut or lopped above the height at which young shoots can be browsed by domestic animals or deer. Like coppice stools, if cutting is carried out on a regular cycle a supply of long straight poles can be produced. Similarly, pollarded willows, cut on a shorter cycle, will produce canes for basket-making. Another practice, mentioned with regard to the elm decline (Section 1.5.3), was the lopping of branches to provide winter feed for cattle. Like coppicing, pollarding also prolongs the life of trees, so that some pollards can be very old. This attribute has been put to use through the deliberate pollarding, or even planting and pollarding, of trees that serve as semi-permanent boundary markers between properties, and are often mentioned in old deeds. They may likewise have been planted and maintained for generations, for example, where several parish boundaries meet.

Question 1.20

According to the metapopulation concept, survival of a species with small isolated populations is achieved by the dispersal of individuals to establish new metapopulations. Where human disturbance of landscape patterns is so great that natural dispersal becomes virtually impossible, the question of deliberate introductions and the establishment of new populations or re-establishment of populations in areas where previously extinction has taken place then needs to be discussed. These are extremely controversial issues, particularly given the unpredictable results of some human introductions of plants and animals into new habitats (Section 1.6).

CHAPTER 2

Question 2.1

It partly supports the theory of a mutualistic interaction, showing that the acacias benefit from the presence of ants. Therefore, when ants are removed the survival rate and growth of the acacia is reduced. Further work could be directed at either supporting this conclusion (e.g. by examining acacia fecundity in the presence and absence of ants) or testing whether the ants benefit from the association (e.g. by putting them on different host-plants). The beneficial effect of acacia is likely to be supported as it has specialized structures which provide food and shelter for the ants.

Question 2.2

See Figure A1. Note the different feeding interactions for *Heliconius* adults and larvae.

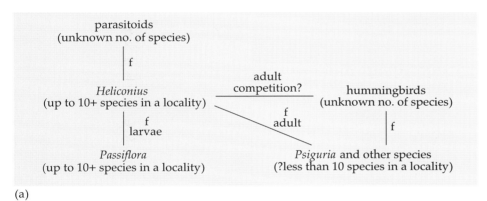

(a)

(b)

Figure A1 Feeding and non-feeding interactions of communities centred on *Heliconius* butterflies and *Cebus albifrons* (f = feeding).

Question 2.3

(a) This would promote the grassland community (as wildebeest grazing has a positive effect on grassland) and lead to a decline in the incidence of fires (see answer to (c)).

(b) This would promote the woodland community (reducing elephant browsing would reduce the negative effect on woodland) and reduce the likelihood of the grassland community.

(c) Increasing the incidence of the fires would promote the grassland community and reduce the likelihood of the woodland community.

Question 2.4

(a) For Table 2.8, all the species occur in the same proportions, hence:

First calculate $\ln(1/8) = -2.079$

and then $1/8 \times -2.079 = -0.2599$

Sum for the eight species:

$8 \times -0.2599 = -2.079$

Make this positive to give the Shannon–Wiener value:

$= +2.079$

For Table 2.9, three of the species occur in the same proportions but the remaining species has a different value and must be calculated separately and summed with the rest, hence:

For species A:

$0.7 \times \ln(0.7) = 0.7 \times -0.3567 = -0.2496$

For species B, C, D:

$0.1 \times \ln(0.1) = 0.1 \times -2.3026 = -0.2302$

Sum for the three species:

$3 \times -0.2302 = -0.6908$

Add the two values:

$-0.2496 + -0.6908 = -0.9403$

Make this positive to give the Shannon–Wiener value:

$= +0.9403$

Note that the second value is lower than the first in agreement with that of the Simpson Index values.

(b) Diversity measures both the number of species (richness) and the relative abundance of species. The fact that there were more species in the unlogged forest is consistent with higher diversity. The higher number of individuals in the unlogged forest (which could be considered as a higher number of individuals per species; 22.4 compared with 15.8) does not necessarily contribute to a higher diversity value. Instead, it is the distribution of individuals between species, rather than the mean number of individuals per species, which contributes to the diversity value. Thus there may be relatively more individuals per species in the unlogged forest and they may be more evenly distributed amongst the species than the individuals in the logged forest.

Question 2.5

(a) Linkage density is the total number of links divided by the number of species (or species groups in some of these examples).

For food web (a), linkage density is $8/7 = 1.14$

For food web (b), linkage density is $28/13 = 2.15$

Hint: to count the links in food web (b), work sequentially from species 1, ten links, through species 2, eight *new* links (i.e. excluding those of species

1), species 3, four new links, species 4, one new link, species 5, one new link, species 6, two new links, species 7, two new links, species 8 to 13, no new links.

(b) The characteristics are physiological and morphological mechanisms of feeding by the predators, e.g. mouthpart structure, digestive system; the local availability of prey species; the defences of prey and the handling and searching times for prey.

Question 2.6

(a) See Figure A2.

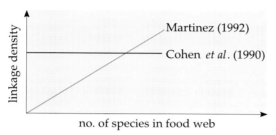

Figure A2   The change in linkage density with number of species in the food web according to the hypotheses of Cohen *et al.* and Martinez.

The relationship of Cohen *et al.* is simply a horizontal straight line (see Book 2, Chapter 2, Box 2.1). The relationship of Martinez is more complicated. If total number of links (T) increases in proportion to the square of number of species (S) in web then:

$T=kS^2$

where k is a constant.

Linkage density $= T/S = kS^2/S = kS$

This is a straight line relationship between linkage density and number of species (S) with a gradient of k.

(b) Data from Question 2.5 indicate that linkage density increases with a higher number of species. This is in agreement with the relationship of Martinez. Of course, the data represent only two points and we need many more before coming to confident conclusions. In fact, the results of Martinez were based on analysis of 175 food webs.

(c) One could either look at different communities and measure linkage density and number of species. Alternatively, one could manipulate communities, e.g. by removing species, and examine the change in linkage density.

Question 2.7

(a) (i) The number of species at 100 area units is about 176; at 80 it is about 167, so the reduction in the number of species is about 9 (the reduction calculated from the corresponding equation is in fact 7.7). The number of species at 40 units is about 146; at 20 it is 127, so the reduction in number of species is about 19. (ii) The estimates of reduction could be improved by substituting values of A in the equation $S = cA^z$ and, knowing z, calculating S.

(b) As the area declines so the rate of loss of species increases. It is worth noting that advocates of the 'loss of species due to destruction of tropical rainforest' theory have made use of the species–area relationship.

Question 2.8

See Figure A3.

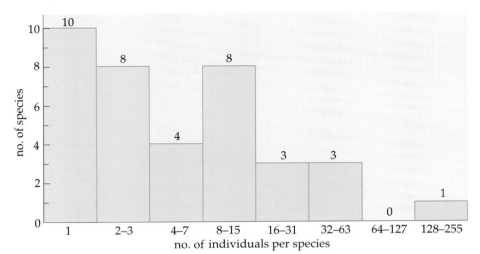

Figure A3 The completed histogram of individuals per species for 37 species of butterfly found in the south-east Trinidad fruit-trapping exercise.

The data do not appear to fit the log-normal distribution. A problem in interpretation is that the left-hand tail of the log-normal distribution is often not present (as in Figure 2.23). The analysis could be improved by (i) using statistical methods to fit the observed distribution to the predicted curve and (ii) using more data (more individuals caught) – it might be that the fit would improve – on the other hand it might get worse!

Question 2.9

The Janzen–Connell model assumes that specialist herbivores significantly reduce seedling densities around parent trees. This would be consistent with top-down control. A high species richness due to grazing would also be an example of top-down control, with grazers determining the abundance of different plant species. The lottery model is not consistent with either hypothesis as it proposes that coexistence is determined by chance events and has no role for predators.

Question 2.10

(a) The highest species richness of encrusting animals are found at the third site from the left of the Figure, where there is an intermediate level of disturbance caused by grazing. It appears that *Stylopus* becomes dominant where grazing is low and that *Cliona* (the boring sponge) is able to increase under high grazing pressure.

(b) These data support the intermediate disturbance hypothesis.

Question 2.11

Comparison of the ratios of species in Trinidad to species in Britain shows that some groups have increased more than would have been expected from studying the plant species. Thus the plant species have increased by a ratio of 2160/1400 = 1.54, whilst butterflies, which might be expected to have a direct relationship to plants, are about ten times more species rich in Trinidad. Breeding birds and mammals have increased slightly more than plants (1.67 and 2.13 respectively) whilst reptiles and amphibians are nine and four times higher respectively.

CHAPTER 3

Question 3.1

The characteristics of communities which change through succession include the composition of species, the identity of the dominant species and the relative abundance of annuals and perennials and herbaceous and woody plants. Other changes outside of the community have been described or hinted at, such as the structure and composition of the soil. These will be covered in Book 4, Chapter 3 under ecosystems.

Question 3.2

(a) This would lead to a secondary succession as most of the vegetation would be removed but the soil, seed bank and vegetatively reproducing structures such as rhizomes would be largely unaffected.

(b) This would lead to a primary succession as all of the vegetation and probably most of the seed bank would be lost and the soil sterilized in the upper layers.

(c) This would accelerate the hydrosere, i.e. continue the primary succession.

(d) This would lead to a secondary succession.

(e) This would lead to a primary succession as no propagules would remain and the rock surface is cleared.

Question 3.3

The characteristics of pioneer species may depend on the succession under consideration and include (i) shade intolerance (tropical forest example), (ii) short life cycle (annuals, old-field, sand dunes; Figure 3.20), (iii) wind dispersal (Figure 3.19), (iv) high reproductive allocation (Figure 3.20).

Question 3.4

This requires some imagination. Two possible hypotheses are:

(i) Bigger seeds have larger seedlings which grow more rapidly after germination and can compete with the denser later successional vegetation.

(ii) More seeds are animal dispersed later in succession and these tend to be larger.

Other hypotheses may occur to you, e.g. concerned with seed dormancy.

The first hypothesis could be tested by first examining if there was a positive correlation between seed size and growth rate under controlled conditions in a greenhouse or field experiment and then recording the fate of seedlings in (for example) a grass mixture. The second hypothesis could be tested by calculating the mean size of seeds which are animal dispersed and those which are not, and determining the statistical significance of the difference between the means.

Question 3.5

The answer to this question is potentially very long, with a wide variety of sources in this Book and the TV programme 'Managing for Biodiversity'.

This theme will be picked up in the TV programme 'Norfolk Broads' and Book 5. Overall there is a large amount of evidence in favour of this assertion. Most of the habitats in Britain (and other temperate regions) are managed in some way. For example, two habitats of high conservation interest in Britain are chalk grasslands and heathlands. These are maintained in a preclimax state by grazing and/or fire. Indeed these habitats are by-products of many years of such management and are at best 'semi-natural'. If succession were allowed to proceed they would lose much of their conservation interest. The mosaic of semi-natural habitats found in Britain, with their associated conservation value, is largely due to the fact that succession has been interrupted at various stages. If Britain were to return to the 'wildwood' before human intervention (Chapter 1) it would be disastrous for most of the present day wildlife. Only in large naturally forested areas such as the new world tropics or the northern forests could one argue that habitat conservation is not dependent on interrupting succession. Yet even there, with increasing exploitation (e.g. Managing for Biodiversity) succession is being manipulated so that secondary forests will become predominant over primary forests.

Question 3.6

(a) Because insecticide treatment may affect the plants directly and will kill other insects besides herbivores. In fact Brown and Gange showed in separate experiments there was no direct effect of the insecticide on the plants.

(b) These data show that the Coleoptera and Thysanoptera fluctuated naturally and widely in abundance in untreated plots. Therefore it is possible that over a short period (e.g. the two years of study by Brown and Gange) that natural fluctuations in insect abundance in untreated plots might affect the interpretation of the insect removal by insecticide.

Question 3.7

(a) The quarries are colonized very quickly (before being abandoned) by birch, a typical pioneer tree species that is dominant after seven years (Figure 3.32a). After 35 years (Figure 3.32b) there are a small number of oaks aged between 15 and 30 years which must have colonized shortly after the quarry was abandoned, but the dominant feature is the large number of hawthorns, which presumably colonized extensively only after 10–25 years had elapsed since abandonment. The birches are still abundant and surviving with some new recruitment.

After 60 years (Figure 3.32c) there are small numbers of old (and presumably large) birch and hawthorns, but oaks aged between 15 and 30 years are the most abundant species. There are no larger older oaks as might be expected from Figure 3.32b, neither are there young oaks present (less than 15 years old). Hawthorn does not appear to be regenerating in this old quarry but small numbers of young birch are present.

(b) A major problem with interpretation is that these data are from separate quarries. Thus, the inconsistencies between the 60- and 35-year-old quarries, for example, in terms of the oaks, may be due to local differences in recruitment. However, if the quarries are taken as a single sequence, then the colonization of the oaks and hawthorn between 7 and 35 years suggests some facilitation (but not tolerance or inhibition). The seed are wind-dispersed so can arrive early, but the oaks and hawthorn are animal dispersed and may need established trees such as the birches to attract birds. Oaks did colonize the quarries early in succession, as predicted by the tolerance and inhibition models. The switch from high abundance of hawthorn after 35 years to high abundance of oaks suggests competition, with the high abundance of oaks inhibiting further colonization by birch.

Question 3.8

(a) Because the normal lifespan (l) of aspen is about 130 years. As, from Figure 3.31a, it has short-lived seeds and is also an I species which cannot regenerate in the successional community, the death of the original invaders will mean loss of aspen from the community.

(b) The same argument explains loss of lodgepole pine after about 180 years: this is longer than the lifespan of adults and of viable seeds.

(c) Lodgepole pine will be lost if fire occurs in a juvenile forest younger than about 20 years because all seeds germinated when the original fire occurred and trees will not have produced fresh seed. The empty box in Figure 3.31b should therefore include aspen, larch, spruce and fir (lodgepole pine lost).

Question 3.9

(a) Items (iii) and (iv): this is an example of cyclic change apparently determined by the life cycle of the dominant species. However, it is puzzling that waves of *total* mortality occur because you would not expect all trees along a wave front to have exactly the same lifespan. It has been suggested that once trees begin to die, this so alters the local environment (e.g. by affecting air flow and frost exposure) that neighbouring trees are killed.

(b) At Hubbard Brook, change occurs in the form of a constantly shifting mosaic as individual trees of several species die. The age structure is random and not in waves of even-aged trees of a single species. Gaps may be colonized by several species.

Acknowledgements

Grateful acknowledgement is made to the following for permission to reproduce material in this Book:

Figures 1.1, 1.10 G. Bateman (1978) *Flowering Plants of the World*, Andromeda Oxford Ltd; *Figures 1.2, 1.3b* F.H. Herring and S.M. Walters (1976) *Atlas of the British Flora*, Botanical Society of the British Isles; *Figure 1.3a* A.M. Emmet and J. Heath (1990) *The Butterflies of Great Britain and Ireland*, B.H. & A. Harley; *Figure 1.7* N. Polunin (1960) *Introduction to Plant Geography and some Related Sciences*, Longmans, Green & Co., Addison–Wesley, Longman; *Figure 1.16* J.S Findley (1993) *Bats: A Community Perspective*, Cambridge University Press; *Figure 1.22* R.A. Spicer and J.L. Chapman (1990) 'Climate change and the evolution of high-latitude terrestrial vegetation and floras' in Sudgeon, A.M., *Trends in Ecology and Evolution*, **5**(9), Elsevier; *Figure 1.23* W. Alvarez (1972) 'Rotation of the Corsica–Sardinia microplate', *Nature Physical Science*, **235**, 7 Feb., Macmillan; *Figure 1.25* B.S. John (1977) *The Ice Age Past and Present*, HarperCollins; *Figure 1.30* E. Hulten (1971) *Circumpolar Plants*, Vol. II, Almquist and Wiskell Int.; *Figure 1.31* M. Follieri *et al.* (1988) '250,000-year pollen record from Valle di Castiglione (Roma)', *Pollen et Spores*, **30**(3–4), pp.329–56, © 1988 M. Follieri, D. Magri and L. Sadori; *Figure 1.32* M. Follieri *et al.* (1990) 'A comparison between lithostratigraphy and palynology from the lacustrine sediments of Valle di Castiglione (Roma) …', *Mem. Soc. Geol. It.*, **45**, pp.889–91, © 1990 M. Follieri, D. Magri and B. Narcisi; *Figure 1.33* J.R. Flenley (1979) *The Equatorial Rain Forest: A Geological History*, Butterworths; *Figure 1.34* R.J. Morley and J.R. Flenley (1987) 'Late Cainozoic vegetational and environmental changes in the Malay Archipelago', in Whitmore, T.C., *Biogeographical Evolution of the Malay Archipelago*, Clarendon Press; *Figure 1.37* © K.S. Brown, B.J. Meggers, J. Haffer, G.T. Prance, reprinted from Whitmore, T.C. and Prance, G.T. (eds) *Biogeography and Quaternary History in Tropical America*, Oxford University Press; *Figure 1.37* G.H. Evans (1970) *New Phytologist*, **69**, Academic Press; *Figure 1.39* G. Anderson and E. Hulten (1971) *Atlas of the Distribution of Vascular Plants of NW Europe*, Kiber Kartor; *Figures 1.44, 1.45* A.P. Conolly; *Figure 1.46* S.M. Peglar, S.C. Fritz and H.J.B. Birks (1989) 'Vegetation and land use history at Diss', *Journal of Ecology*, **77**, pp.203–22, British Ecological Society; *Figure 1.53* K.J. Kirby, G.F. Peterken, J.W. Spencer and G.W. Walker (1984) 'Inventories of ancient semi-natural woodland', in *Focus on Nature Conservation*, **6**, Nature Conservancy Council / English Nature; *Figures 1.54, 1.55* Charles Turner; *Figure 2.3a* R.S.K. Barnes and R.N. Hughes (1988) *An Introduction to Marine Ecology*, 2nd edn, Blackwell; *Figure 2.3b* L. Guldwasser and J. Roughgarden (1993) 'Construction and analysis of a large Caribbean food web', *Ecology*, **74**, pp.1216–33, copyright © 1993 Ecological Society of America; *Figure 2.4* D.H. Wise (1993) *Spiders in Ecological Webs*, Cambridge University Press; *Figures 2.5, 3.16, 3.17* M. Begon *et al.* (1986) *Ecology*, Blackwell; *Figure 2.8* D.A. Murawski and L.E. Gilbert (1986) 'Pollen flow in *Psiguria warscewiczii* …', *Oecologia*, **68**, pp.161–7, © 1986 Springer–Verlag; *Figure 2.9* L.E Gilbert and J.T. Smiley (1978) 'Determinants of local diversity in phytophagous insects …', *Symposium Royal Entomological Society*, **9**, pp.89–104, Royal Entomological Society; *Figures 2.10, 2.11* J. Terborgh (1983) *Five New World Primates: A Study in Comparative Ecology*, copyright © 1983 Princeton University Press; *Figure 2.14* O. Rackham (1975) *Hayley Wood – Its History and Ecology*, Cambs

& Isle of Ely Naturalist Trust Ltd; *Figure 2.18* S.C. Pimm (1982) *Food Webs*, Chapman & Hall; *Figure 2.19* M.R. Gardner and W.R. Ashby (1970) 'Connectance of large dynamic (cybernetic) systems', *Nature*, **228**, p.784, Macmillan; *Figure 2.21* J.G. Dony (1977) 'Species–area relationships in an area of intermediate size', *Journal of Ecology*, **65**, pp.457–84, British Ecological Society; *Figure 2.22* R. Condit *et al.* (1996) 'Species–area relationships for tropical trees …', *Journal of Ecology*, **84**, British Ecological Society; *Figure 2.23* S.L. Sutton *et al.* (1983) *Tropical Rain Forest: Ecology and Management*, © 1983 British Ecological Society/Blackwell; *Figure 2.24* C.E.J. Kennedy and T.R.E. Southwood (1984) 'The number of species of insects associated with British trees …', *Journal of Animal Ecology*, **53**, pp.455–78, Blackwell; *Figure 2.26* 'Rapid asymptotic species accumulation in phytophagous insect communities …', *Science*, **185**, © 1974 AAAS; *Figure 2.27* M.G. Morris (1971) 'Grassland and conservation of invertebrate animals', in Duffy, E. and Watts, A.S. *The Scientific Management of Animal and Plant Communities for Conservation*, Blackwell; *Figure 2.30* R.W. Kimmerer and T.F.H. Allen (1982) 'The role of disturbance in pattern of a riparian Bryophyte community', *American Midland Naturalist*, **107**, pp.370–83, American Midland Naturalist; *Figure 2.31* A.M. Ayling (1980) 'The role of biological disturbance in temperate subtidal encrusting communities', *Ecology*, **62**(3), pp.830–47, Ecological Society of America; *Figures 3.2, 3.13* S.T.A. Pickett (1982) 'Population patterns through 20 years of oldfield succession', *Vegetatio*, **49**, pp.45–9, © Dr W. Junk Publishers, The Hague; *Figures 3.7, 3.8* F.H. Bormann and G.E. Likens (1976) *Pattern and Process in a Forested Ecosystem*, © 1979 Springer–Verlag NY Inc.; *Figures 3.10, 3.11* C.J. Krebs (1994) *Ecology: The Experimental Analysis of Distribution and Abundance*, 4th edn, copyright © 1994 HarperCollins College Publishers; *Figures 3.12, 3.19* J. Miles (1987) 'Vegetation succession …' in Gray, A.J. *et al.*, *26th Symp. British Ecological Society Colonization, Successional Stability*, © 1987; *Figures 3.14, 3.15* M.D. Swaine and J.B. Hall (1983) 'Early succession on cleared forest land in Ghana', *Journal of Ecology*, **71**, pp.601–27, British Ecological Society; *Figure 3.18* T.R.E. Southwood *et al.* (1979) 'The relationship of plant and insect diversities in succession', *Biol. J. Linn. Soc.*, **12**, © Linnean Society of London, Academic Press; *Figure 3.21* A. Smith (1986) *The Great Rift: Africa's Changing Valley*, BBC Books; *Figure 3.22* A.S. Watt (1974) 'Senescence and rejuvenation in ungrazed chalk grassland (grassland B) in Breckland …', *Journal of Applied Ecology*, **11**, p.1164, Blackwell; *Figures 3.23, 3.24* V.K Brown and A.C. Gange (1989) 'Differential effects of above- and below-ground insect herbivory during early plant succession', *Oikos*, **54**, pp.67–76, Munksgaard International Booksellers & Publishers; *Figure 3.25* J.H. Brown and E.J. Heske (1990) 'Control of a desert–grassland transition by a keystone rodent guild', *Science*, **2**, Dec., AAAS; *Figure 3.29* W.P. Sousa (1979) 'Experimental investigations of disturbance and ecological succession in a rocky intertidal algal community', *Ecological Monographs*, **49**, © 1979 Ecological Society of America; *Figure 3.30* J.R. Connell and R.O. Slatyer (1977) 'Mechanisms of succession in natural communities and their role in community stability and organization', *The American Naturalist*, **111**(982), © 1977 University of Chicago Press.

INDEX

Entries and page numbers in **bold type** refer to key words which are printed in **bold** in the text. Pages indicated in *italics* refer to a figure or caption.

Abies spp., *see* silver fir
abundance of species 142–3, 145
Acer spp., *see* maple
Acer campestre, see field maple
Acer pseudoplatanus, see sycamore
Acer saccharum, see sugar maple
Achatina fulica, see giant snail
'acid rain' 97
Aeonium spp., endemic in Canary Islands 23
Aesculus hippocastaneum, see horse chestnut
Agabiformis lentus, see under woodlice
aggradation phase (forest succession) **171**
agriculture, early 78, 79
   in East Anglia 82–8
alder (*Alnus* spp.) 49, 51, 95, 165
Alnus spp., *see* alder
Alnus glutinosa, see common alder
alpha diversity 131
Ammophila arenaria, see marram grass
ancient woodland 95, **96**–7
   flora and fauna 101–2
   management 97–101
anemochores 178
   see also wind-dispersed seeds
Anglo-Saxon Britain 87, *88*
Anolis spp., feeding relationships, 111, *112*
Antarctic Kingdom, *13*
Anthriscus sylvestris, see cow parsley
Aphantopus hyperantus, see ringlet butterfly
Arecaceae, *see* palm family
Argiope spp., *see under* spiders
Artemisia spp., *see* mugwort
Arum maculatum, see lords and ladies
ash (*Fraxinus* spp.) 49, 100, 171
aspen (*Populus tremuloides*) 191–2
Asplenium adiantum-nigrum, see black spleenwort fern
Asteraceae, see daisy family
atmospheric circulation *14*
Australia, isolation 32–4
Australian Kingdom *13*
Australian region *13, 16,* **18,** *19*

Barbarea vulgaris, see winter-cress
Barfield Tarn 79–80

barochores 178
Barro Colorado Island, tree species–area relationships 141
Batesian mimicry 119
bats
   distribution 26
   pollinators *117*
   seed dispersal by 178
beating tray (sampling technique) 144–5
beech (*Fagus* spp.) 49, 52, 171
beetles, indicator species 78
beta diversity, 131
Betula spp., *see* birch
Betula pendula, see silver birch
Betula pubescens, see downy birch
biodiversity 129
biogeographical regions 12–20
biogeography 9
   changes in Quaternary 39–55
   historical 12
   recent changes 90–3
biological diversity 129
birch (*Betula* spp.) 49, 52, 171
   in ancient northern forest 95, 97
   regeneration in forest clearings 51, 81
   in sedge fen 165
birds
   changes with secondary succession 177
   pollinators *117*
   seed dispersal by 178, *178*–9
black hairstreak butterfly (*Satyrium pruni*) 101, 105
black spleenwort fern (*Asplenium adiantum-nigrum*), distribution 10–11
Blelham Tarn 70–73, *74,* 79
bloody cranesbill (*Geranium sanguineum*), distribution 102
blue-green algae, pioneer species 167
bluebell (*Hyacinthoides non-scriptus*) 102
Boreal Kingdom *13,* **15**
Bosumtwi Lake, Ghana, palynological profile *66,* 67
bottom-up processes (community regulation) 148–9
bracken fern (*Pteridium aquilinum*)
   colonization of clearings 81
   distribution 20

bramble (*Rubus fruticosus*), introduced to New Zealand 93
Bronze Age
   Early 86, *88*
   Later 87, *88*
brook saxifrage (*Saxifraga rivularis*), distribution *54*
brown capuchin (*Cebus apella*) 122–4
bryophytes, diversity on stream banks 150–1
bulrush (*Schoenoplectus lacustris*) 165
burning of vegetation (forest clearance) 78, 80
butterflies
   species richness in tropical forest 127–8, 147, *148*
   see also individual genera and species

cacao, insect pests 145
Caledonian Forest 97
Calluna vulgaris, see heather
Canadian pondweed (*Elodea canadensis*), introduced species **92**–3
Cannabis sativa, see hemp
canopy fogging (sampling technique) 128–9
carpenter bees 116
Carpinus spp., *see* hornbeam
Castanea sativa, see sweet chestnut
Cebus albifrons, see white-fronted capuchin
Cebus apella, see brown capuchin
Ceratocystis ulmi 82, 91
cereals, cultivation 80, *81,* 82, 83, 87
Cervus elaphus see red deer
Cetti's warbler (*Cettia cetti*), spread into Britain 93
chalkhill blue butterfly (*Lysandra corydon*), distribution 11–12
Chamaerops humilis, see dwarf palm
Chenopodiaceae 59, 60
Cherleria sedoides, see mossy cyphel
Cladium mariscus, see saw sedge
climatic belts *14*
climatic climax 181
climax forest 171
climax state **161,** 180–2
Clupea harengus, see herring

Cocha Cashu, primate community 121–4
coconut palm (*Cocos nucifera*), distribution 10
cold stages 41–2
  see also glacial stages
collared dove (*Streptopelia decaocto*), spread into Britain 93
colonization
  forest clearings 81, 170–1, *190*
  volcanic islands 23–4, 167
colugo (flying lemur, *Cynocephalus variegatus*) 19
common alder (*Alnus glutinosa*) 49, 51, 165
common ash (*Fraxinus excelsior*) 49, 171
common reed (*Phragmites australis*) 165
  distribution 20
communities, *see* ecological communities
community complexity 125
  measurement 126–33
  related to community stability 135–9
community matrix 133, 136–9
community regulation 148–51
  non-equilibrium processes 149–51
  top-down and bottom-up processes 148–9
community stability 125, 132–3
  related to community complexity 135–9
competition coefficients, matrix 133
connectance 132
conservation
  use of bird perches 178–9
  of woodland species 105
continental drift 27
Convallaria majalis, *see* lily-of-the-valley
convergent evolution 18, *19*
coppice 97, **99**–100, 104
coppice with standards *99*, **100**–1
coppice stools 99
Corylus avellana, *see* hazel
cosmopolitan distribution **20**
cow parsley (*Anthriscus sylvestris*) 101
cow-wheat (*Melampyrum pratense*) 101, 104
cowslip (*Primula veris*), dispersal 102
coypu (*Myocastor coypus*), introduced species 91
crop species, insect pests 145
crowberry (*Empetrum*) 52
cyclic changes 161, **194**–5
Cynocephalus variegatus, *see* colugo

daisy family (Asteraceae), distribution 20
Dama dama, *see* fallow deer
Darwin, Charles, predicts pollinator's existence 116
Darwin's finches, endemic in Galapagos Islands 23
Daucus carota, *see* wild carrot

dense-flowered orchid (*Neotinea maculata*), spread into Britain 93
Devensian stage 69, 73
Dipodomys spectabilis, *see* kangaroo rat
disjunct distributions 20–2, 33, 35
  mechanisms 23–4
dispersal 23, 24, 35
  mechanisms 178–9
Diss Mere 82–8, 95
distribution patterns 9–12
  and drift of tectonic plates 31–6
  types of 20–3
  see also biogeographical regions
diversity (ecosystems) **24**
diversity indices 129
  see also Shannon–Wiener index; Simpson diversity index
dog's mercury (*Mercurialis perennis*) 102
Domesday survey 98
dominant species 130, 131, 143
  in forest successions 171, 175–6
  in old-field succession 163, *164*, 165
donor control 148
Douglas fir (*Pseudotsuga menziesii*) 191–2, 195
downy birch (*Betula pubescens*) 49, 165
duckweeds (*Lemna* spp.), distribution of fossil 76–7
Dutch elm disease 82, 91
dwarf palm (*Chamaerops humilis*), distribution 9
dwarf serapias (*Serapias parviflora*), spread into Britain 93

Early Bronze Age 86, *88*
early-glacial substage *52*, *53*
early-temperate substage *52*, *53*
ecological communities 109–113
egg mimicry 120
eigenvalues 133, 139
elm (*Ulmus* spp.) 40, 49, 100
elm decline
  Neolithic 75, **79**, 81–2
  20th-century 82
Elminius modestus, *see* New Zealand barnacle
Elodea canadensis, *see* Canadian pondweed
Elodea nuttallii, introduced species 93
Elton, Charles 135
Ely Cathedral 98
Empetrum, *see* crowberry
Emys orbicularis, *see* pond tortoise
endemics 22–3
endozoochores 178
English oak (*Quercus robur*) 49, 165
Epilobium nerterioides, *see* New Zealand willowherb
epizoochores 178

equitability of community **129**, 151
Ethiopian region *13*, *16*, **17**–18
evenness (equitability) of community **129**, 151
extinctions 36
  at onset of Quaternary Ice Age 40–1, 63
  of isolated populations 103–5
  result of hunting 36, 43, 78

facilitation model of succession **188**, *190*, 191
Fagus spp., *see* beech
fallow deer (*Dama dama*), introduced species 91
Faunal Regions 12–13, *15*–18
fen carr 165
ferns
  pioneer colonists 23, 81, 167
  see also black spleenwort fern; bracken fern
field maple (*Acer campestre*) 49
finite rate of increase 133
fire climaxes 182
fishes, species–area relationships in lakes 141
Flandrian stage **41**, 60
  environmental changes 69–88
  human impacts 78–82
  thermal maximum 77, 79
  vegetational history 75–8
flattened meadow-grass (*Poa compressa*) 165
Floral Kingdoms/Subkingdoms 12–13, *15*–18
flying lemur, *see* colugo
food webs 111–13, 132
forest
  clearance 79–81, 95
    succession following 170–1, 174–6, *190*–3
  successional models for 170–2
  see also tropical forest
fossils
  marine organisms 43
  plants 20–22, 30, 34, 35, *54*, 76–7, 90
  Quaternary 43–4
  see also pollen analysis
Fraxinus spp., *see* ash
Fraxinus excelsior, *see* common ash
frugivores 116, 121–4
fruit traps (sampling technique) **127**–8, 147–8
fungi, successional sequence in pine needle litter 176

gamma diversity 131
garden snail (*Helix aspersa*), introduced species 91
generation time, successional changes in 179

Geranium sanguineum, see bloody cranesbill

giant redwood (*Sequoia* spp.), extinction in Europe 40

giant snail (*Achatina fulica*), introduced species 135

Gigartina caniculata, colonizing species 189, 190

Ginkgo biloba, see maidenhair tree

glacial stages 41–2

   environments 53–5, 63, 67

glacial–interglacial cycles 39, 41, 52, *53*

goldenrod (*Solidago*), successional changes in seed size 179, *180*

Gondwanaland 32

Gosse, Philip, quoted 114–5

grass family (Poaceae) *165*

   distribution 20

   see also marram grass

greenhouse mode (climate) 36

grey squirrel (*Sciurus carolinensis*), introduced species 91

grouse, interactions with other species 110

guilds (in tropical forest) 115–16

Gurania spp. 118

habitat complexity, and diversity 24–5

Hayley Wood, plant species richness 126

hazel (*Corylus avellana*) 49, 51, 81

   coppice *99*, 100

   distribution of fossil 76

heath fritillary butterfly (*Mellicta athalia*) 104, *105*

heather (*Calluna vulgaris*), regeneration cycle 194

Hedera helix, see ivy

Heliaster kubinji, *see under* starfish

Heliconia spp., insect communities in 137–9

Heliconiinae (butterflies) 116–20

Helix aspersa, see garden snail

Helix pomatia, see Roman snail

hemp (*Cannabis sativa*) 83, 87–8

herb paris (*Paris quadrifolia*) 101

herring (*Clupea harengus*), feeding relationships 111, 132

heterotrophic succession 188

Hippocrepis comosa, see horseshoe vetch

Hippophae rhamnoides, see sea buckthorn

historical biogeography 12

Holarctic region 15

holly (*Ilex aquifolium*) 50

Holocene Period 41, 60

   see also Flandrian stage

hornbeam (*Carpinus*) spp. 40, 49, 51, 100

horse chestnut (*Aesculus hippocastaneum*), introduced species 88

horseshoe vetch (*Hippocrepis comosa*), distribution 11–12

Hoxnian sediments, pollen analysis 48–53, 55

Hubbard Brook Forest, model for succession 170–1, 194

human activities

   during Flandrian Period 78–82

   responsible for extinctions 36, 43, 78

   see also agriculture; introduced species

Hyacinthoides non-scriptus, see bluebell

hydrosere 165–7, 181

Ice Age, Quaternary 36, *37*, 39–42

icehouse mode (climate) 36, 39

Ilex aquifolium, see holly

inhibition model of succession **189**, *190*, 191

insects

   effects on succession of herbivorous 184–6

   pollinators 117–20

   species diversity in woodland succession 177–8

   species richness on trees 143–6

   in tropical forest canopy 128–9

interaction coefficients 132–3

interglacial stages 41

   fauna 53

   vegetational history 48–53, 63–5, 67

intermediate disturbance hypothesis 150–1

interstadials 41, 63

introduced species 88, 90–3, 100, 135

Irish lady's tresses (*Spiranthes romanzoffiana*), spread into Britain 93

Iron Age 87

ivy (*Hedera helix*) 50, 101

juniper (*Juniperus communis*) 50

kangaroo rat (*Dipodomys spectabilis*), effect of removal on vegetation 186–7

keystone species 122, 123, 187

kinkajou (*Potos flavus*) 17

Krakatoa (Krakatau) islands

   primary succession on 167–9

   recolonization after eruption 23–4

Laguna de Fuquerne sediments, pollen analysis 63–5

lakes

   fish species–area relationships 141

   species richness in 153

   see also hydrosere

land bridges 42, 70

landnam phases **80**, 86

Lantana camara 118

larch (*Larix occidentalis*) 191–2

Larix occidentalis, see larch

Late-glacial Interstadial 70, 75

late-glacial stage *52*, *53*, 73

   vegetational history 73, 74–5

late-temperate substage *52*, *53*

Later Bronze Age 87, *88*

Lemna spp., see duckweeds

life-history traits, successional changes 179–80

lily-of-the-valley (*Convallaria majalis*) 101

lime (*Tilia* spp.) 42, 95

   coppice 100

   decline 87

linkage density 132

Liriodendron spp., see tulip tree

lithospheric plates 27–30

Livistona spp. 10

Loch Lomond Stadial 70, 75

lodgepole pine (*Pinus contorta*) 191–2

log-normal curves **142**–143

lords and ladies (*Arum maculatum*) 101

lottery model of species coexistence **150**

lowland vegetation 63

Lysandra corydon, see chalkhill blue butterfly

Magnolia spp.

   distribution 20, *21*

   extinction in Europe 40

maidenhair tree (*Ginkgo biloba*), distribution 22, *24*, 38, 39

mammoth (*Mammuthus primigenius*) *43*

maple (*Acer* spp.) 171

Mariscus spp., see saw sedge

mark–release–recapture methods **127**

Marks Tey sediments, pollen analysis 48–53, 55, 73

marram grass (*Ammophila arenaria*) 172, 188

marsupial mammals 17, 18, *19*

May, Robert 136

medieval Britain 87, *88*

Mediterranean vegetation 58, *59*, 60

megathermal species **10**

Melampyrum pratense, see cow-wheat

Mellicta athalia, see heath fritillary butterfly

Mercurialis perennis, see dog's mercury

Mesolithic period **78**

metapopulations 103–105

Mid-Atlantic Ridge 28

mimicry 119, 120

mink (*Mustela vison*), introduced species 91

monoclimax 181

montane vegetation 58, *59*, 60, 63, 66

mossy cyphel (*Cherleria sedoides*), distribution *54*

mountain-building 30

mugwort (*Artemisia* spp.) 52, *59*, 60

Mullerian mimicry 119

multiple successional pathways 173–4

Mustela vison, see mink

Myocastor coypus, see coypu

Myristicaceae, *see* nutmeg family

myxomatosis 183

natural selection 137

Nearctic region 13, **15**, *16*

Neolithic period **78**–9, 80, 86, *88*

Neotinea maculata, see dense-flowered orchid

Neotropical Kingdom 13

Neotropical region 13, 16, **17**

New Guinea, vegetational changes 65–6

New Zealand, species introduced to 93

New Zealand barnacle (*Elminius modestus*), introduced species 91, 94

New Zealand willowherb (*Epilobium nerterioides*), introduced species 90, *91*

niche pre-emption 143

Nipa 32

Nothofagus spp., *see* southern beeches

nutmeg family (Myristicaceae), distribution 31

oak (*Quercus* spp.) 40, 49, 51, 95, 165, 171

timber tree 98, 100

obligatory succession, *see* facilitation model of succession

ocean circulation 42

oceanic islands, endemic species 22–3

old-field succession 161–3, *164*, *165*, 174

propagule dispersal in 178–9

orchids

pollinator predicted 116

spread into Britain 93

Oriental region 13, 16, **17**–18

Oryctolagus cuniculus, see rabbit

oviposition strategies 120

Oxalis acetosella, see wood sorrel

Oxford ragwort (*Senecio squalidus*), introduced species 91

oxlip (*Primula elatior*), dispersal 102

Palaearctic region 13, **15**, *16*

palaeoclimate 31, 32, 36, *37*, 39–42, 52

palaeoecology 42–4

Palaeolithic period **78**

Palaeotropic Kingdom 13

palm family, distribution 9–10, 31, 32, 34, *35*

palynology 44

see also pollen analysis

Pandanus spp., *see* screw-pines

Paris quadrifolia, see herb paris

passion flower family (Passifloraceae) 117, 120

pastoralism, early 78, 87

peat 165, 167

permafrost 42

Phasianus colchicus, see pheasant

pheasant (*Phasianus colchicus*), introduced species 91

Phoenix theophrasti, distribution 9

Phragmites australis, see reed

Picea spp., *see* spruce

pin cherry (*Prunus pensylvanica*) 171

pine (*Pinus* spp.) 49, 191–2

in ancient forest 51, *52*, 95, 97

fungi in needle litter 176

unsuitable for coppice 100

Pinus spp., *see* pine

Pinus contorta, see lodgepole pine

Pinus sylvestris, see Scots pine

pioneer species 51, **170**

in forest clearings 51, 171, 174, *175*, 189

on rocky shores 189

on volcanic islands after eruption 23, 167

Pisaster ochraceous, see under starfish

placental mammals *19*

plagioclimaxes 182

plane (*Platanus* spp.), introduced species 88

plant biomass, changes over succession 170–1

plant defences 118, 149

Plantago lanceolata, see ribwort plantain

plantations 95, 97

Platanus spp., *see* plane

plate tectonics, theory of 27–30

and distribution of organisms 31–6

Pleistocene refugia 67, *68*

Poa compressa, see flattened meadow-grass

Poaceae, *see* grass family

pollarded trees 96, **98**, *99*

pollen analysis 31, 33, 34, 35, **44**–7, 61, 70

of Andean lake sediments 63–4

of Barfield Tarn sediments 79–80

of Blelham Tarn sediments 70–3, *74*

of Diss Mere sediments 82–8

of Flandrian sediments 70–3, *74*, 75–6, 82

of Late-glacial sediments 73, *74*–5

of Marks Tey sediment 48–53, 55

of southern European lake sediments 58–60, 61–3

pollen zones 50–2

pollinators (in tropical forest) 116–20

Polylepis forest 64

pond tortoise (*Emys orbicularis*), distribution 77

Populus tremuloides, see aspen

post-temperate substage 52, *53*

Potos flavus, see kinkajou

pre-temperate substage 52, *53*

primary succession **161**

on mining sites 178–9

on volcanic islands 167–9

see also hydrosere

primrose (*Primula vulgaris*), dispersal 102

Primula elatior, see oxlip

Primula veris, see cowslip

Primula vulgaris, see primrose

Prunus pensylvanica, see pin cherry

Pseudotsuga menziesii, see Douglas fir

Psiguria spp. 118

Pteridium aquilinum, see bracken fern

Pterocarya spp., *see* wingnut

Ptilostemon casabonae, distribution 38

purple saxifrage (*Saxifraga oppositifolia*), distribution *54*

Quaternary Ice Age 36, *37*, 39–42

Quaternary Period **39**

fossils 43–4

Quercus spp., *see* oak

Quercus petraea, see sessile oak

Quercus robur, see English oak

rabbit (*Oryctolagus cuniculus*)

introduced species 91

population fall following myxomatosis 183–4

radiocarbon dating 45

radioisotope labelling, food chain studies 112, *113*

raised bog 167, 181

rare species 141, 142–3

Ray, John 102

red clover (*Trifolium pratense*) *165*

red deer (*Cervus elaphus*) 97

introduced species 135

reed (*Phragmites australis*) 165

distribution 20

reedmace (*Typha latifolia*) 165

refugia 24, *54*

temperate 60–3

tropical 63–8

regeneration cycles 194–5

regional diversity, *see* gamma diversity

relative abundance of species **129**

relict taxa 22, 24

reorganization phase (forest succession) **170**–1

reproductive effort, successional changes in 179

Rhododendron ponticum, introduced species 90

ribwort plantain (*Plantago lanceolata*) 79, 86, *165*

ringlet butterfly (*Aphantopus hyperantus*) 101
Roman Britain 87, *88*
Roman snail (*Helix pomatia*), introduced species 91
Rubus fruticosus, *see* bramble

saddle-backed tamarin (*Saguinus fuscicollis*) 122–4
Saguinus fuscicollis, *see* saddle-backed tamarin
Saimiri sciureus, *see* squirrel monkey
St Martin food web 111, *112*
Salix spp., *see* willows
sampling methods
    beating tray 144–5
    canopy fogging 128–9
    fruit traps 127–8, 147–8
    walk-and-count transects 127–8
sand dunes
    climax communities on 181
    successional changes on 172–4, 188
Sargassum muticum, introduced species 91
Satyrium pruni, *see* black hairstreak butterfly
savannah 66–7, **181–2**
saw sedge (*Cladium mariscus*, *Mariscus* spp.) 165
    distribution of fossil 76–7
Saxifraga oppositifolia, *see* purple saxifrage
Saxifraga rivularis, *see* brook saxifrage
Schoenoplectus lacustris, *see* bulrush
Sciurus carolinensis, *see* grey squirrel
Scots pine (*Pinus sylvestris*) 49, 95
screw-pines (*Pandanus* spp.) 18
sea buckthorn (*Hippophae rhamnoides*) 50
sea-level changes 30, 41, 42, 70
secondary succession **161**
    changes in life-history traits in 179
    effects of insect herbivory in 184–6
    in Hubbard Brook Forest 170–1
    see also old-field succession
secondary woodland 97
seed size, successional changes in 179
Senecio squalidus, *see* Oxford ragwort
Sequoia spp., *see* giant redwood
seral stages **161**
Serapias parviflora, *see* dense-flowered orchid
seres 161
service tree (*Sorbus domestica*) 96
sessile oak (*Quercus petraea*) 49, 95
shade-tolerant plants 171, 174, 189
Shannon–Wiener index 131
shifting mosaic steady state (climax forest) **171**
silver birch (*Betula pendula*) 49
silver fir (*Abies*) spp. 48, 50, 51
Simpson diversity index 129–31, 151

sink populations 104
snails, introduced species 91
Solidago spp., *see* goldenrod
Sorbus domestica, *see* service tree
Sorbus torminalis, *see* wild service tree
source populations 104
South African Kingdom 13
southern beeches (*Nothofagus* spp.), distribution 33–4
specialization 115–16
species–abundance curves 142–3
species–area curves 140–2
species diversity 24
    in birch woodland 177–8
    measurement 129–31
    in old-field succession 174
    types 131
species interactions 11–12, 109–13
    feeding 111–13, 132
    non-feeding 113
    notation 109–10, 132–3
    strength 110
species richness 25–6, **126–9**, 171
    effects of herbivorous insects on plants 184–6
    patterns 140–6
    related to latitude 152–5
    successional changes 171–6
species turnover, *see* beta diversity
Sphagnum palustre (sphagnum moss) 167
Sphenodon spp. 93
spiders, diet of *Argiope* spp. 112, *113*
Spiranthes romanzoffiana, *see* Irish lady's tresses
sporopollenin 45
spruce (*Picea* spp.) 48, 50, 100, 191–2
squirrel monkey (*Saimiri sciureus*) 122–4
stability matrix, *see* community matrix
standards (timber trees) **99**, 100
starfish, food webs 134, *135*, 149
'steppe' vegetation 60
stone tools 78, 80, *81*
Streptopelia decaocto, *see* collared dove
structural diversity and species richness **145–6**, 153
submontane vegetation 58, *59*, 60
succession 161
    community changes during 170–80
    mechanisms 183–92
    methods of studying 161–3
    roles of animals 182–7
    see also primary succession; secondary succession
sugar maple (*Acer saccharum*) 171
Sumatra, vegetational changes 65
swamp cypress (*Taxodium* spp.), extinction in Europe 40

sweet chestnut (*Castanea sativa*)
    coppice 100, 101
    introduced species 90
sweet violet (*Viola odorata*) 101
sycamore (*Acer pseudoplatanus*), introduced species 88, 90, 100
Symphonia spp., distribution 22, 35

Taxodium spp., *see* swamp cypress
Taxus baccata, *see* yew
tectonic plates 27–30
    boundaries 12
Tethys Ocean **30**, 32, 34, 35
thermal maximum (Flandrian) **77**, 79
thrush, niche 154, 155
Tilia spp., *see* lime
timber (distinct from wood) **98**
tolerance model of succession **189**, *190*, 191
top-down processes (community regulation) 148–9
transition phase (forest succession) **171**
Trapa natans, *see* water chestnut
trees
    coexistence in tropical forest 149–50
    pollen, *see* pollen analysis
    species richness of insects on 143–6
    see also coppice; forest; pollarded trees; standards
Trichorhina tomentosa, *see under* woodlice
Trifolium pratense, *see* red clover
trophic levels 132, 148
tropical forest
    butterfly species richness 127–8
    coexistence of tree species in 149–50
    communities 114–24
    fruit-bearing trees in 178
    glacial–interglacial changes 66–7, *68*
    insect species in canopy 128–9
    species–area relationships 141–2
    stratification and species richness 24–5
    successional changes in 175–6
tropical montane vegetation 64
tropicalpine vegetation 63, 64
Tsuga heterophylla, *see* western hemlock
tulip tree (*Liriodendron* spp.)
    distribution 20, *21*, 24, 35
    extinction in Europe 40
Typha latifolia, *see* reedmace

Ulmus spp., *see* elm
Ulva spp., role in intertidal succession 189, *190*
Urtica atrovirens, distribution 38

Valle di Castiglione sediments, pollen analysis 58–60, *61*, *62*

vegetational belts *14*
   changes 48–53, 58–67
vicariance 23, 24, 31–2, 34, 35
vicariance biogeography 23
vicariant species 23
Viola odorata, see sweet violet
vital attributes 191–2
volcanic activity, mountain-building 30
volcanic islands
   colonization after eruption 23–4
   primary succession on 167–9

walk-and-count transects 127–8
Wallacea 34
Wallace's Line *13*, **34**

water chestnut (*Trapa nutans*), distribution of fossil 76
Weber's Line 34
West Java, vegetational changes 65
western hemlock (*Tsuga heterophylla*), regeneration cycles 195
white-fronted capuchin (*Cebus albifrons*) 122–4
wild carrot (*Daucus carota*) 165
wild service tree (*Sorbus torminalis*) 101
wildwood 95, *96*, 103
willows (*Salix* spp.) 50, 165
wind-dispersed seeds 51, 93, 178
wind-pollinated plants 44, *117*
wingnut (*Pterocarya* spp.) 48, 50, 51
winter-cress (*Barbarea vulgaris*) 165

wood (distinct from timber) **98**
wood sorrel (*Oxalis acetosella*) 101
woodbank 98
woodland 95–7
   plant species richness in temperate 126
   species diversity changes with age 177–8
   stratification of temperate 24
   see also ancient woodland
woodlice, introduced species 91
woodmanship 98

xeric vegetation 58, *59*, 60, 63

yew (*Taxus baccata*) 50, 51